Enhancing
Classroom
Practice

with Research behind *Principles to Actions*

Edited by
Denise A. Spangler
and Jeffrey J. Wanko

NATIONAL COUNCIL OF
TEACHERS OF MATHEMATICS

Copyright © 2017 by
The National Council of Teachers of Mathematics, Inc.
1906 Association Drive, Reston, VA 20191-1502
(703) 620-9840; (800) 235-7566; www.nctm.org
All rights reserved
ISBN 978-0-87353-978-4
Library of Congress Cataloging-in-Publication Data

Names: Spangler, Denise A., editor. | Wanko, Jeffrey J., editor. | National Council of Teachers of Mathematics.
Title: Enhancing classroom practice with research behind Principles to actions / edited by Denise A. Spangler,
    University of Georgia, and Jeffrey J. Wanko, Miami University of Ohio.
Other titles: Principles to actions
Description: Reston, VA : National Council of Teachers of Mathematics,
    [2017] | Includes bibliographical references.
Identifiers: LCCN 2017010676 (print) | LCCN 2016059785 (ebook) | ISBN 9781680540048 (pbk.) |
    ISBN 781680540055 (ebook)
Subjects: LCSH: Mathematics--Study and teaching--United States. | Effective teaching. | Curriculum planning.
Classification: LCC QA13 .E49 2017 (ebook) | LCC QA13 (print) | DDC 510.71/073--dc23
LC record available at https://lccn.loc.gov/2017010676

The National Council of Teachers of Mathematics is the public voice of mathematics education, supporting teachers to ensure equitable mathematics learning of the highest quality for each and every student through vision, leadership, professional development, and research.

Printed in the United States of America

Contents

Contents

Acknowledgments

All chapters in this book were reviewed by at least two reviewers. We wish to thank the following mathematics educators for their thorough, thoughtful, and timely reviews: Shelby Aaberg, Scottsbluff (Nebraska) High School; Vickie Anderson, Rising Starr Middle School, Fayetteville, Georgia; Elizabeth Coyne, Heritage Academy, Atlanta, Georgia; Natalie Crist, Baltimore (Maryland) County Public Schools; Liza Dallavalle, Hampstead Elementary School, Westminster, Maryland; Sandra Hogan, Newnan, Georgia; DeAnn Huinker, University of Wisconsin–Milwaukee; Susie Katt, Lincoln (Nebraska) Public Schools; Steven Leinwand, American Institutes for Research, Washington D.C.; LouAnn H. Lovin, James Madison University; Robyn L. B. Ovrick, University of Georgia, Griffin; Ami N. Rivera, Rocky Branch Elementary School, Bogart, Georgia; Gregory P. Sand, Omaha (Nebraska) Central High; Kyle T. Schultz, James Madison University; Karina S. Scott, Decatur (Georgia) High School; Margaret Smith, University of Pittsburgh; Wendy M. Smith, University of Nebraska–Lincoln; Laura Steward, Conyers (Georgia) Middle School; Christy Sutton, Lee County Primary School, Leesburg, Georgia; Matthew D. Timm, Indian Hill Elementary School, Omaha, Nebraska; Andrew Tyminski, Clemson University; Cori Wilson, Landmark Christian School, Peachtree City, Georgia; Kim Zeugner, Kingswood Elementary School, Cary, North Carolina.

We were also assisted in the preparation of this book by graduate students at our universities, and we wish to extend our appreciation to them for their diligent and thoughtful work on this book: Ángel M. Carreras-Jusino, University of Georgia; and Alex Trassare, Miami University.

Introduction

Denise A. Spangler, *University of Georgia*
Jeffrey J. Wanko, *Miami University*

In 2014 the National Council of Teachers of Mathematics (NCTM) released *Principles to Actions: Ensuring Mathematical Success for All* (*PtA*) to describe "the conditions, structures, and policies that must exist for all students to learn" (p. vii). *PtA* articulates eight guiding principles and five essential elements that are necessary for effective mathematics teaching and learning—regardless of the standards, curriculum, type of school, age of students, or other circumstances. This book was commissioned as a companion to *PtA* to enact NCTM's longstanding commitment to linking research and practice. In the remainder of this introduction we describe the purpose of the book, its intended audiences, and suggestions for how this book might be used by a range of mathematics education professionals.

Purpose of This Book

The purpose of this book is to summarize and synthesize the research behind each of the guiding principles and essential elements and to offer examples of what they might look like in classroom practice. While each of the principles and elements is backed by an extensive body of research, our goal was not to offer a comprehensive, exhaustive, or detailed review of the literature. Rather, the goal was to give readers a sense of where the field stands in its knowledge and its hypotheses about the big ideas put forth in *PtA*. In addition, the goal was to make the principles and elements—as well as the research—concrete for readers by offering examples from classroom practice. Again, however, our goal was not to be comprehensive and detailed, so the examples do not cover every grade level or every content area, nor do they contain full-fledged lesson plans. Rather, the illustrative examples are meant to give readers a flavor of what a principle or element might look like in practice. It is up to the reader to tailor the examples to a particular context.

Many of the chapters in this book were written collaboratively by school-based mathematics educators and university-based mathematics educators in a deliberate effort to exemplify NCTM's commitment to linking research and practice. Working together in teams allowed the authors to combine and integrate their expertise, to craft chapters that reflect a balance of research and practice examples in ways that meet the needs of practitioners in both schools and universities. To further ensure that the book would meet the needs of practitioners at both levels, every chapter was reviewed by both school-based and university-based mathematics educators.

Audience for and Uses of This Book

This book was designed to be useful to many audiences, including preservice teachers, in-service teachers, instructional coaches, administrators, professional developers, and mathematics teacher educators. For example, preservice teachers might read the tasks chapter as part of a mathematics methods course to gain a sense of how tasks with high cognitive demand can be implemented on a daily basis in classrooms. Administrators might read the discourse chapter to gain a lens for thinking about what to expect when observing a teacher who is trying to create a discourse-rich classroom environment. A group of teachers in a school might use the equity chapter as a springboard for ongoing critical conversations about the ways the practices they enact in their classrooms, as well as school-wide practices related to tracking, are or are not supportive of all students learning mathematics. Instructional coaches and professional developers might suggest particular chapters to teachers who are trying to grow their practice in specific areas or to gain ideas for how to support teachers.

And some readers may wish to read the entire book in order to gain a high-level overview of the professional commitments of mathematics educators and how those commitments play out in classrooms.

Whatever use is made of this book, readers might wish to read the relevant section of *PtA* along with the corresponding chapter in this book in order to gain a full picture of NCTM's recommendations, the research that supports those recommendations, and the implementation of the recommendations in classrooms. It is important to note that chapter authors did not reproduce *PtA* in its entirety in this book. In most cases, only a very short summary of the principle or element from *PtA* is included, so we encourage readers to visit the *PtA* document for full details of the recommendations.

Conclusion

As noted in *PtA*, we all have a role to play in ensuring that every student is engaged in mathematics learning that is a vibrant, dynamic, enriching experience. This book is but one small part in supporting mathematics educators and other professionals in developing the knowledge base, attitudes, beliefs, and skills to make that vision a reality.

Reference

National Council of Teachers of Mathematics (NCTM). *Principles to Actions: Ensuring Mathematical Success for All.* Reston, Va.: NCTM, 2014.

Chapter 1

The Nature and Role of Goals in and for Mathematics Instruction

Mary Kay Stein and Erin Meikle, *University of Pittsburgh*

The first teaching practice in *Principles to Actions: Ensuring Mathematical Success for All* (NCTM 2014) relates to teachers' goals for student learning: "Effective teaching of mathematics establishes clear goals for the mathematics that students are learning, situates goals within learning progressions, and uses the goals to guide instructional decisions" (p. 10). The leading position of this practice is notable in that it points to the importance of lesson preparation and lesson reflection as essential components of effective mathematics teaching (Mills 2015). It also acknowledges the key role that goals play in the overall enterprise of mathematics teaching and learning: "Goals set the stage for everything else" (Hiebert et al. 2007, p. 51). In this chapter, we begin by clarifying what we mean by goals for student learning at the lesson level. Then, we argue for the importance of specifying learning goals and provide some suggestions for how teachers could go about specifying learning goals for student learning.

Getting Clear on Our Terms: Defining Learning Goals

The importance of learning goals echoes inside school buildings and is felt daily in the lives of teachers. Some districts require that teachers post learning objectives for each lesson on the corner of the board, available for all to see, including students and evaluators. Others require teachers to use state standards as their learning goals. Theoretically, goals should also make an appearance on the lesson plans that most teachers are required to hand in regularly, a common district mandate.

In short, teachers are obliged to have goals for student learning, some of which are provided to them, others of which they must create. It is worth noting that, in addition to goals related to content, sometimes teachers have other kinds of goals they want students to achieve, such as wanting students to be engaged and share their thoughts or wanting their students to be able to use technology to support their mathematics learning (see Lampert 2001). In this chapter, the focus is on the goals that are related to content.

Devoting attention to content goals for student learning has never been more important. In "traditional textbooks," attention to student learning goals was not as critical because what students were supposed to learn was directly reflected in the exercises that they were asked to do, in part because of the procedural nature of the goals of most traditional lessons. For example, when students were asked to complete twenty worksheet problems on adding fractions, they were supposed to be learning "how to add fractions." There was no need for teachers to deliberate over the goal for student learning or whether students had met that goal.

In contrast, the relationship between what students are supposed to learn and the activities in which they are asked to engage is not as straightforward in standards-based materials. Standards-driven lessons often embody goals of a more conceptual nature; students are not directly "taught" the concept, however. Rather, they are asked to engage with a task or small project that requires them to think and reason about what they are doing, the purpose of which is to "surface" ideas that— upon carefully orchestrated discussions led by the teacher—become consolidated into an understanding of the concept. As such, teachers need to spend more time before the lesson identifying the elements of conceptual understanding that they want students to walk away from the lesson with and how they might build bridges between students' thinking during class activities and the concept.

To illustrate the above contrast, consider the different ways in which traditional versus standards-based curricula might define student learning goals around "average." In traditional curricula what students would be expected to learn would directly align with what they would be asked to do: Students would learn "how to find the average" by finding the average of a set of numbers (computing the sum of the numbers in the set and dividing the sum by the number of addends), presumably after demonstrations by the teacher.

In standards-based curricula, on the other hand, the student learning goal would be to understand the meaning of *average*. The lesson would not start with the definition of *average* or with routine problem sets. Instead, the lesson might ask students to engage in a "leveling" task that exposes students to one particular meaning of *average* (see fig. 1.1).

The task asks students to sketch the height of two numbers before and after they are leveled off and then to write a statement about how their method of leveling off was related to finding the average of the two numbers. As students perform this task, they experience how the average that is found algorithmically represents the equal distribution of both numbers and thus can begin to understand one meaning of an average (i.e., it evens out all of the data values of a given population to find the value that all of the data values in the set would be if they were the same).

Preparations for such lessons involve understanding the mathematical content that the task affords students the opportunity to learn and how those ideas relate to lesson-level learning goals. The overt specification of concepts that underlie a learning goal is a hallmark of instruction that supports students' development of conceptual understanding (Hiebert and Grouws 2007). Not surprisingly, teachers find this kind of planning challenging. In a study of thirteen coach-teacher pairs over an eighteen-month period, Hunt and Stein (2016) found that, despite being primed to bring a goal

statement and a cognitively demanding task to their pre-observation conference, only one teacher was able to state a specific learning goal for an individual lesson. The others stated vague goals or talked about other kinds of goals (e.g., "students will be able to complete this worksheet"), not what students would learn or be able to do mathematically. All of this suggests that it is time for mathematics educators to turn their attention to the nature and role of goals in mathematics teaching and to how teachers can be helped to develop learning goals.

The pairs of numbers in a–d below represent the heights of stacks of cubes to be leveled off. On grid paper, sketch the front views of columns of cubes with these heights before and after they are leveled off. Write a statement under the sketches that explains how your method of leveling off is related to finding the average of the two numbers.

a) 9 and 5 b) 16 and 7 c) 7 and 12 d) 13 and 15

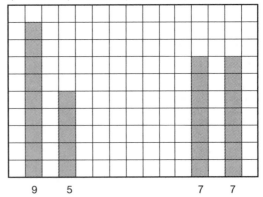

By taking 2 blocks off the first stack and giving them to the second stack, I've made the two stacks the same. So the total # of cubes is now distributed into 2 columns of equal height. And that is what average means.

Fig. 1.1. An example of a standards-based task. From Linda Cooper Foreman and Albert B. Bennett Jr., *Visual Mathematics III/Math Alive*, The Math Learning Center, mathlearningcenter.org. Used with permission.

Features of Goals That Support Instructional Decision Making

There appears to be growing consensus among mathematics educators regarding the features of goals that teachers should identify or develop. Key to most of the recommendations is the criterion that the goal must explicitly address what students should learn in the *language of the discipline* (Charles 2005; Hiebert et al. 2007; Smith and Stein 2011). As noted by Hiebert and colleagues (2007), "A goal of '80% correct by each student on the quiz at the end of the lesson' is not as useful as a goal of 'students should construct relationships between the value of a decimal fraction, the sum of the values of each of its digits, and increasing [and decreasing] powers of 10' " (p. 51).

Also key is the notion of specificity. For example, it is possible to distinguish three different kinds of learning goals for an eighth-grade lesson on the Pythagorean theorem (see fig. 1.2). Goal A identifies what students should learn but at a very general level. Goal B identifies what the teacher would like students to be able to do by the end of a lesson but does not unpack *how* they would explain why $c^2 = a^2 + b^2$. Both goals fail to unpack the learning goal into underlying concepts, ideas, or procedures that would help the teacher identify evidence in students' work of whether or not the learning goal had been achieved. In addition, the lack of specificity in these learning goals probably would not make them very useful to teachers as they select instructional tasks or teach the lesson. Learning Goal C, on the other hand, identifies the mathematical relationship that is at the heart of the Pythagorean theorem. Learning Goal C begins to unpack the explanation for why the Pythagorean theorem works. However, this learning goal could be unpacked even more. For example, Learning Goal C could highlight the reason we know that the side length of the hypotenuse is c and the side lengths of the legs of the triangle are a and b. The reason that c is the length of the hypotenuse is because its corresponding square has an area of c^2, which by definition has a side length of c. The *specificity* of this goal provides the teacher with a clear instructional target that can guide the selection of tasks and serve as a referent for monitoring and advancing student thinking during the lesson.

A third criterion for goals that can productively guide teachers' lesson planning and instruction is that they must be situated within a *learner-driven model* of how understanding of important mathematical concepts develops over time. In this way, goals are different from the traditional scope and sequence charts that mark the pathway of instruction. Although some curricula have

begun to incorporate research on student learning in their design of task sequences, most curricula rely on the logic of the discipline and on what has traditionally been taught at various grade levels (decisions that have not been based in research on student learning). But as teachers work to refine and specify learning goals across multiple lessons or a course, they should be developing deeper knowledge of the progression of student thinking and how all of the learning goals fit into that progression.

Learning Goal A. Students will learn the Pythagorean theorem

Learning Goal B. Students will also be able to explain why $c^2 = a^2 + b^2$.

Learning Goal C. Students will be able to explain why $c^2 = a^2 + b^2$.

–Students will recognize that the area of the square built on the hypotenuse of a right triangle is equal to the sum of the areas of the squares built on the legs.

–Students will conjecture that $c^2 = a^2 + b^2$ (where c is the length of the hypotenuse and a and b are the lengths of the other two sides of the triangle).

Fig. 1.2. Three different goal statements for a lesson on the Pythagorean theorem. Adapted from Smith and Stein (2011), p. 14.

Why Is Specifying Learning Goals Important?

A teacher might ask, "Why is it so important for me to spend time specifying learning goals for individual lessons when the standards are already defined for me?" First, the Common Core State Standards for Mathematics (CCSSM) (NGA Center and CCSSO 2010) are written to identify the content students should learn about different mathematical topics and/or concepts at different grade levels, but, in general, each standard in the CCSSM necessitates multiple lessons for students to achieve (e.g., "Represent proportional relationships by equations"). Although these general learning goals may suffice for units or multiple lessons, these kinds of goals will provide little help for individual lessons.

Making Instructional Decisions

One logical argument for identifying specific learning goals for individual lessons is that a higher degree of specificity will help teachers make better instructional decisions *during* lessons. For example, after students have worked on a high-level task individually or in small groups, the teacher's role is to orchestrate a productive whole-class discussion that builds on their thinking but also pushes it further toward the goal of the lesson. Instead of gently steering students' individual and collective thinking toward canonical understandings of mathematics, however, many classrooms become "show and tells" in which students take turns sharing their approaches to solving problems with little filtering by the teacher about which mathematical ideas each approach helps to illustrate (Ball 2001; Lampert 2001; Schoenfeld 1998). In addition, teachers do not typically draw connections among different ways of solving problems or tie them to important disciplinary methods (Ball 1993; Boaler and Humphreys 2005).

It could be argued that this phenomenom stems from teachers' lack of clear learning goals for their lessons. In a widely cited article, "With an Eye on the Mathematical Horizon," Ball (1993) argued that the field needed to take responsibility for helping teachers learn how to continually "size up" whether important mathematical ideas were being developed and how to step in and redirect classroom work when needed. Clear learning goals can help teachers do this by helping them to consider (a) the alignment between their instructional task and their goal for student learning, (b) which solution strategies to the mathematical task would have the most potential to uncover ideas underlying the learning goal, and (c) which questions could be asked during a class discussion that would support students in thinking about key ideas underlying the learning goal.

All of this suggests that mathematical learning goals can serve as reference points for "sizing up" and guiding mathematical discussions of student work. When used by skilled teachers, goals become the "north star" by which to select and steer students' partially formed ideas toward important and shared mathematical ideas and concepts. There is emerging evidence that greater specificity of goals leads to better instruction, specifically to instruction in which the cognitive demand of high-level tasks is maintained throughout the lesson. Hunt and Stein (2016) found that teachers who had spent more time in a pre-observation conference with a coach clarifying goals by working and reflecting on the mathematics available in the task were also more likely to maintain the level of cognitive demand of that task when they actually enacted the task.

Diagnosing Students' Understanding

A second argument for identifying specific learning goals is that these types of learning goals will support teachers in diagnosing students' levels and ways of understanding the mathematics required to do instructional tasks (Hiebert, Morris, and Spitzer forthcoming). Even with a highly detailed learning goal, there is sometimes the need to break the goal into subgoals in order to be prepared to "analyze student thinking with sufficient depth" (Phelps, Shore, and Spitzer 2014). For example, consider the learning goal from Phelps, Shore, and Spitzer (2014):

> Students will understand that in a number line model, a fraction a/b signifies a specific location, which is a distance of a multiples of the length of $1/b$ from 0. Students will recognize that this distance from 0 represents a quantity of size a/b. (p. 165)

Teachers may find it helpful to break this learning goal down even further into subgoals. For example,

> SC1. On a number line, each number signifies a unique point on the number line and quantifies the point's distance from 0 (magnitude).
>
> SC2. That distance—and any other equivalent distance or length on the number line—is equal to the quantity the number represents.
>
> SC3. A fraction a/b is the quantity (or magnitude on a number line) that equals a multiple of the unit fraction $1/b$.
>
> SC4. A unit fraction $1/b$ can be formed by partitioning the quantity 1 (or its magnitude on the number line) into b equal units.
>
> SC5. Exactly b copies of the magnitude of $1/b$ results in a magnitude of 1.
>
> (Phelps, Shore, and Spitzer 2014, p. 165)

Without unpacking the learning goal into these subconcepts, a teacher might not initially know what evidence to look for in student work that would indicate partial or complete understanding of the learning goal. The high degree of specificity of these subconcepts makes the intended evidence much easier to identify.

Developing Mathematical Knowledge for Teaching

A third argument for specifying learning goals is that, in theory, the work in which teachers engage in order to specify learning goals will help them develop better understandings of the content. As teachers analyze students' work or use curricular materials to refine learning goals, they are developing deeper specialized content knowledge (Ball, Thames, and Phelps 2008; Hiebert et al. 2007). For example, teachers could develop a deeper understanding of students' common solution strategies or difficulties they encounter when trying to achieve a particular learning goal. Furthermore, teachers will not only develop a deeper understanding of how all of the concepts, ideas, and procedures underlying learning goals across multiple lessons are related but also how they build on each other. As learning goals become more specific, the connections between different lesson-level learning goals become more easily identifiable.

A relatively recent development that holds promise for specifying the pathways that students traverse as they learn mathematical concepts over time is the identification of students' learning progressions in various domains of mathematics (Simon 1995). These trajectories could be especially useful in supplying a map of the terrain that lies between "where students are" and "where they need to be" (the goal of the lesson or unit). As teachers develop a better understanding of the concepts, ideas, and procedures underlying learning goals across multiple lessons, they should have a better idea how these learning goals build on each other. Examples of learning progressions can be found at http://ime .math.arizona.edu/progressions/ or http://turnonccmath .net/index.php).

Learning progressions map the successively more sophisticated ways students think about a topic over a broad span of time (National Research Council 2007). So, essentially, learning progressions can be viewed as a mapping out of lesson-level learning goals over a span of time and, ideally, highlight connections between

lesson-level learning goals. They are researcher-conjectured and supported by empirical research (Confrey et al. 2009). Although defined differently by different researchers, most agree that the progression of cognition represented in a learning progression is not necessarily linear, but it is also not random (Confrey and Maloney 2010). They also agree that instruction plays a critical role in students' development along a learning trajectory (Daro, Mosher, and Corcoran 2011).

The lion's share of research in this area consists of studies that conjecture and test various learning progressions. Increasingly, though, there are calls for research on how learning trajectory-based tools *can be used by teachers* as they prepare for and teach lessons. Several such studies (as reported in Sztajn et al. 2012) have found that teachers' knowledge of learning trajectories "can support growth in mathematical knowledge, selection of instructional tasks, interactions with students in classroom contexts and use of students' responses to further learning" (p. 148).

Recent research suggests that teachers' opportunities to study a learning-based trajectory (in this case, a pathway that students traverse as they learn about equipartitioning [see Confrey et al. 2009]) can also shape the kinds of goals they set for student learning. Specifically, Edgington (2012) found that teachers' knowledge of the equipartioning learning trajectory helped them to more clearly specify learning goals. Additional research within this same project extended this finding with a design study that examined *how* teachers used the specific dimensions of the learning trajectory (i.e., proficiency levels and task parameters) to create their goals (Wilson et al. 2015). For example, a third-grade teacher stated that her goal was for students to "construct a fair share from multiple wholes and practice naming a mixed number." This goal directly referenced the terminology from the multiple wholes and naming proficiency level of the learning trajectory.

In these studies of teachers' use of learning trajectories, goals are defined as increasingly sophisticated versions of student thinking as they get closer to a full understanding of a key mathematical concept or big idea. In other words, higher levels of student thinking along the trajectory can be viewed as the goals for students less far along. In this way, teachers can be assured that goals are not only specific and cast in the language of mathematics but also that they are sequenced in an order that research suggests is most logical to the learner.

The Process of Specifying Learning Goals

The articulation of specific learning goals is hard work. As noted earlier, it is difficult to develop learning goals that go beyond general statements of what students should learn as a result of the planned lesson (Hunt and Stein 2016). In early attempts to do so, teachers often request feedback from others and want to know: "Is this a good learning goal?" or "Is this the correct learning goal?"

Another way to think about goals is as "hypotheses about what specific ideas students must learn to achieve broader, value-based goals" (such as standards) (Hiebert, Morris, and Spitzer forthcoming). According to this perspective, learning goals identify the intended content students should learn by the end of an individual lesson (i.e., *not* for multiple lessons, a unit, or a course) and are viewed as hypotheses about what students should learn by the end of a lesson. Teachers learn how their instruction is (or is not) benefiting students by (a) setting learning goals (hypotheses about what students should learn) and then (b) analyzing evidence from student work to assess the extent to which those learning goals are reached. The in-depth examination of evidence can then lead to refined learning goals.

If learning goals are thought of as hypotheses, teachers can write learning goal statements in ways that make the most sense to them. For example, if teachers write learning target statements from the students' perspective (e.g., "I will understand why the common denominator algorithm works for subtraction of fractions according to the 'take away' meaning of subtraction.") for their learning goals, these learning goal hypotheses can be refined and tested over time, as long as the teachers' learning goal statements identify the content they want their students to learn for individual lessons (see Hiebert, Morris, and Spitzer forthcoming).

In the next sections, a different set of questions is posed to help focus teachers' thinking when specifying learning goals. Because learning goals can be thought of as hypotheses, a teacher's answers to these questions might change, evolve, or become more detailed over time.

Identifying Content

As noted earlier, teachers have competing goals for mathematics instruction (Lampert 1985, 2001), such as learning goals (e.g., "students will understand why the common denominator algorithm for addition of fractions works"), student engagement goals (e.g., Common Core Standards for Mathematical Practice) (NGA Center and CCSSO 2010), or social justice learning goals (e.g., "relating mathematics to all cultures so all students can be involved") (Bartell 2013, p. 139). These other types of goals can be just as important, but they are not the focus of what this chapter aims to help teachers learn how to do, that is, write *learning* goals. For example, it is important for students to engage in the Common Core Standards for Mathematical Practice (e.g., make sense of problems and persevere in solving them). In particular, conceptual understanding necessitates these practices. So, having other goals related to how students will engage with the mathematics is important for students' conceptual learning, but these other types of goals are not about the content students should learn by the end of a lesson.

Identifying the Type of Understanding

The CCSSM focuses on both conceptual understanding and procedural understanding. Conceptual understanding consists of "mental connections among mathematical facts, procedures, and ideas" (Hiebert and Grouws 2007, p. 380). Consequently, it makes sense that conceptual learning goals should focus on these types of connections. For example, consider the following learning goal: "Students will understand how the slope of a linear equation is represented in the tabular, graphical, and symbolic representations of that equation and understand relationships between these different representations of slope." The first part of the learning goal (students will understand how the slope of a linear function is represented in the tabular, graphical, and symbolic representations of that equation) might only require procedural understanding if the different connections between the representations are not made explicit. For example, a student easily might be able to calculate slope from a table or graph or identify the slope by looking at the linear function without considering connections between these representations. Another student could recognize that the ratio of the difference in *y*-values to the difference in *x*-values for any two points in a tabular representation of a linear function remains constant. The same student could then discover that this ratio represents the relationship of the vertical change to the horizontal change of any two points on the graph of the line. This student is able to identify a relationship between the slope represented in a table and the slope represented in a graph. In table 1.1, for each consecutive increase in *x*-values, the *y*-values increase by 2. Similarly, in figure 3, a student can count the vertical difference between two points on the graph and the horizontal difference between two points on the graph to calculate the ratio of 2/1.

Table 1.1
Table of values for finding slope

x	*y*
−2	1
−1	3
0	5
1	7
2	9

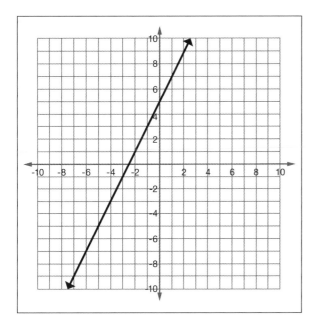

Fig. 1.3. Graph for finding slope

The point is, without considering these connections, the learning goal would only be procedural in nature. Just because students are asked to use different representations does not mean the learning goal necessarily is about conceptual understanding, unless connections are made between these different representations.

At first glance, some action words in learning goals might appear to be about conceptual understanding. For example, consider the following learning goal: "Students will explain the common denominator algorithm for subtraction of fractions." Because this learning goal requires students to explain, one might think this learning goal supports conceptual understanding. But, due to the vagueness of this learning goal, the teacher might intend for students to explain only the algorithm procedurally, step-by-step. If the learning goal is more specified to state, "Students will explain why the common denominator algorithm for subtraction of fractions works according to the 'take away' meaning of subtraction," then this learning goal now requires connections between the take-away meaning of subtraction and the common denominator algorithm to be able to achieve it. Consequently, this new learning goal requires conceptual understanding.

Using Student Work to Refine Learning Goals

Teachers will likely have difficulty specifying learning goals the first time they teach a course, and research suggests that time spent in trying to write "the perfect learning goal" may not pay off. Rather, teachers can turn to curricular materials as a resource (Drake, Land, and Tyminski 2014) or seek knowledge from colleagues who have taught the course in the past to support them in specifying learning goals for the first time. After that, making the process of refining learning goals a deliberate part of practice can be a way to systematically try to improve instruction (and learning goals) over time. According to Hiebert and colleagues (forthcoming), there is no such thing as a perfectly written learning goal, but it is important to analyze evidence against a learning goal to try to improve instruction over time and to diagnose students' competence.

So, if there is no such thing as a perfect learning goal statement, then when is a learning goal specific enough? Because learning goals are our best hypotheses about what students should be able to understand at the end of a lesson, the learning goal might not ever be specific enough. But, ideally, as a teacher refines a learning goal over time, the learning goal should become more specified. Figure 1.4 shows an example of a learning goal that seems pretty specific because it uses the language of the subject and it unpacks the learning goal into subgoals (Hiebert et al. 2007; Hiebert, Morris, and Spitzer forthcoming).

Students will be able to compare fractions without converting the fractions to decimals or percents.

- The numerator represents the number of pieces of size 1/*n*.

- The denominator represents the size of the pieces. Therefore, we need to represent fractions in terms of the same size pieces to be able to compare them.

Fig. 1.4. Learning goal for subtraction of fractions

Imagine a teacher named Mrs. Barnes teaches a lesson to the learning goal in figure 1.4. One of the tasks the teacher uses during the lesson to help students achieve this learning goal is shown in figure 1.5. Figure 1.6 includes some hypothetical student solution strategies to the task in figure 1.5.

Compare $5/7$ and $3/5$ without converting the fractions to decimals or percents. Which one is bigger?

Fig. 1.5. Task to meet the learning goal

After analyzing the students' solution strategies, Mrs. Barnes realizes there was something important missing from the learning goal. In particular, she realizes after analyzing solution strategy 3 the importance of both fractions having the same referent, in this case the same size whole. It appears the student who used solution strategy 3 did not understand that the fractions have to be referring to the same whole and instead made the pieces the same size before drawing two wholes of the same size.

Solution Strategy Number	Students' Solution Strategy
1	I folded one fraction strip into 7 equal-sized pieces and shaded in 5 of them to represent 5/7. I folded another fraction strip into 5 equal-sized pieces and shaded in 3 of them to represent 3/5. 5/7 is slightly larger than 3/5 because a larger piece of the whole fraction strip is shaded. 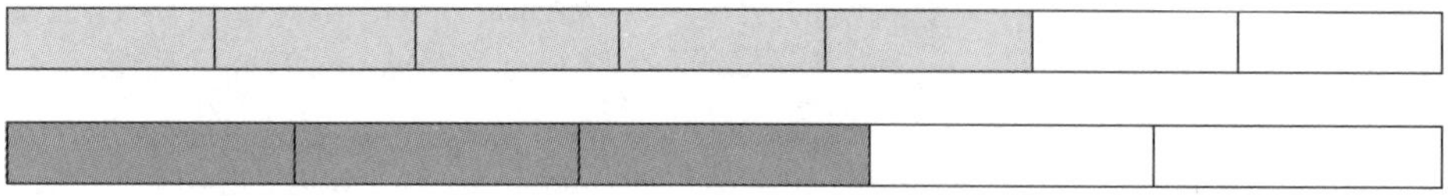
2	5/7 has 5 pieces of size 1/7. 3/5 has 3 pieces of size 1/5. 1/5 pieces are bigger than 1/7 size pieces because the whole is divided into only 5 equal-sized pieces instead of 7. For 5/7, we only need 2 more pieces to fill the whole. For 3/5, we also only need two more pieces to fill the whole, but the pieces need to fill the whole are bigger. 5/7 is bigger than 3/5 because the pieces needed to fill the whole for 5/7 are smaller.
3	5/7 is bigger because the shaded area is larger. 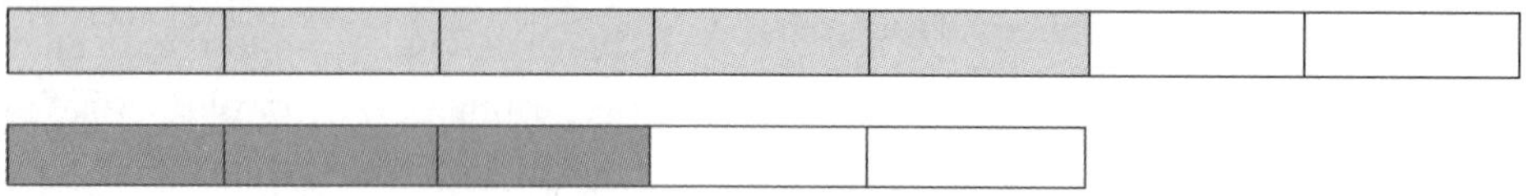

Fig. 1.6. Possible student solutions to the task

Mrs. Barnes also realizes that the students did not necessarily need equal-sized pieces to compare the fractions. Solution strategy 2 uses understanding of the meaning of the numerator (the number of pieces of size $1/n$) and the meaning of the denominator (the size of the pieces) to reason how far away each fraction is from 1.

Based on these analyses, Mrs. Barnes refined her learning goal to reflect the importance of the referent and the reasoning strategy that did not require equal-sized pieces. Mrs. Barnes' revised learning goal is shown in figure 1.7.

Students will be able to compare fractions using different strategies (e.g., compare fractions by representing the fractions in terms of the same-sized pieces and determining the distance away each fraction is from 1) without converting the fractions to decimals or percents.

- *In order to be able to compare fractions, the fractions must be in reference to the same-sized whole.*

- The numerator represents the number of pieces of size $1/n$.

- The denominator represents the size of the pieces. ~~Therefore, we need to represent fractions in terms of the same size pieces to be able to compare them.~~

Fig. 1.7. Revised learning goal

Some studies have found that analyzing solution strategies can be supportive for teachers in helping them identify concepts or ideas underlying a learning goal (Meikle 2016; Phelps and Spitzer 2012). In particular, Phelps and Spitzer (2012) found that comparing and contrasting different solution strategies was supportive for teachers in analyzing evidence in the solution strategies for concepts. The example of Mrs. Barnes above demonstrates the need to analyze multiple solution strategies or pieces of data from a lesson. Solution Strategies 2 and 3 helped Mrs. Barnes refine the learning goal, but in different ways. Consequently, they both were needed to help her refine the learning goal.

Conclusion

We stand at an interesting moment in time; the public is calling for increased levels of academic rigor in the classroom, and states are now more empowered to demand rigorous instruction and higher levels of student achievement. States and districts also can decide whether and how to design and provide the resources for professional development needed to attain those levels of instructional rigor and student success. The deep levels of student understanding called for by the CCSSM will require renewed effort on the part of teachers and teacher educators to prepare for and deliver high-quality lessons. The design, identification, and/or adaptation of learning goals will surely need to be a part of this process.

Teachers have access to a range of resources, many of which purport to contain learning goals, albeit under a variety of names and different meanings. As noted earlier, there may be educational objectives that teachers are required to address by their school, district, or state/province. Some districts specify learning targets; others require that teachers use the Common Core or state/province standards as learning goals. Depending on their specific content, these may be more or less suitable to serve as learning goals for a particular lesson.

Some scholars have cautioned that many learning goals are susceptible to the *name* of the entity becoming the thing that is taught and learned instead of the ideas, connections, and reasoning that underlie the entity. As noted by Daro, Mosher, and Corcoran (2011), what students need to learn comprises

> mental actions on mental objects, reasoning maneuvers and rules, representational systems and languages for mathematical objects and relations, cognitive schema and strategies, webs of structured knowledge, conventions, and so on. (p. 47)

They go on to say that many of the "things" that we want students to learn are not things at all but systems that interact with other systems in thinking, knowing, and doing. Unfortunately, a complete cognitive "map" of this system—an overview of the mathematical terrain driven by the logic of student thinking—does not (yet) exist. What does exist are standards, textbooks, pacing guides, and assessments. All of these name and provide labels for competencies but do not unpack the learning or the understanding that undergirds them. Yet, because of their prevalence in the learning environment, things such as interim assessments often become the goals for day-to-day lessons. As Daro and colleagues aptly note, "Teachers end up teaching the standards instead of teaching mathematics" (2011, p. 48).

The approaches outlined in this chapter are not quick fixes, but they promise to lead to teaching that is informed by the mental processes that underlie the development of deep conceptual understanding rather than attribute labels to it. They situate responsibility for recognizing and productively using and/or developing specific learning goals directly with the teacher. Whether she is using a well-articulated learning trajectory to situate her learning goal for the day or is constructing her own learning goal in terms of a hypothesis of what students should learn from her lesson, the teacher will need to be deeply knowledgeable about and deeply engaged with the notion of what and how students are learning.

References

Ball, Deborah Loewenberg. "With an Eye on the Mathematical Horizon: Dilemmas of Teaching Elementary School Mathematics." *Elementary School Journal* 93, no. 4 (1993): 373–97.

———. "Teaching, with Respect to Mathematics and Students." In *Beyond Classical Pedagogy: Teaching Elementary School Mathematics*, edited by Terry Wood, Barbara Scott Nelson, and Janet E. Warfield, pp. 11–22. Mahwah, N.J.: Erlbaum, 2001.

Ball, Deborah Loewenberg, Mark Hoover Thames, and Geoffrey Phelps. "Content Knowledge for Teaching: What Makes it Special"? *Journal of Teacher Education* 59, no. 5 (2008): 389–407.

Bartell, Tonya. "Learning to Teach Mathematics for Social Justice: Negotiating Social Justice and Mathematical Goals." *Journal for Research in Mathematics Education* 44, no. 1 (2013): 129–63.

Boaler, Jo, and Cathy Humphreys. *Connecting Mathematical Ideas: Middle School Video Cases to Support Teaching and Learning.* Vol. 1. Portsmouth, N.H.: Heinemann, 2005.

Charles, Randall I. "Big Ideas and Understandings as the Foundation for Elementary and Middle School Mathematics." *Journal of Mathematics Education* 7, no. 3 (2005): 9–24.

Confrey, Jere, and Alan Maloney. "The Construction, Refinement, and Early Validation of the Equipartitioning Learning Trajectory." In *Learning in the Disciplines: Proceedings of the 9th International Conference of the Learning Sciences–Volume 1, Full Papers*, edited by Kimberly Gomez, Leilah Lyons, and Joshua Radinsky, pp. 968–75. Chicago: International Society of the Learning Sciences, 2010.

Confrey, Jere, Alan Maloney, Kenny H. Nguyen, Gemma Mojica, and Marielle Myers. "Equipartitioning/Splitting as a Foundation of Rational Number Reasoning Using Learning Trajectories." Paper presented at the 33rd Conference of the International Group for the Psychology of Mathematics Education, Thessaloniki, Greece, July 19–24, 2009.

Daro, Phil, Frederic A. Mosher, and Tom Corcoran. *Learning Trajectories in Mathematics: A Foundation for Standards, Curriculum, Assessment, and Instruction.* CPRE Research Report #RR-68. Madison, Wis.: Consortium for Policy Research in Education, 2011.

Drake, Corey, Tonia Land, and Andrew Tyminski. "Using Educative Curriculum Materials to Support the Development of Prospective Teachers' Knowledge." *Educational Researcher* 43, no. 3 (2014): 154–62.

Edgington, Cynthia Page. "Teachers' Uses of a Learning Trajectory to Support Attention to Students' Mathematical Thinking." PhD diss., North Carolina State University, Raleigh, 2012.

Hiebert, James, Thomas Carpenter, Elizabeth Fennema, Karen Fuson, Diana Wearne, et al. *Making Sense: Teaching and Learning Mathematics with Understanding.* Portsmouth, N.H.: Heinemann, 1997.

Hiebert, James, and Douglas A. Grouws. "The Effects of Classroom Mathematics Teaching on Students' Learning." In *Second Handbook of Research on Mathematics Teaching and Learning*, edited by Frank K. Lester Jr., pp. 371–404. Charlotte, N.C: Information Age Publishing, and Reston, Va.: National Council of Teachers of Mathematics, 2007.

Hiebert, James, Anne K. Morris, Dawn Berk, and Amanda Jansen. "Preparing Teachers to Learn from Teaching." *Journal of Teacher Education* 58, no. 1 (2007): 47–61.

Hiebert, J., Anne K. Morris, and S. M. Spitzer. "Diagnosing Learning Goals: An Often Overlooked Teaching Competency." In *Diagnostic Competence in Mathematics Teacher Education*, edited by K. Philipp, T. Leuders, and J. Leuders. New York: Springer, forthcoming.

Hunt, Jessica, and Mary Kay Stein. "Coaching and Mathematical Goal Setting." Unpublished manuscript, last modified November 15, 2016.

Lampert, Magdalene. "How Do Teachers Manage to Teach? Perspectives on Problems of Practice." *Harvard Educational Review* 55, no. 2 (1985): 178–95.

———. *Teaching Problems and the Problems of Teaching.* New Haven, Conn.: Yale University Press, 2001.

Meikle, Erin. "Exploring Factors That Influence Pre-service Teachers' Selections of Solution Strategies for Discussion." Unpublished manuscript, last modified October 22, 2016.

Mills, Valerie L. "Redefining the Work of Teaching: Acknowledging What it Takes to Prepare Powerful and Productive Mathematics Lessons." *National Council of Supervisors of Mathematics Newsletter* 46, no. 1 (2015): 4–6.

Morris, Anne K., James Hiebert, and Sandy M. Spitzer. "Mathematical Knowledge for Teaching in Planning and Evaluation Instruction: What Can Preservice Teachers Learn?" *Journal for Research in Mathematics Education* 40, no. 5 (2009): 491–529.

National Council of Teachers of Mathematics (NCTM). *Principles to Actions: Ensuring Mathematical Success for All.* Reston, Va.: NCTM, 2014.

National Governors Association Center for Best Practices (NGA Center) and Council of Chief State School Officers (CCSSO). *Common Core State Standards for Mathematics.* Washington, D.C.: NGA Center and CCSSO, 2010. http://www.corestandards.org

National Research Council. *Taking Science to School.* Washington, D.C.: National Academy Press, 2007.

Phelps, Christine, Felice Shore, and Sandy Spitzer. "Using Classroom Evidence to Inform and Improve Teaching." In *Annual Perspectives in Mathematics Education 2014: Using Research to Improve Instruction*, edited by K. Karp and A. R. McDuffie, pp. 163–70. Reston, VA: National Council of Teachers of Mathematics, 2014.

Phelps, Christine, and Sandy Spitzer. "Systematically Improving Lessons in Teacher Education: What's Good for Prospective Teachers Is Good for Teacher Educators." *Teacher Educator* 47 (2012): 328–47.

Schoenfeld, Alan H. "Toward a Theory of Teaching-in-Context." *Issues in Education* 4, no. 1 (1998): 1–94.

Simon, Martin A. "Reconstructing Mathematics Pedagogy from a Constructivist Perspective." *Journal for Research in Mathematics Education* 26, no. 2 (1995): 114–45.

Smith, Margaret S., and Mary Kay Stein. *5 Practices for Orchestrating Productive Mathematics Discussions.* Reston, Va.: National Council of Teachers of Mathematics, 2011.

Sztajn, Paola, Jere Confrey, P. Holt Wilson, and Cynthia Edgington. "Learning Trajectory Based Instruction: Toward a Theory of Teaching." *Educational Researcher* 41, no. 5 (2012): 147–56.

Wilson, P. Holt, Paola Sztajn, Cyndi Edgington, and Marrielle Myers. "Teachers' Uses of a Learning Trajectory in Student-Centered Instructional Practices." *Journal of Teacher Education* 66, no. 3 (2015): 227–44.

Chapter 2

Implementing Tasks That Promote Reasoning and Problem Solving

Successes and Obstacles in Making Day-to-Day Mathematics High Level

Melissa D. Boston and Kayla Madler, *Duquesne University*
Christopher Cutone, *Dorseyville Middle School, Fox Chapel School District, Pittsburgh, Pennsylvania*

"Is there a way to make the day-to-day more high-level? . . . That's what I have been wrestling with all year in my algebra class."

Across decades of research, tasks that promote reasoning and problem solving have been identified as essential in supporting students' learning of mathematics with understanding (Doyle 1983; Silver 2010; Stein, Grover, and Henningsen 1996). Research provides examples of teachers, schools, and districts successfully selecting and implementing tasks that promote reasoning and problem solving (Boaler and Staples 2008; Boston and Smith 2009; Stein and Lane 1996; Tarr et al. 2008). However, research also indicates that the use of such tasks in teaching mathematics has not taken hold on a national scale (Hiebert et al. 2003; Kane and Staiger 2012; Weiss et al. 2003). This suggests the presence of common and overarching obstacles in selecting and implementing tasks that promote reasoning and problem solving in the work that teachers do on a daily basis in teaching mathematics.

The research summarized in this chapter identifies the importance and complexity of implementing tasks that promote reasoning and problem solving. *Principles to Actions: Ensuring Mathematical Success for All* asserts, "For students to learn mathematics with understanding, they must have opportunities to engage *on a regular basis* with tasks that focus on reasoning and problem solving and make possible multiple entry points and varied

solution strategies" (NCTM 2014, p. 23; emphasis added). To illustrate the complexities of implementing tasks that promote reasoning and problem solving on a "regular basis," consider the quote at the start of this chapter, a sentiment that was expressed during the last day of a year-long professional development workshop focused on the selection and implementation of cognitively challenging mathematical tasks:

> *Teacher 1*: . . . [Thinking Through a Lesson Protocol] is useful for high-level tasks but not for an everyday lesson.
>
> *Facilitator [referring to tasks teachers had previously identified as having high-level demands (fig. 2.1) and low-level demands (fig. 2.2)]*: Does this suggest that a high-level task can't be an everyday lesson? So you have occasions where you do the "S-Pattern" [*fig. 2.1*] and you have days where you learn FOIL [*fig. 2.2*]?
>
> *Teacher 2*: Where I thought you were going . . . Is there a way to make the day-to-day more high-level? . . . That's what I have been wrestling with all year in my algebra class. (Boston 2013, p. 28)

This discussion lasted approximately fifteen minutes, with contributions from four additional teachers, and thirteen (of eighteen) teachers referring to this discussion in their final reflections or interviews. The discussion highlights the tension between teaching with high-level tasks (e.g., tasks that promote reasoning and problem solving) and teachers' typical practices (Johnson et al. 2016), their own day-to-day experiences in

The ESP Professional development workshop discussed in this chapter was supported by a grant from the National Science Foundation (DUE-0301962). Any opinions expressed herein are those of the authors and do not necessarily represent the views of the Foundation. The authors would like to thank the ESP Principal Investigators: Margaret (Peg) Smith, Ellen Ansell, Beverly Michaels, and Paul Gartside, all from the University of Pittsburgh. The first and third authors would also like to thank Peg Smith for her ongoing support personally and for her work in the field at large, particularly in bringing research-to-practice around the implementation of tasks that promote reasoning and problem solving.

teaching (and learning) mathematics, and perhaps the everyday tasks available in their curriculum.

We begin this chapter with a review of research establishing both the importance and the complexity of *Principles to Actions*' effective teaching practice of "implementing tasks that promote reasoning and problem solving" (NCTM 2014, p. 17). We then provide the perspectives of a middle school mathematics teacher (Chris Cutone, third author) and a secondary mathematics preservice teacher (Kayla Madler, second author) on the successes and obstacles encountered when implementing tasks that promote reasoning and problem solving. We close by connecting their successes and obstacles to ideas in *Principles to Actions* and prevalent research findings. By identifying how research and theories reflect the experiences of teachers and preservice teachers (PSTs), we hope to provide insight and ideas that support teachers' and PSTs' selection and implementation of tasks that promote reasoning and problem solving in the day-to-day teaching of mathematics.

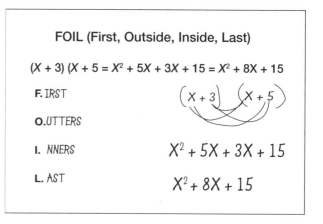

Fig. 2.2. The FOIL procedure

Tasks That Promote Reasoning and Problem Solving

A *mathematical task* is defined as a set of problems or a single complex problem that focuses students' attention on a particular mathematical idea (Stein, Grover, and Henningsen 1996). Doyle (1983) defined *tasks* to include the intellectual and physical products expected of students, the operations students might use to obtain those products, and the resources available to create those products. Doyle posited that "tasks form the basic treatment unit in classrooms" (1983, p. 162) because tasks focus students' attention on specific mathematical concepts, and tasks set parameters for how students are to engage with mathematical concepts. In other words, students have an opportunity to learn the concepts and processes embedded in the tasks they complete, and they have far less opportunity to learn concepts and processes not embedded in tasks (Hiebert et al. 1997; Stein, Grover, and Henningsen 1996).

A rich history of research identifies the importance of tasks that promote reasoning and problem solving in supporting students' learning of mathematics (e.g., Boaler and Staples 2008; Hiebert and Wearne 1993; Stein and Lane 1996; Tarr et al. 2008). Previous literature used labels such as "worthwhile tasks" (NCTM 2000), "cognitively challenging" or "high-level" tasks (Stein, Grover, and Henningsen 1996), and "making connections" tasks (Hiebert et al. 2003). Hiebert and colleagues (1997) identified three important features of tasks that promote reasoning and problem solving:

S-Pattern Task

Write a description that could be used to define any figure in the pattern shown below, including an expression for the total number of square tiles in the figure. You may use drawings, words, and numbers to determine your expression. Your answer should be clear enough so that another person could read it and understand your thinking. After describing the pattern one way, find a second way and show that the expression is equivalent to the expression for your first pattern.

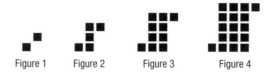

Figure 1   Figure 2   Figure 3   Figure 4

Fig. 2.1. The S-Pattern task. Adapted from Linda Cooper Foreman and Albert B. Bennett Jr., *Visual Mathematics Course 2,* lessons 1–10, The Math Learning Center, mathlearningcenter.org.

(1) the mathematics is problematic for students—students see the task as an interesting and challenging problem to solve; (2) the task connects with students' prior knowledge—students must be able to use existing knowledge to develop a method for solving the problem; and (3) the task engages students in thinking about important mathematics. Furthermore, Stein and colleagues (1996, 2009) delineated two categories of tasks with higher level cognitive demands (or high-level tasks): "doing mathematics" (open-ended tasks that require complex and non-algorithmic thinking) and "procedures with connections" (tasks that suggest a broad general procedure in order to support students' development and/or understanding of mathematical concepts and procedures). Stein and colleagues' work also identified two categories of tasks with lower level cognitive demands: "memorization" (recall of facts, definitions, or formulas) and "procedures without connections" (rote application of procedures).

Selecting and Implementing Tasks That Promote Reasoning and Problem Solving

"Implementing tasks that promote reasoning and problem solving" (NCTM 2014, p. 17) is one of eight effective Mathematics Teaching Practices outlined in *Principles to Actions*. The authors of *PtA* assert that "effective teaching of mathematics engages students in solving and discussing tasks that promote mathematical reasoning and problem solving and allow multiple entry points and varied solution strategies" (p. 17). In fact, large national studies (e.g., Cobb and Smith 2008; Kane and Staiger 2012; Weiss et al. 2003) and international studies (e.g., Hiebert et al. 2003) have analyzed the selection and implementation of cognitively challenging tasks as a measure of the nature and quality of mathematics instruction in the United States and abroad.

Principles to Actions summarizes three major research findings on the use of mathematical tasks generated over the last two decades. First, "Not all tasks provide the same opportunities for student thinking and learning" (NCTM 2014, p. 17). Based on the findings of several large-scale studies (e.g., Cobb and Smith 2008; Hiebert et al. 2003; Kane and Stagier 2012; Silver and Stein 1996), tasks appear to "set the ceiling" for students' engagement in reasoning and problem solving throughout a lesson (Boston and Wilhelm 2015):

> Tasks with low cognitive demands simply do not provide fodder for teachers to engage students in thinking, reasoning, or mathematical discourse. . . . If opportunities for high-level thinking and reasoning are not embedded in instructional tasks, these opportunities rarely materialize during mathematics lessons. This finding, robust in its consistency across several studies, suggests that . . . high-level instructional tasks are a necessary condition for ambitious mathematics instruction. (p. 24)

Hence, selecting tasks that promote reasoning and problem solving is an essential first step in supporting students' learning of mathematics with understanding.

Second, "Student learning is greatest in classrooms where tasks consistently encourage high-level student thinking and reasoning and least in classrooms where tasks are routinely procedural in nature" (NCTM 2014, p. 17). Research examining differences in mathematics teaching and learning between teachers and schools using different types of curriculum consistently associates higher student achievement with mathematics curricula containing cognitively challenging tasks at the elementary level (Fuson, Carroll, and Druek 2000; Hiebert and Wearne 1993; Schoenfeld 2002), middle school level (Cai et al. 2011; Post et al. 2008; Reys et al. 2003; Riordan and Noyce 2001; Stein and Lane 1996; Tarr et al. 2008), and high school level (Boaler and Staples 2008; Grouws et al. 2013; Ridgeway et al. 2003; Schoen et al. 2003). Research originating with the QUASAR project (Quantitative Understanding: Amplifying Student Achievement and Reasoning; Silver and Stein 1996) highlights the importance of task implementation as *the key factor* affecting students' learning. Stein and Lane (1996) found significantly higher learning gains on a test of reasoning and problem solving for students whose teachers regularly maintained high-level demands. Similarly, Schoenfeld (2002) identified significantly higher student achievement in elementary and middle school classrooms with teachers rated as "high implementers" of reform-oriented mathematics curricula than students having teachers rated as "low implementers." In the Third International Mathematics and Science Study (TIMSS) (Hiebert et al. 2003), task implementation at the level of "making connections" was significantly higher in countries whose students outperformed U.S. students, even though percentages of "making connections" tasks were not significantly different. In other words, while different countries selected similar percentages of high-level tasks for mathematics instruction, significant differences occurred in the percentages of tasks implemented at a high level, and these differences were associated with student achievement.

Third, "Tasks with high cognitive demands are the most difficult to implement well and are often transformed into less demanding tasks during instruction" (NCTM 2014, p. 17). As described by Stein and colleagues (2009), the cognitive demands of a task can be maintained or can decline as the task is implemented during instruction. Classroom observation studies consistently identify large percentages of lessons that begin with high-level tasks but do not maintain students' engagement in high-level thinking (Boston and Wilhelm 2015). In TIMSS, while 15 percent of tasks in U.S.

lessons began at the "making connections" level, less than 1 percent of tasks were implemented in ways that provided opportunities for students to engage in "making connections" (Hiebert et al. 2003). Discomfort with the "productive struggle" that often accompanies high-level tasks can lead students to press the teacher for step-by-step directions, thereby reducing the cognitive demands. (See chapter 7 for a more detailed description of productive struggle.) Alternatively, by asking questions, encouraging conceptual connections, and holding students accountable for explanations and meaning, teachers can maintain students' engagement in high-level thinking and reasoning throughout a lesson (Henningsen and Stein 1997). Henningsen and Stein (1997) identified a set of classroom-based factors

Factors Associated with the Decline of High-level Cognitive Demands	Factors Associated with the Maintenance of High-level Cognitive Demands
1. Problematic aspects of the task become routinized (e.g., students press the teacher to reduce the complexity of the task by specifying explicit procedures or steps to perform; the teacher "takes over" the thinking and reasoning and tells students how to do the problem).	1. Scaffolding of students' thinking and reasoning
2. The teacher shifts the emphasis from meaning, concepts, or understanding to the correctness or completeness of the answer.	2. Students are provided with means of monitoring their own progress.
3. Not enough time is provided to wrestle with the demanding aspects of the task or too much time is allowed and students drift into off-task behavior.	3. Teacher or capable students model high-level performance.
4. Classroom management problems prevent sustained engagement in high-level cognitive activities.	4. Sustained press for justifications, explanations, and/or meaning through teacher questioning, comments, and/or feedback
5. Inappropriateness of tasks for a given group of students (e.g., students do not engage in high-level cognitive activities due to lack of interest, motivation, or prior knowledge needed to perform; task expectations not clear enough to put students in the right cognitive space).	5. Tasks build on students' prior knowledge.
6. Students are not held accountable for high-level products or processes (e.g., although asked to explain their thinking, unclear or incorrect student explanations are accepted; students are given the impression that their work will not "count" toward a grade).	6. Teacher draws frequent conceptual connections. 7. Sufficient time to explore (not too little, not too much)

Figure 2.3. Factors associated with the maintenance and decline of high-level cognitive demands
(Henningsen and Stein 1997)

(fig. 2.3) that serve to support or inhibit students' engagement in thinking and reasoning.

Research highlights the value of professional development (Arbaugh et al. 2006; Boston and Smith 2009, 2011; Marrongelle, Sztajn, and Smith 2013; Senk and Thompson 2003) and teacher preparation (Franke, Kazemi, and Battey 2007; Steele and Hillen 2012) for supporting mathematics teachers and preservice teachers to implement cognitively challenging tasks. In contrast to studies of national samples of U.S. classrooms, research in the classrooms of teachers pursuing professional development focused on the selection and implementation of cognitively challenging tasks provides far more positive results (e.g., McMeeking, Orsi, and Cobb 2012; Shoen et al. 2003; Tarr et al. 2008). For example, Boston and Wilhelm (2015) identified significant differences in high-level task implementation (53.7% vs. 3.5%) between observed mathematics lessons in a district with ongoing, content-focused professional development compared to a district with minimal professional development opportunities.

Research has also generated a variety of tools and professional development materials to support teachers' selection and implementation of high cognitive demand tasks during a lesson. Here are a few examples:

- The "Task Analysis Guide" (Smith and Stein 1998) and the "Task-Sorting Activity" (Smith et al. 2004) support task selection by engaging teachers in assessing the level of cognitive demand of mathematical tasks.

- "Thinking Through a Lesson Protocol" (Smith, Bill, and Hughes 2008) provides a tool for planning lessons around high-level tasks.

- Jackson and colleagues (2012) provide strategies for launching high-level tasks.

- The "5 Practices" provide a framework for orchestrating discussions that promote thinking and reasoning (Smith and Stein 2011) delineated from research (Stein et al. 2008).

- Classroom observation instruments originally designed for research can be used to support teachers' reflection task selection and implementation (cf. Boston et al. 2015).

Connecting to Practice

In this section, we provide the perspectives of a teacher (Chris Cutone) and a preservice teacher (Kayla Madler) on selecting and implementing tasks that promote reasoning and problem solving on a regular basis. When possible, we connect to research to provide rationales for successes and obstacles and suggestions for overcoming obstacles.

The Perspective of a Mathematics Teacher

I have been teaching middle school mathematics for eighteen years in a midsized school district noted for academic success. I participated in the "Enhancing Secondary Mathematics Teacher Preparation" (ESP) project (Boston and Smith 2009) during the 2004–2005 and 2005–2006 school years. In the second year of ESP, I served as mentor to a secondary mathematics PST during a year-long internship. The intern and I attended the third ESP workshop together, and she was experiencing the same ideas about tasks and task implementation in her teacher preparation courses that I was experiencing in the ESP project.

During this year, my school moved to full implementation of a new reform-oriented mathematics curriculum. I had been frustrated with the traditional text and the extent to which mathematics class seemed to promote rote mathematics. Students were "understanding" the lesson that day but not learning the mathematics long-term. The new curriculum featured great problems that engaged students, helped them to make connections among mathematical ideas, and allowed them to discover the mathematics (in other words, tasks that promoted reasoning and problem solving).

The new curriculum and professional development converged at a point in my teaching (at eight years of experience) where I was looking to change, but I did not know what that change would be. The new curriculum provided high-level tasks and detailed teacher materials to guide the implementation of the lesson, and ESP provided strategies such as asking questions that assess and advance students' understanding, and facilitating whole-group discussions. Furthermore, mentoring an intern provided the unique opportunity of having a collaborator in the classroom on a daily basis. We were able to observe each other's teaching and reflect on what was working—or not working—supported by the tools, ideas, and strategies from the ESP workshop. Through opportunities to share ideas and work together to create and try new approaches, we developed and refined strategies and materials for implementing the new curriculum. To be sure, this was hard work (e.g., analyzing one's own teaching, sometimes critically; providing formative and sometimes critical feedback for the PST; considering and reconsidering different strategies; developing materials such as presentation slides, student handouts, communication with parents), time-consuming, and certainly not completed in one year. Still, it was well worth the initial effort.

Successes and Obstacles in Implementing Cognitively Challenging Tasks on a Regular Basis

Cutone identifies many important successes and challenges in selecting and implementing cognitively challenging tasks on a regular basis. Aspects of Cutone's experience can be generalized beyond his specific setting to inform other mathematics teachers and teacher educators engaged in this work.

Collegial support. Cutone attributes his long-term use of high-level tasks to collegial support. In piloting and fully implementing the curriculum, Cutone had the support of the mathematics teachers in his department, the mathematics curriculum coordinator, his peers in the ESP project, and the intern in his classroom. The success of reform efforts, such as selecting and implementing tasks that promote reasoning and problem solving, requires support at the district level and alignment with a district's vision of high-quality teaching (Cobb and Jackson 2011; Kaufman and Stein, 2010; Nelson and Sassi 2000). For example, adopting a reform-oriented curriculum often requires approval at the district level, and teaching in ways that promote reasoning and problem solving is more likely to be sustained when such practices align with a district's vision for high-quality teaching (e.g., with teacher-evaluation criteria).

At the classroom level, observing the PST's enactment of high-level tasks in the role of the mentor teacher allowed Cutone to see firsthand the factors

for supporting *or* inhibiting students' engagement in high-level thinking in action (fig. 2.3), to note what was effective, and to make suggestions or brainstorm with the intern for future adjustments (Boston and Smith 2011). Conversations between Cutone, the intern, and the university supervisor following lesson observations consistently emphasized aspects of the lesson central to implementing cognitively challenging tasks. This "reinforcing culture" (Sykes and Bird 1992) served to support both Cutone and the intern in considering how to maintain students' engagement throughout a lesson. More generally, teachers beginning the journey of selecting and implementing tasks that promote reasoning and problem solving with at least one other colleague can establish this same type of support and culture through collaborative planning, observing or video recording mathematics lessons, and reflecting on instruction using the tools identified in this chapter.

Tools and strategies. Research suggests that tools and frameworks for selecting and implementing cognitively challenging tasks are effective in changing, supporting, or enhancing teachers' practices (Arbaugh and

Books

Implementing Standards-Based Mathematics Instruction (Stein et al. 2009)

5 Practices for Orchestrating Mathematical Discussions (Smith and Stein 2011)

Improving Instruction in Algebra, Vol. 2 of *Using Cases to Transform Mathematics Teaching and Learning* (Smith, Silver, and Stein 2005)

Articles in NCTM journals

"Launching Complex Tasks" (Jackson et al. 2012)

"Thinking Through a Lesson: Successfully Implementing High-Level Tasks" (Smith, Bill, and Hughes 2008)

Web-based resources

NCTM *Principles to Actions* Toolkit (http://www.nctm.org/PtAToolkit/)

Fig. 2.4. Materials that can help in the selection and implementation of cognitively challenging tasks

Brown 2005; Boston and Smith 2009, 2011; National Academy of Education 1999). The ESP workshop provided many tools and strategies to support the selection and implementation of cognitively challenging tasks, and many of these materials (or materials created since then) are available in various formats. Some of these materials are listed in figure 2.4. Such materials could be used by teams of teachers engaged in book studies, professional learning communities, lesson study, or other types of face-to-face or online collaborations.

Getting started with tasks that promote reasoning and problem solving. The reform-oriented curriculum presented new ways of teaching and learning mathematics for Cutone and his students. Middle school students reacted to differences in the structure and format of mathematics classes from their previous experiences, as well as to the fact that they had to read in math class. To ease students' transition into the new curriculum and set the tone for the new way math class would operate, Cutone and his colleagues developed patterning task units (see Smith, Hillen, and Catania 2007) to implement in each of their courses at the beginning of the school year. Each teacher selected a few pattern tasks aligned with their course and grade level.

Specific to his course (Algebra, grade 8), Cutone selected patterns that would support students' understanding of quadratic relationships (e.g., how they grow, what they look like in a graph or table, how they compare to linear relationships), such as the S-Pattern task (fig. 2.1). Pattern tasks enable students to use and connect mathematical representations (see chapter 3) and use multiple strategies. Pattern tasks also provide a context for students to understand what a variable is, how to represent a quantity that varies, and functional relationships between the figure number and some quantitative aspect of the pattern (e.g., perimeter, area, number of tiles). By engaging in patterning tasks, students realize that there can be multiple strategies for solving a mathematics problem—and this can be revolutionary. Cutone describes his own experiences in solving a pattern task with other teachers in the ESP workshop: "I thought my strategy was the only way to solve it: how I solved it was how everyone else was solving it. But there were all these strategies from sixth-grade math through Algebra 1 and 2, statistics,

and calculus." Pattern tasks also provide opportunities for familiarizing students with norms for working in groups (see Lotan 2003 for characteristics of "group-worthy" tasks), sharing solutions with peers, and responding to teacher's questions (e.g., being asked to "explain your thinking" does not mean you have made a mistake).

Challenges in implementing high-level tasks *at a high level.* *PtA* states, "Although selecting tasks that promote reasoning and problem solving is a critical first step, giving the task to students does not guarantee that students will actually engage in the task at a high level" (NCTM 2014, p. 22). The comparison of two teaching episodes using the same high-level task provided in *PtA* (p. 23) makes salient that what happens during a lesson determines whether a task lives up to its potential to engage students in high-level thinking. Cutone indicates that implementing high-level tasks is often hard work, especially in the initial efforts. Planning and teaching mathematics lessons with high-level tasks requires new and different practices and, as with any new endeavor, initial efforts have varying degrees of success. Fortunately, tools exist to support planning and teaching with high-level tasks (Smith, Bill, and Hughes 2008; Smith and Stein 2011) and to identify observable classroom-based factors that serve to support or inhibit high-level implementation (Henningsen and Stein 1997; fig. 2.3).

Reflecting on one's own practice or providing feedback to a colleague or a preservice teacher about aspects of a lesson that inhibited or reduced students' opportunities for high-level thinking can be uncomfortable; however, it can also be constructive and insightful for enhancing future lessons. One approach suggested in research is for teams of teachers to begin by collectively analyzing written or video cases of mathematics lessons (e.g., Sherin and van Es 2005), especially where teachers have identified aspects of the lesson that served to reduce students' engagement in high-level cognitive demands (such as cases featured in Smith, Silver, and Stein 2005). Teachers can use the ideas generated during case discussions to consider the implementation of high-level tasks beyond the specific task featured in the case. In future discussions, teachers may feel more comfortable identifying aspects of their own lessons that resonate with the case and the factors that supported or inhibited students' engagement in cognitively demanding thinking and reasoning.

Preparing students for the next course and for high school mathematics. Preparing students with the procedures needed to be successful in the next mathematics course can be perceived as an obstacle for regularly implementing tasks that promote reasoning and problem solving. Cutone teaches eighth-grade Algebra and Accelerated Algebra using a reform-oriented curriculum as the main "textbook." His students progress to the next mathematics course in the sequence (geometry) as ninth graders in high school. Cutone believes that students learn mathematics best when they can "explore, discover, and understand *first*, … then practice." The reform-oriented curriculum provides high-level tasks on a day-to-day basis; however, this curriculum provides fewer opportunities for practice, particularly of skills that Cutone's students will need to be successful in high school mathematics (e.g., factoring).

Cutone's solution, to use the reform-oriented curriculum as the main text but to supplement with extra practice, is similar to recommendations in several NCTM resources. *PtA* states, "It is important to note that tasks that focus on learning and applying procedures do have a place in the curriculum and are necessary for developing fluency. Such tasks, however, should not dominate instruction and preempt the use of tasks that promote reasoning. Instead, these tasks should build on and emerge from these sense-making and problem-solving experiences" (NCTM 2014, p. 23). Similarly, in her November 2014 NCTM Presidential Message, Diane Briars asserted, "No materials are perfect. Inevitably, an evaluation process will uncover gaps, omissions, or inadequate treatment of some content. The key question is how easily teachers, the school, or the district can fill the gaps. For example, providing additional practice on a skill may be relatively easy; providing lessons to address a gap in concept development is probably more difficult" (Briars 2014). Tasks and curricula that regularly promote reasoning and problem solving provide opportunities for students to develop the conceptual understanding necessary for fluency with important mathematical procedures and

require the least effort to supplement so that students receive opportunities to explore, discover, understand, *and practice*. More generally, considering high-level tasks as the norm for everyday instruction and supplementing with extra practice appears to be a promising perspective.

In summary, Cutone provides insight into successes and obstacles in regularly using tasks that promote reasoning and problem solving across a course more broadly. In the next section, Kayla Madler shares her perspective as a PST learning about (and learning to teach with) high-level tasks.

The Perspective of a Preservice Teacher

My initial exposure to teaching with high-level tasks was during my first mathematics methods class, as my prior experiences in learning mathematics were very traditional: direct instruction, modeled examples, and independent work (e.g., "1–49 odd"). Initially, I disliked the idea of teaching mathematics using high-level tasks. Throughout the first methods class, I was constantly wrestling with the ideas of teaching with high-level tasks and the more traditional ways of teaching mathematics. Teaching a lesson with high-level tasks seemed to require putting on a "huge performance." All the examples from methods class had manipulatives, exploration paired with assessing and advancing questions, and an impressive whole-group discussion with multiple solutions and engaging conversations about the mathematical concept(s). I could not imagine how to enact such a huge performance in a typical mathematics class of approximately forty-five minutes!

However, after participating in a second mathematics methods course and seeing Chris Cutone's algebra class, I knew I could make high-level tasks work in the classroom. Specifically, I saw how students reacted to the investigations. Contrary to my initial perceptions, I witnessed how high-level tasks can be implemented on a day-to-day basis, giving students opportunities to discover and investigate mathematics rather than just practicing twenty-five problems that all look the same. While planning lessons around high-level tasks is intense (e.g., anticipating students' strategies and misconceptions, and planning assess and advance questions [Smith and Stein 2011]), the time spent planning makes a difference when implementing high-level tasks in the classroom.

I also realized that high-level tasks can be a combination or sequence of lessons. For example, two lessons from our curriculum formed an interesting high-level task that provided the conceptual foundation for the procedure of multiplying binomials. In the first lesson, students are asked to find the area of a square lot (n by n) and then find the area of a rectangular lot that has a length 2 meters greater than the square lot ($n + 2$) and a width 2 meters less than the square lot ($n - 2$). Additional questions in the investigation ask students to compare the relationship between the areas of the squares and rectangles using equations, graphs, and by determining whether different expressions are equivalent. The second lesson visually represents a rectangle resulting from changing one or more dimensions of a square (Lappan et al. 2014). Each rectangle is subdivided into two or four smaller rectangles (fig. 2.5a). Students are asked to find two expressions for the area of the rectangle—essentially, one in factored form and one in expanded form. Although each problem does not have multiple solutions, the task is high level because "students need to engage with the conceptual ideas that underlie the procedures in order to successfully complete the task" (e.g., "procedures with connections," from Stein et al. 2009, p. 16). A sample of students' work is provided in figure 2.5.

I enjoyed teaching this lesson because it took something I remember learning in a very traditional, procedural way (through direct instruction) and created a much deeper thinking activity. In using high-level tasks, students explore problems that build off of prior knowledge (like area of a square and rectangle) and allow students to develop their own understanding of new mathematical ideas. These two specific lessons set the groundwork for students to understand the very useful procedure of FOIL (fig. 2.2). Once we finished teaching these two lessons, students very smoothly transitioned to multiplying binomials using the FOIL method.

Successes and Obstacles in Implementing Cognitively Challenging Tasks on a Regular Basis

Many aspects of Madler's experiences connect to salient findings in research on the selection and implementation of tasks that promote reasoning and problem solving. Madler's perspectives, successes, and obstacles can benefit other PSTs and teachers transitioning to teaching with high-level tasks and provide insights for mathematics teacher education and professional development.

Student learning. Madler connected her increased appreciation for high-level tasks to the changes she observed in students' learning: "I enjoy teaching high-level tasks because students tend to remember the concepts more. Typically, students forget what they learn once they have been tested on the material, because mathematics traditionally was more memorizing and less understanding. But throughout my student teaching experience I have noticed that I can refer back to specific lessons, and students remember the process." Similarly, Cutone became convinced of the value of using high-level tasks after seeing his students' engagement in the pilot units.

Experiencing ways in which high-level tasks elicit students' thinking may support teachers' desire to implement high-level tasks (Ball and Cohen 1999; Elliott et al. 2009; Kazemi and Franke 2004; Smith 2001). Such experiences can occur in professional development or teacher preparation as well as in the classroom or in school-based learning communities. Some ideas include solving challenging mathematical tasks together as learners; examining student work and attending to students' thinking in professional development materials or from teachers' own classrooms; reading and discussing narrative or video cases of other teachers engaged in the work of implementing cognitively challenging tasks; and reviewing research on the value of high-level tasks in supporting students' learning.

Anticipating students' strategies and questions. Madler identified one of her biggest struggles as a PST as "anticipating students' strategies and questions." She commented, "Because high-level tasks allow students to investigate mathematical problems differently, there are many creative responses students can come up with. It is hard for me as a preservice teacher to anticipate all the possible strategies, but with time and more experience I can see myself overcoming this obstacle." Smith and Stein (2011) identified the process of anticipating students' strategies, responses, and misconceptions as a critical component in orchestrating discussions that maintain students' engagement in thinking and reasoning. Anticipating students' strategies allows teachers to consider ahead of time how to facilitate discussions that surface the main mathematical ideas and connections at the heart of a lesson (i.e., the goals for students' learning), rather than having to interpret and connect all students' strategies and reasoning in the moment. In this way, *PtA*'s effective mathematics teaching practices of "establishing mathematics goals to focus learning" and "facilitating meaningful mathematical discourse" interact to support the implementation of tasks that promote reasoning and problem solving. When using a high-level task for the first time, tools and strategies to anticipate students' solutions might include consulting a teachers' edition for sample solutions, or solving the task with colleagues and considering how students might approach the task. Such discussions might occur during common planning time or professional development meetings, informally in the teachers' lounge, or with distant colleagues using technology.

Time and perseverance. Madler's reflection that time and experience will enhance her ability to implement high-level tasks is sound advice for other PSTs and for any teacher beginning to teach with high-level tasks. Teachers, schools, and school leaders often give up too soon on reform-oriented curricula and teaching methods. Research on reform-oriented curricula identifies the correlation between improvements in teachers' implementation and students' achievement over time, with significant increases typically occurring in and beyond the second year of use (Bray 2005; Post et al. 2008; Reys et al. 2003). Studies generally associate "a longer implementation in the school . . . with a greater score advantage for students" (Riordan and Noyce 2001, p. 383). Boston and Smith (2009) identified changes in ESP teachers' practice along a progression from task selection, to task implementation, and then to discussion—continual, gradual improvement as teachers and students became accustomed to teaching and learning using high-level tasks. These findings suggest the importance of persevering with reform-oriented curricula and teaching.

A Common Obstacle: Making the Day-to-Day More High Level

Cutone and Madler both initially perceived tasks such as the S-Pattern task (fig. 2.2) as the *only* type of high-level task. Such tasks are often used in professional development and teacher education (e.g., http://www.nctm.org/PtAToolkit/; Smith, Silver and Stein 2005), because they are engaging for participants, position teachers or PSTs as learners, and enable facilitators to model effective teaching practices. As Cutone noted, patterning tasks provided opportunities for him to see multiple strategies and representations and provided similar opportunities for his students. Even with important underlying mathematics, tasks such as the S-Pattern gain more traction when used within sequences of tasks that develop students' understanding of larger mathematical ideas or processes. For example, different strategies for generalizing the S-Pattern lead students to produce different expressions. Initially, students may evaluate the expressions to show they are equivalent for a given figure number, but the need to justify the equivalence of the expressions, in general, motivates the need for multiplying binomials. The tasks that Madler discussed might serve as the next tasks in the sequence. First, students explore an area model comparing a square with side length n to a rectangle with dimensions $(n + 2)$ and $(n - 2)$. The area model is continued in the next problem, shown with samples of student work in figure 2.5a–d. The task first provides an area model for multiplying binomials (fig. 2.5a), then asks students to create area models (fig. 2.5b), then transitions students to use of the distributive property (fig. 2.5c), and finally asks students to generalize for a special case (fig. 2.5d). In this progression of tasks, students are asked questions to make connections (e.g., "Show how using the distributive property to multiply $(x + 3)$ and $(x + 5)$ is the same as using a rectangular model") that support their understanding of multiplying binomials, including the distributive property and FOIL. This sequence of tasks illustrates how tasks that promote reasoning and problem solving might be used to make the day-to-day more high level.

Conclusion

In considering how to implement tasks that promote reasoning and problem solving on a regular basis, it may be helpful for mathematics teachers, teacher educators, and professional development providers to consider progressions of tasks that build up students' understandings. Open-ended problem-solving tasks (fig. 2.1) might be connected to tasks that develop conceptual foundations (fig. 2.5) in order to support students' mathematical understanding and procedural fluency. We provided a specific example here in the content of algebra, but our ideas and suggestions could generalize to any content or grade level.

Based on research and connections to practice, suggestions to alleviate the obstacles and complexities of teaching day-to-day mathematics with tasks that promote reasoning and problem solving include a curriculum that provides a source of high-level tasks; collegial support and collaboration; changes in students' and parents' beliefs about effective mathematics teaching and learning; and support from district leadership. In addition to time and perseverance, other supports for implementing high-level tasks that promote reasoning and problem solving include tools and strategies for lesson planning, orchestrating mathematical discussions, and reflecting on teaching and learning.

Consistent with research, we end by noting the im-

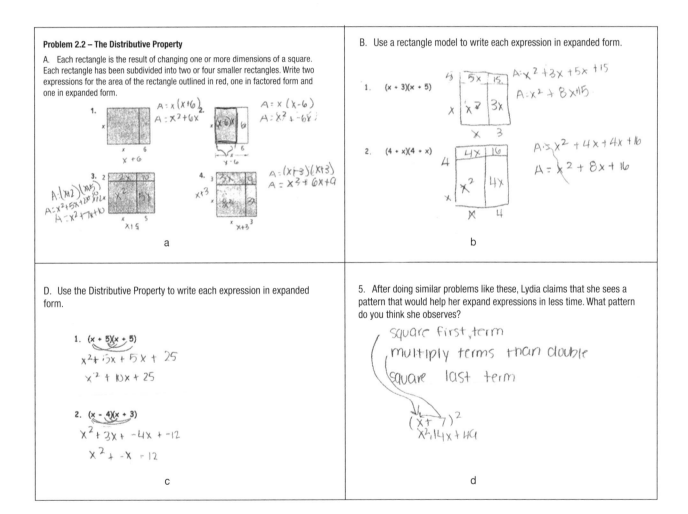

Fig. 2.5. Student work on a progression of tasks to develop understanding of multiplying binomials: (a) Students are provided with area models. (b) Students create area models. (c) Students apply the distributive property. (d) Students generalize for a special case. Class handout adapted from *Connected Mathematics 3: Frogs, Fleas, and Painted Cubes*, Investigation 2.2, Changing Dimensions (Lappan et al. 2014).

portance of task *implementation*. Many research-based resources for supporting teachers and PSTs in planning and enacting high-level tasks have been identified in this chapter, including the suggestion of collaborating with colleagues. *Consistently selecting* high-level tasks, even to teach day-to-day mathematical topics and procedures, is only the first step. *Consistently maintaining* high-level demands throughout the lesson is the critical factor in supporting students' mathematical learning.

References

Arbaugh, Fran, and Catherine A. Brown. "Analyzing Mathematical Tasks: A Catalyst for Change?" *Journal of Mathematics Teacher Education* 8, no. 6 (2005): 499–536.

Arbaugh, Fran, John Lannin, Dustin L. Jones, and Meredith Park-Rogers. "Examining Instructional Practices in Core-Plus lessons: Implications for Professional Development." *Journal of Mathematics Teacher Education* 9 (2006): 517–50.

Ball, Deborah Loewenberg, and David K. Cohen. "Developing Practice, Developing Practitioners: Toward a Practice-based Theory of Professional Education." *Teaching as the Learning Profession: Handbook of Policy and Practice* 1 (1999): 3–22.

Boaler, Jo, and Megan Staples. "Creating Mathematical Futures through an Equitable Teaching Approach: The Case of Railside School." *Teachers College Record* 110, no. 3 (2008): 608–45.

Boston, Melissa D. "Connecting Changes in Secondary Mathematics Teachers' Knowledge to Their Experiences in a Professional Development Workshop." *Journal of Mathematics Teacher Education* 16, no. 1 (2013): 7–31.

Boston, Melissa, Jonathan Bostic, Kristin Lesseig, and Milan Sherman. "A Comparison of Mathematics Classroom Observation Protocols." *Mathematics Teacher Educator* 3, no. 2 (2015): 154–75.

Boston, Melissa D., and Margaret S. Smith. "Transforming Secondary Mathematics Teaching: Increasing the Cognitive Demands of Instructional Tasks Used in Teachers' Classrooms." *Journal for Research in Mathematics Education* 40, no. 2 (2009): 119–56.

———. "A 'Task-Centric Approach' to Professional Development: Enhancing and Sustaining Mathematics Teachers' Ability to Implement Cognitively Challenging Mathematical Tasks." *ZDM: International Journal of Mathematics Teacher Education* 43, no. 6–7 (2011): 965–77.

Boston, Melissa D., and Annie Garrison Wilhelm. "Middle School Mathematics Instruction in Instructionally Focused Urban Districts." *Urban Education* (2015): 1–33. doi:1177/0042085915574528

Bray, Megan S. "Achievement of Eighth Grade Students in Mathematics after Completing Three Years of the Connected Mathematics Project." PhD diss., University of Tennessee, 2005. http://trace.tennessee.edu/utk_graddiss/1866

Briars, Diane J. "Curriculum Materials Matter: Evaluating the Evaluation Process." National Council of Teachers of Mathematics President's Message, November 2014. https://www.nctm.org/News-and-Calendar/Messages-from-the-President/Archive/Diane-Briars/Curriculum-Materials-Matter_-Evaluating-the-Evaluation-Process/

Cai, Jinfa, Ning Wang, John C. Moyer, Chuang Wang, and Bikai Nie. "Longitudinal Investigation of the Curricular Effect: An Analysis of Student Learning Outcomes from the Lie-Cal Project in the United States." *International Journal of Educational Research* 50, no. 2 (2011): 117–36.

Cobb, Paul, and Kara Jackson. "Towards an Empirically Grounded Theory of Action for Improving the Quality of Mathematics Teaching at Scale." *Mathematics Teacher Education and Development* 13, no. 1 (2011): 6–33.

Cobb, Paul, and Thomas M. Smith. "District Development as a Means of Improving Mathematics Teaching and Learning at Scale." In *Participants in Mathematics Teacher Education: Individuals, Teams, Communities, and Networks* (Vol. 3), edited by K. Krainer and T. Wood, pp. 213–54. Rotterdam, The Netherlands: Sense Publishers, 2008.

Doyle, Walter. "Academic Work." *Review of Educational Research 43*, no. 2 (1983): 159–99.

Elliott, Rebekah, Elham Kazemi, Kristin Lesseig, Judith Mumme, Cathy Carroll, and Megan Kelley-Petersen. "Conceptualizing the Work of Leading Mathematical Tasks in Professional Development." *Journal of Teacher Education* 60, no. 4 (2009): 364–79.

Foreman, Linda C., and A. B. Bennett Jr. *Visual Mathematics: Course II.* Salem, Ore.: The Math Learning Center, 1996.

Franke, Megan Loef, Elham Kazemi, and Daniel Battey. "Mathematics Teaching and Classroom Practice." In *Second Handbook of Research on Mathematics Teaching and Learning,* edited by Frank K. Lester Jr., pp. 225–56. Charlotte, N.C.: Information Age Publishing, and Reston, Va.: National Council of Teachers of Mathematics, 2007.

Fuson, Karen C., William M. Carroll, and Jane V. Drueck. "Achievement Results for Second and Third Graders Using the Standards-Based Curriculum Everyday Mathematics." *Journal for Research in Mathematics Education* 31, no. 3 (2000): 277–95.

Grouws, Douglas A., James E. Tarr, Óscar Chávez, Ruthmae Sears, Victor M. Soria, and Rukiye D. Taylan. "Curriculum and Implementation Effects on High School Students' Mathematics Learning from Curricula Representing Subject-Specific and Integrated Content Organizations." *Journal for Research in Mathematics Education* 44, no. 2 (2013): 416–63.

Henningsen, Marjorie, and Mary Kay Stein. "Mathematical Tasks and Student Cognition: Classroom-Based Factors that Support and Inhibit High-Level Mathematical Thinking and Reasoning." *Journal for Research in Mathematics Education* 28, no. 5 (1997): 524–49.

Hiebert, James, Tom P. Carpenter, Elizabeth Fennema, Kathleen C. Fuson, Diana Wearne, Hanlie Murray, Alwyn Olivier, and Peter Human. *Making Sense: Teaching and Learning Mathematics with Understanding.* Portsmouth, N.H.: Heinemann, 1997.

Hiebert, James, Ronald Gallimore, Helen Garnier, Karen Bogarhughes Givvin, Hilary Hollingsworth, Jennifer Jacobs, Angel Miu-Ying Chui, et al. *Highlights from the TIMSS 1999 Video Study of Eighth-Grade Mathematics Teaching.* Washington, D.C.: U.S. Department of Education, National Center for Education Statistics, 2003.

Hiebert, James, and Diana Wearne. "Instructional Tasks, Classroom Discourse, and Students' Learning in Second-Grade Arithmetic." *American Educational Research Journal* 30, no. 2 (1993): 393–425.

Jackson, Kara J., Emily C. Shahan, Lynsey K. Gibbons, and Paul A. Cobb. "Launching Complex Tasks." *Mathematics Teaching in the Middle School* 18, no. 1 (2012): 24–29.

Johnson, Raymond, Samuel Severance, William R. Penuel, and Heather Leary. "Teachers, Tasks, and Tensions: Lessons from a Research-Practice Partnership." *Journal of Mathematics Teacher Education* 19, no. 2–3 (2016): 169–85.

Kane, Thomas J., and Doug O. Staiger. "Gathering Feedback for Teaching: Combining High-Quality Observations with Student Surveys and Achievement Gains." Research paper: MET Project, 2012. Bill & Melinda Gates Foundation.

Kaufman, Julia Heath, and Mary Kay Stein. "Teacher Learning Opportunities in a Shifting Policy Environment for Instruction." *Educational Policy* 24, no. 4 (2010): 563–601.

Kazemi, Elham, and Megan Loef Franke. "Teacher Learning in Mathematics: Using Student Work to Promote Collective Inquiry." *Journal of Mathematics Teacher Education* 7, no. 3 (2004): 203–35.

Lappan, Glenda, James T. Fey, William M. Fitzgerald, Susan Friel, and Elizabeth D. Phillips. *Connected Mathematics 3.* Boston: Pearson Prentice Hall, 2014.

Lotan, Rachel A. "Group-Worthy Tasks." *Educational Leadership* 60, no. 6 (2003): 72–75.

Marrongelle, Karen, Paola Sztajn, and Margaret Smith. "Scaling Up Professional Development in an Era of Common State Standards." *Journal of Teacher Education* 64, no. 3 (2013): 202–11.

McMeeking, Laura B., Rebecca Orsi, and R. Brian Cobb. "Effects of a Teacher Professional Development Program on the Mathematics Achievement of Middle School Students." *Journal for Research in Mathematics Education* 43, no. 2 (2012): 159–81.

National Academy of Education (NAEd). *Recommendations Regarding Research Priorities: An Advisory Report to the National Educational Research Policy and Priorities Board.* Washington, D.C.: NAEd, 1999.

National Council of Teachers of Mathematics (NCTM). *Principles and Standards for School Mathematics.* Reston, Va.: NCTM, 2000.

———(NCTM). *Principles to Actions: Ensuring Mathematical Success for All.* Reston, Va.: NCTM, 2014.

Nelson, Barbara Scott, and Annette Sassi. "Shifting Approaches to Supervision: The Case of Mathematics Supervision." *Educational Administration Quarterly* 36, no. 4 (2000): 553–84.

Post, Thomas R., Michael R. Harwell, Jon D. Davis, Yukiko Maeda, Arnie Cutler, Edwin Andersen, Jeremy A. Kahan, and Ke Wu Norman. "Standards-Based Mathematics Curricula and Middle-Grades Students' Performance on Standardized Achievement Tests." *Journal for Research in Mathematics Education* 39, no. 2 (2008): 184–212.

Reys, Robert, Barbara Reys, Richard Lapan, Gregory Holliday, and Deanna Wasman. "Assessing the Impact of Standards-Based Middle Grades Mathematics Curriculum Materials on Student Achievement." *Journal for Research in Mathematics Education* 34, no. 1 (2003): 74–95.

Ridgeway, James, Judith Z. Zawojewski, Mark Hoover, and Diana Lambdin. "Student Attainment in the Connected Mathematics Curriculum." In *Standards-Based Mathematics Curricula: What Are They? What Do Students Learn?*, edited by Sharon L. Senk and Denisse R. Thompson, pp. 193–224. Mahwah, N.J.: Lawrence Erlbaum Associates, 2003.

Riordan, Julie E., and Pendred E. Noyce. "The Impact of Two Standards-Based Mathematics Curricula on Student Achievement in Massachusetts." *Journal for Research in Mathematics Education* 32, no. 4 (2001): 368–98.

Schoen, Harold L., Kristin J. Cebulla, Kelly F. Finn, and Cos Fi. "Teacher Variables That Relate to Student Achievement when Using a Standards-Based Curriculum." *Journal for Research in Mathematics Education* 34, no. 3 (2003): 228–59.

Schoenfeld, Alan H. "Making Mathematics Work for All Children: Issues of Standards, Testing, and Equity." *Educational Researcher* 31, no. 1 (2002): 13–25.

Senk, Sharon L., and Denisse R. Thompson, eds. *Standards-Based School Mathematics Curricula: What Are They? What Do Students Learn?* Mahwah, N.J.: Lawrence Erlbaum Associates, 2003.

Sherin, Miriam, and Elizabeth van Es. "Using Video to Support Teachers' Ability to Notice Classroom Interactions." *Journal of Technology and Teacher Education* 13, no. 3 (2005): 475–91.

Silver, Edward. "Examining What Teachers Do when They Display Their Best Practice: Teaching Mathematics for Understanding." *Journal of Mathematics Education at Teachers College* 1, no. 1 (2010): 1–6.

Silver, Edward A., and Mary Kay Stein. "The Quasar Project: The 'Revolution of the Possible' in Mathematics Instructional Reform in Urban Middle Schools." *Urban Education* 30, no. 4 (1996): 476–521.

Smith, Margaret Schwan. *Practice-Based Professional Development for Teachers of Mathematics.* Reston, Va.: National Council of Teachers of Mathematics, 2001.

25

Smith, Margaret S., Victoria Bill, and Elizabeth K. Hughes. "Thinking Through a Lesson: Successfully Implementing High-Level Tasks." *Mathematics Teaching in the Middle School* 14, no. 3 (2008): 132–38.

Smith, Margaret S., Amy F. Hillen, and Christy L. Catania. "Using Pattern Tasks to Develop Mathematical Understandings and Set Classroom Norms." *Mathematics Teaching in the Middle School* 13, no. 1 (2007): 38.

Smith, Margaret S., Edward A. Silver, and Mary Kay Stein. *Improving Instruction in Algebra.* Vol. 2 of *Using Cases to Transform Mathematics Teaching and Learning.* New York: Teachers College Press, 2005.

Smith, Margaret S., and Mary Kay Stein. "Selecting and Creating Mathematical Tasks: From Research to Practice." *Mathematics Teaching in the Middle School* 3, no. 5 (1998): 344–50.

———. *5 Practices for Orchestrating Productive Mathematics Discussions.* Reston, Va.: National Council of Teachers of Mathematics, 2011.

Smith, Margaret S., Mary Kay Stein, Fran Arbaugh, Catherine A. Brown, and Jennifer Mossgrove. "Characterizing the Cognitive Demands of Mathematical Tasks: A Task-Sorting Activity." In *Professional Development Guidebook for Perspectives on the Teaching of Mathematics: Companion to the Sixty-Sixth Yearbook*, edited by Rheta N. Rubenstein and George Bright, pp. 45–72. Reston, Va.: National Council of Teachers of Mathematics, 2004.

Steele, Michael D., and Amy F. Hillen. "The Content-Focused Methods Course: A Model for Integrating Pedagogy and Mathematics Content." *Mathematics Teacher Educator* 1, no. 1 (2012): 53–70.

Stein, Mary Kay, Randi A. Engle, Margaret S. Smith, and Elizabeth K. Hughes. "Orchestrating Productive Mathematical Discussions: Five Practices for Helping Teachers Move Beyond Show and Tell." *Mathematical Thinking and Learning* 10, no. 4 (2008): 313–40.

Stein, Mary Kay, Barbara W. Grover, and Marjorie Henningsen. "Building Student Capacity for Mathematical Thinking and Reasoning: An Analysis of Mathematical Tasks Used in Reform Classrooms." *American Educational Research Journal* 33, no. 2 (1996): 455–88.

Stein, Mary Kay, and Suzanne Lane. "Instructional Tasks and the Development of Student Capacity to Think and Reason: An Analysis of the Relationship between Teaching and Learning in a Reform Mathematics Project." *Educational Research and Evaluation* 2, no. 1 (1996): 50–80.

Stein, Mary Kay, Margaret S. Smith, Marjorie Henningsen, and Edward A. Silver. *Implementing Standards-Based Mathematics Instruction: A Casebook for Professional Development.* 2nd ed. New York: Teachers College Press, 2009.

Sykes, Gary, and Tom Bird. "Teacher Education and the Case Idea." *Review of Research in Education* 18 (1992): 457–521.

Tarr, James E., Robert E. Reys, Barbara J. Reys, Oscar Chavez, Jeffrey Shih, and Steven J. Osterlind. "The Impact of Middle-Grades Mathematics Curricula and the Classroom Learning Environment on Student Achievement." *Journal for Research in Mathematics Education* 39, no. 3 (2008): 247–80.

Weiss, Iris R., Joan D. Pasley, P. Sean Smith, Eric R. Banilower, and Daniel J. Heck. *Looking inside the Classroom: A Study of K–12 Mathematics and Science Education in the United States.* Chapel Hill, N.C.: Horizon Research, 2003.

Chapter 3

Representations as Tools for Mathematical Understanding

Thomas E. Hodges, *University of South Carolina*
Malisa Johnson, *Oak Pointe Elementary School, Irmo, South Carolina*

"I think that's what I took away the most from today . . . paying attention to how the tasks and our discussions really all center on what representations the students are using, what connections they are making, and what that says about their mathematical understanding."

In our collaborative work designing, delivering, and studying field-based mathematics methods courses (Hodges and Mills 2014), we anticipate how our structures and strategies might give students opportunities to communicate and give teacher candidates access to students' mathematical understandings. The quote above, from one of our classroom teacher colleagues engaged in hosting field-based courses, occurred as we reflected on a demonstration lesson co-taught by Hodges and the classroom teacher. Her reflection highlights the centrality of mathematical representation in two areas of effective teaching: (1) making connections among and with representational tools and (2) deepening students' mathematical understandings. These two areas form the foundation of the role of representations as illustrated in *Principles to Actions: Ensuring Mathematical Success for All* (NCTM 2014).

In the broadest sense, representations can be viewed as "standing for," or representing, particular objects, concepts, mental images, and/or processes. Mathematical representations occur both internally and externally in support of reasoning, problem solving, and communicating mathematical ideas. As one of the eight effective teaching practices in *Principles to*

Actions (*PtA*), the Use and Connect Mathematical Representations practice explicates how teachers' and students' use of representations form the vehicle through which mathematical ideas are explored, considered, and justified (Goldin and Shteingold 2001; Heritage and Niemi 2006; National Research Council 2001). The authors of *PtA* note that "effective mathematics teaching includes a strong focus on using varied mathematical representations" (NCTM 2014, p. 24); as students learn to express and justify their thinking through connections between representations, they demonstrate deeper conceptual understandings (Fuson, Kalchman, and Bransford 2005; Lesh, Post, and Behr 1987).

In this chapter, we highlight those two key roles of representation. First, we describe the varied representations that teachers and students may use in the course of mathematics teaching and learning. Marshall, Superfine, and Canty (2010, p. 40) note the important role of the teacher in purposefully choosing representations when designing and selecting problem-solving tasks. Using the work of Malisa Johnson, the teacher author in this chapter, we illustrate the challenges of selecting problem contexts that illuminate both useful representations and important mathematical ideas. Second, we describe the relationship between students' use of and connections between varied representations alongside their deepening mathematical understanding. In particular, we illustrate how students begin to see representational systems as tools for solving and communicating their thinking across a variety of problem types.

Representations as Tools for Problem Solving

The notion of representation as highlighted in *Principles to Actions* follows a rich history of practitioners' and researchers' attempts to unpack beneficial representations in mathematics, including representations invented by students in conjunction with those presented by teachers. The mathematics education community has developed a shared set of categories of representations, which may be introduced by teacher or student in the course of mathematical learning and problem solving. Lesh, Post, and Behr (1987) describe five types of representations: contextual, visual, verbal, physical, and symbolic. Furthermore, Lesh, Post, and Behr note the importance of students' ability to move fluently between representations as they engage in problem-solving situations (see fig. 3.1).

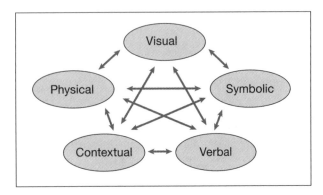

Fig. 3.1. Important connections among mathematical representations

Later, Lesh and Doerr (2003) extended these representational categories to include tabular and graphical, explicating the role that tabular and graphical representations play in the teaching and learning of mathematics.

Each mode serves as an external representation, or a representation that can be communicated to others. That is, they can be seen, felt, and/or heard. A focus on external representations is important for two reasons. First, mathematics as a discipline has historical roots in developing and refining representational systems, which are subsequently shared with students as they learn to work, solve problems, and communicate with representations (Lesh, Landau, and Hamilton 1983). Second, through the lens of mathematical understanding, external representations provide some insight into

how students are reasoning about mathematical concepts, relationships, and/or symbols. In other words, there is a bidirectional process in which representations serve as an externalization of students' internal mental images while also functioning as a way for students to internalize ("see" or "imagine") external representations (Pape and Tchoshanov 2001).

Seeing beyond a Single Task

In *PtA*, each Mathematics Teaching Practice is highlighted using both teacher and student actions, which illustrate the interwoven norms that are negotiated between teachers and students as they engage in shared methods of reasoning (Dixon, Andreasen, and Stephan 2009; Yackel and Cobb 1996). It is meaningful to consider the usefulness of and distinction between representations that are modeled by teachers as compared to those that students create (Cuoco and Curcio 2001). First, there are representations that teachers use and/or promote that may encourage students' selection of a particular representation and/or make explicit connections between representation modes. However, the ultimate goals for students are to use representations to learn about concepts and procedures and as tools to solve future problems. Van Den Heuvel-Panhuizen (2003) refers to these student uses of representation as *model of* and *model for*—signifying the distinction between models that are developed as a representation *of* a problem situation and those that have become generalized tools *for* solving problems. For example, Lobato and Thanheiser (2002) describe a classroom teaching experiment where students design wheelchair ramps using dynamic geometry software that maintain the "same steepness" as a ramp that is 3 units high and 12 units long. Although a student, Brian, could correctly identify 0.25 as the slope, he did not understand the meaning of the generated value within the context of the problem (e.g., that the length of the ramp was four times its height, thus resulting in a ratio of ¼, or 0.25). That is, he could create a *model of* this one problem situation and compute an accurate solution, but he could not make generalizations about slope. Through a series of dynamic sketches connected to symbolic representations and by teacher probing, Brian was able to see that 0.25 described the multiplicative relationship of height to length. Maintaining this multiplicative relationship across examples meant that he was generating ramps with the same steepness. The teacher then posed follow-up activities using dynamic geometry software that would help Brian begin to use his understanding of slope as ratio in new problem situations—thus developing a way for him to use dynamic sketches as a *model for* slope as a ratio.

In order for students to see representations as generalized tools for solving problems (i.e., moving from *model of* to *model for*), they must consider a particular representation as appropriate in the given problem situation and judge it against other possible representations (Lesh and Doerr 2012; Lesh and Zawojewski 2007). Furthermore, students must interpret the underlying mathematical structures and relationships highlighted through the representation and then identify other mathematical situations that maintain the corresponding structure. Doing so requires mathematical representations to be viewed as "part of a wider system within which meanings and conventions have been established" (Goldin and Shteingold 2001, p. 1), rather than an isolated *model of* any particular problem situation. Correspondingly, students' abilities to see representations as *models for* require flexibility in moving between representations modes (Huinker 2013; Lesh, Post, and Behr 1987; Superfine, Canty, and Marshall 2009). Pedagogical moves made by the teacher provide opportunities to showcase relationships among representations, highlighting generalizable mathematical structures evident across representational modes.

Developing *Models for* through Purposeful Representation Sequencing

"The challenging part is choosing rich tasks to do with my students. I try to think about how the math is likely to be used to solve the problem, rather than simply choosing problems to practice skills they already know."

In her selection and implementation of rich tasks for daily instruction, Johnson shares the same challenges as Chris Cutone, the middle school teacher highlighted in chapter 2, and his preservice teacher, Kayla Madler. In terms of representations, Johnson is concerned not only about the representations students may draw upon

with the current task but also how those representations help to construct a broad conceptual and procedural understanding of the mathematics at hand. As Meyer (2001) describes, the grain size for representational choice is much larger than a single lesson; instead, it spans an extended period of time as students move through increasingly sophisticated levels of abstraction through their use of a variety of representations. Thus, teachers' knowledge of mathematics as a discipline alongside purposeful pedagogical moves provides the basis for students' mathematical reasoning and, consequently, student learning. This sort of representational "nudging" by the teacher is grounded in concurrent commitments to both the mathematics and the ideas that students generate as they engage in carefully selected mathematics tasks (cf. Ball and Bass 2000).

The iceberg model (see fig. 3.2) provides a visualization of the important role various representations play in helping students make sense of more formal procedures and symbolic representations (the tip of the iceberg) (Webb, Boswinkel, and Dekker 2008). The "floating capacity," or underwater portion, of the iceberg includes a collection of less formal representations of mathematical ideas that form the conceptual basis for the more formal "tip." For Johnson, this means choosing problem contexts that serve to highlight useful representations and sequencing and connecting representations that provide pathways to more formal representations.

Johnson's fourth-grade class began an introductory unit on fractions by engaging in the "Field Trips and Fund-Raisers" (Fosnot 2007) unit. To begin the unit, students are told a story about sharing submarine sandwiches on a field trip, with 3 subs shared by 4 people, 4 subs shared by 5 people, 7 subs shared by 8 people, and 3 subs shared by 5 people. Students work together to determine how much of a sub each person in each group receives and whether or not the subs were distributed fairly. Selecting a context involving submarine sandwiches is not done haphazardly. As students make use of physical materials (e.g., fraction towers or strips) and/or draw pictures, they are likely to make use of a length model for the fractional parts. Given the importance of the length model when exploring fraction concepts (e.g., Fosnot and Dolk 2002; Siegler et al. 2010; Usiskin 2007; Watanabe 2006), students are able

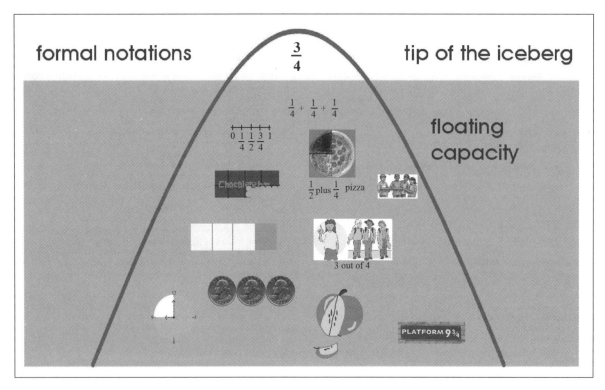

Fig. 3.2. The iceberg model. Adapted from Webb, Boswinkel, and Dekker (2008).

to construct representations that afford opportunities to explore key "big ideas," such as—

- seeing fractions as relation;
- iterating unit fractions;
- partitioning a whole into unit fractions; and
- generating constant ratios for equivalence.

A vast body of mathematics education literature highlights the importance of problem context in insinuating strategies and encouraging particular representations of problem situations (e.g., Carpenter et al. 2015; Friedlander and Tabach 2001; Gravemeijer and Doorman 1999; Verschaffel, Greer, and De Corte 2007). Students generally begin their explorations by directly modeling the situation in the problem context to generate representational models of the situation (Gravemeijer 1999). This is not unlike young children's differing interpretations and solution strategies of problem contexts that involve, for example, subtraction with separate-result unknown (e.g., Terrence has

7 toy cars. He loses 2. How many does he have left?) and separate-start unknown (e.g., Terrence had some cars. He lost 2. Now he has 5. How many did he have to start?). Later, as students explore fraction equivalence and comparison, sub sandwiches, for example, can be a beneficial context for encouraging students' use of a length model, while pans of brownies, visually represented as an area model, can support students' sense-making of the standard algorithm for multiplying fractions. The importance of such contexts highlights the critical role of task selection in encouraging students' representational choice.

As students explored the submarine tasks, one student group elected to use fraction towers, which Johnson made available in the class. Providing students opportunities to select and/or create their own representations better positions them to understand various representations and move fluently between them. Furthermore, students who select and/or create their own representations are more successful when encountering novel high-demand tasks (Terwel et al. 2009). When exploring 3 subs shared by 4 people, for example, they used 3 of the fourths fraction towers, giving each person $1/4$ from each sub. When prompted, students combined the three $1/4$ pieces, noting that it was $3/4$ of one sub sandwich (see fig. 3.3). Other student groups arrived at the same solution through drawings. However, students' solution strategies differed by representation choice when they began to explore whether the distribution of subs had been completed fairly. Opportunities to make use of various representations when exploring mathematical concepts is important, as students using different representations may contribute different strategies or mechanisms for arriving at a solution (Goldin and Shteingold 2001). Students who used the fraction towers successfully tended to continue to use them when making comparisons. They reasoned that $4/5$ of a sub is more than $3/4$ of a sub because, while "both were missing one piece to make it a whole, $1/5$ is smaller than $1/4$ [showing the pieces from the fraction towers], so the people that got $4/5$ were missing less than the people who got $3/4$." Likewise, those that were successful with drawings tended to continue using drawings for their comparisons. Through trial and error, students eventually determined that a common multiple for the number of people (in this case, 40) would allow for easier comparisons (see fig. 3.4).

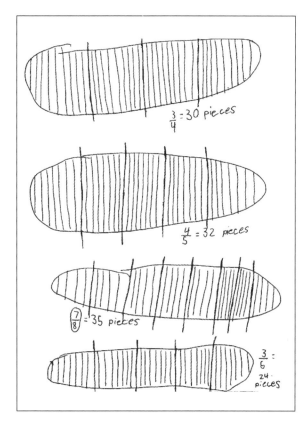

Fig. 3.4. Using a common multiple of 40 (common denominator) to compare fractional parts

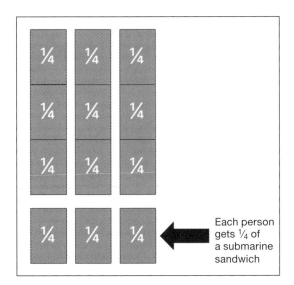

Fig. 3.3. Students' use of fraction towers to share 3 subs among 4 people

An important next step was to help students begin to see these representations as part of an interconnected system requiring flexibility in translating between representation modes (Huinker 2013). As students presented their ideas to the class, Johnson recorded their thinking, using symbols to help bridge the "floating capacity" of representations students had been exploring with the more formal "tip of the iceberg" symbolic representations students would be expected to move toward. For Johnson, students' future use of symbols and their ability to make connections between strategies highlights a need to be purposeful in her task selection and intentional in her questioning of students' strategic and representational choices.

Deepening Students' Understanding through Representational Connections

As students solved a multi-digit multiplication problem, Johnson noticed that several students struggled to see the relationship between the standard algorithm (a tip of the iceberg representation) and the partial products generated when using other student-invented algorithms.

Some students used the standard algorithm, yet others had generated a visual representation by breaking apart the numbers into 10s and 1s. While many students had generated a correct solution using each strategy, they had trouble seeing the relationship between the visual model and the standard algorithm.

One might argue that, because almost all students in the class arrived at a correct solution and could generally describe their strategy, further exploration was unnecessary. However, taking students' end solutions as a strong indicator of their mathematical understanding is problematic given students' struggles with seeing relationships between visual, symbolic, and contextual representations. Students who fail to see connections among representations have difficulty understanding computation strategies and solving problems (Huinker 2013; Lesh et al. 2003). In the case of Johnson's students, it was likely that many using the standard algorithm were unaware they were computing partial products.

The Importance of Representational Fluency

Mathematics education research has consistently shown that students who can move fluently between representations have deeper understandings than those who cannot (Fuson, Kalchman, and Bransford 2005; Lesh, Post, and Behr 1987; Pape and Tchoshanov 2001; Webb, Boswinkel, and Dekker 2008; Yee and Bostic 2014). Students' understanding of mathematical concepts deepens as teachers highlight, or encourage students to highlight, similarities that occur across representational forms (Zimba 2011). Over time, once students are able to move flexibly between representations, our work has shown that students tend to drop less efficient for more efficient representations.

To address gaps in students' representational fluency with multiplication, Johnson selected a context that suggested the use of an area/array visual representation to help reconcile students' ideas about partial products in both student-invented and standard algorithms. As a result, she posed the task shown in figure 3.5.

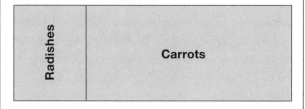

John wants to plant radishes and carrots. His fields are rectangular and next to one another, similar to the picture below:

The radish field has 25 rows of radishes, with 5 radishes in each row. John plants three times as many carrots as radishes. How many radishes and carrots did he plant?

Fig. 3.5. Radishes and Carrots task

Johnson began the task debrief by asking Jorrie to share her solution strategy.

> *Jorrie*: I tried to draw a picture of 25 rows with 5 radishes in each row, but then I realized it would take too long because I would have to count them. So then I drew a picture of a square and I put 25 rows and 5 at the top. I multiplied 5 times 20 and got a 100. And I multiplied 5 times 5 and got 25. So then I got 125. Then I did 125 × 3 [*stacked*] and I got 365. [*See fig. 3.6.*]

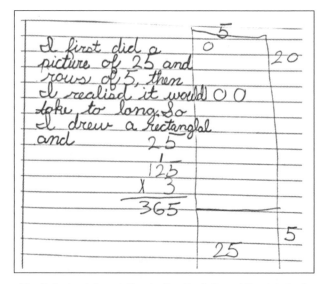

Fig. 3.6. Jorrie's solution to the Radish and Carrots task

We take Jorrie's use of the area model to solve 25 × 5 and her shift to the standard algorithm to solve (incorrectly, because of a computational error) 125 × 3 as a demonstration that, for Jorrie, the area model was a *model of* this particular problem situation rather than a *model for* solving multiplication problems more generally. Further, whereas Jorrie could explain the partial products in 25 × 5 using her visual model, she could not explain them in 125 × 3. Rather, Jorrie explained the procedure for using the standard algorithm. In other words, Jorrie was unable to make connections between representations that might highlight her understanding of multiplication. However, Jorrie's solution proved powerful for her classmates. Other students in the class had used a standard algorithm to calculate 25 × 5. Through a series of probes, Johnson was able to show-case the connection between Jorrie's partial products and the standard algorithm. Next, she encouraged the class to try out Jorrie's strategy to determine 125 × 3. Many students constructed an area model similar to Jor-rie's (see fig. 3.7). Johnson concluded the lesson by ask-ing students to compare the partial products apparent in the visual model with the calculations made using the standard algorithm. We use this example to illustrate the power of connections between contextual, visual, and symbolic representations in the course of devel-oping mathematical understanding. It is through these constellations of representations alongside purposeful mathematical discourse that students' conceptual and procedural understandings of mathematics occur.

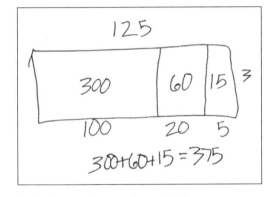

Fig. 3.7. A student's use of "Jorrie's method" (area model) to solve 125 × 3

Challenges in the Design of Classroom Instruction

Representations form the vehicle through which students' mathematical thinking is communicated, and without an overt focus on students' ability to move fluently between representations, mathematical understanding is difficult to achieve. However, many times students' use of representations results in more

questions than answers. Making sense of which ideas to capitalize on, how to make records of students' representational choices and connections, and how to sequence at both a task and unit level that honors stu-dents' ideas and the mathematics remain challenging. However, such challenges are common. As Greeno and Hall (1997) state:

> As in any classroom setting, the extent to which students give fully articulated versions of their work varies, but the practices found in these classrooms often involve extensive use of interrelated representational forms to communicate understanding. A heterogeneous mix of representational forms becomes a valuable resource for students when they communicate the sense of their work to teammates, to other students in the class, and to their teachers. (p. 361)

Students will often demonstrate partial abilities to translate between representations, rather than simply being capable of doing so or not (Superfine, Canty, and Marshall 2009). It is important to recognize that differ-entiated instruction may be needed as students' abilities to move fluently between representations vary. As il-lustrated in *PtA*, Marshall, Superfine, and Canty (2010) have identified promising practices that include pur-posefully selecting representations and alternating the direction of connections made between representations while discussing the connections between those repre-sentations. Implicit in their suggestions is a purposeful focus on teacher and student use of representations in the course of mathematics teaching and learning.

Implications for Classroom Design and Research

Research on the influence of reform curriculum materials (e.g., Reys et al. 2003; Senk and Thompson 2003) along with more thorough understanding of developmental learning progressions within content domains (e.g., Clements and Sarama 2004; Simon and Tzur 2004) both serve as critical sources of support when making classroom-level decisions regarding when and how to promote particular representation forms. Certainly, there is space for the mathematics education community to increase our understanding of progressions at both an individual student and class-room level. In particular, technology affords dynamic visual models, which allow us to *see the unseen* (Arcavi 2003). These unseen connections between representations, presented in real time, provide innovative ways to design lessons and sequence mathematical ideas.

Finally, sense making in mathematics is a nonlinear, complex process. Students are often encouraged to move toward abstract symbolic representations without grounding and connecting their use of symbols in more concrete representations. We know from our own experiences that expectations placed upon teachers by testing practices, curricular fidelity, and limited instructional time can serve as constraints when deciding when and how to move students toward increased abstraction. However, such decisions are also undergirded by teachers' orientations in teaching mathematics (Thompson et al. 1994). That is, teachers with conceptual orientations toward mathematics are more likely to focus attention on materials and tasks that bring out representational choices that will eventually be used as *models for*. Conversely, teachers with *calculational* orientations are more likely to focus exclusively on procedures without considering the role of context or the relevant alternative representations. These orientations provide significantly different visions of both the role of representation and mathematical reasoning more broadly. As such, those working in support of teachers must maintain a dual focus on deepening teachers' understanding of effective representational choices alongside promoting orientations toward mathematics teaching in order to afford teachers opportunities to see mathematics in conceptually sound ways for themselves.

References

Arcavi, Abraham. "The Role of Visual Representations in the Learning of Mathematics." *Educational Studies in Mathematics* 52, no. 3 (2003): 215–41.

Ball, D. L., and Hyman Bass. "Interweaving Content and Pedagogy in Teaching and Learning to Teach: Knowing and Using Mathematics." In *Multiple Perspectives on the Teaching and Learning of Mathematics*, edited by Jo Boaler, pp. 83–104. Westport, Conn.: Ablex, 2000.

Carpenter, Thomas P., Elizabeth Fennema, Megan Loef Franke, Linda Levi, and Susan B. Empson. *Children's Mathematics: Cognitively Guided Instruction*. 2nd ed. Portsmouth, N.H.: Heinemann, 2015.

Clements, Douglas H., and Julie Sarama. "Learning Trajectories in Mathematics Education." *Mathematical Thinking and Learning* 6, no. 2 (2004): 81–89.

Cuoco, Albert A., and Frances R. Curcio, eds. *The Roles of Representation in School Mathematics: 63rd Yearbook of the National Council of Teachers of Mathematics*. Reston, Va.: National Council of Teachers of Mathematics, 2001.

Dixon, Juli K., Janet B. Andreasen, and Michelle Stephan. "Establishing Social and Sociomathematical Norms in an Undergraduate Mathematics Content Course for Prospective Teachers: The Role of the Instructor." In *Scholarly Practices and Inquiry into the Preparation of Mathematics Teachers*, edited by Denise S. Mewborn and Hollylynne S. Lee, pp. 43–66. San Diego, Calif.: Association of Mathematics Teacher Educators, 2009.

Fosnot, Catherine Twomey. *Field Trips and Fund-raisers: Introducing Fractions, Contexts for Learning Mathematics*. Portsmouth, N.H.: Heinemann, 2007.

Fosnot, Catherine Twomey, and Maarten Dolk. *Young Mathematicians at Work, 3: Constructing Fractions, Decimals, and Percents*. Portsmouth, N.H.: Heinemann, 2002.

Friedlander, Alex, and Michal Tabach. "Promoting Multiple Representations in Algebra." In *The Roles of Representation in School Mathematics: 63rd Yearbook of the National Council of Teachers of Mathematics*, edited by Albert A. Cuoco and Frances R. Curcio, pp. 173–85. Reston, Va.: National Council of Teachers of Mathematics, 2001.

Fuson, Karen C., Mindy Kalchman, and John D. Bransford. "Mathematical Understanding: An Introduction." In *How Students Learn: History, Mathematics, and Science in the Classroom*, edited by M. Suzanne Donovan and John D. Bransford, pp. 217–56. Washington, D.C.: National Academies Press, 2005.

Goldin, Gerald, and Nina Shteingold. "Systems of Representations and the Development of Mathematical Concepts." In *The Roles of Representation in School Mathematics: 63rd Yearbook of the National Council of Teachers of Mathematics*, edited by Albert A. Cuoco and Frances R. Curcio, pp. 1–23. Reston, Va.: National Council of Teachers of Mathematics, 2001.

Gravemeijer, Koeno. "How Emergent Models May Foster the Constitution of Formal Mathematics." *Mathematical Thinking and Learning* 1, no. 2 (1999): 155–77.

Gravemeijer, Koeno, and Michiel Doorman. "Context Problems in Realistic Mathematics Education: A Calculus Course as an Example." *Educational Studies in Mathematics* 39, no. 1–3 (1999): 111–29.

Greeno, James G., and Rogers P. Hall. "Practicing Representation: Learning with and about Representational Forms." *Phi Delta Kappan* 78, no. 5 (1997): 361.

Heritage, Margaret, and David Niemi. "Toward a Framework for Using Student Mathematical Representations as Formative Assessments." *Educational Assessment* 11, no. 3–4 (2006): 265–82.

Hodges, Thomas E., and Heidi Mills. "Embedded Field Experiences as Professional Apprenticeships." In *Annual Perspectives in Mathematics Education 2014: Using Research to Improve Instruction*, edited by Karen Karp and Amy Roth McDuffie, pp. 249–60. Reston, Va.: National Council of Teachers of Mathematics, 2014.

Huinker, DeAnn. "Examining Dimensions of Fraction Operation Sense." In *Defining Mathematics Education: Presidential Yearbook Selections, 1926–2012: Seventy-fifth Yearbook of the National Council of Teachers of Mathematics*, edited by Tim Jacobbe, Gary Kader, and Rose Mary Zbiek, pp. 373–79. Reston, Va.: National Council of Teachers of Mathematics, 2013.

Lesh, Richard, Kathleen Cramer, Helen Doerr, Thomas Post, and Judith Zawojewski. "Model Development Sequences." In *Beyond Constructivism: Models and Modeling Perspectives on Mathematics Problem Solving, Learning, and Teaching*, edited by Richard Lesh and Helen Doerr, pp. 35–38. Mahwah, N.J.: Lawrence Erlbaum Associates, 2003.

Lesh, Richard, and Helen Doerr. "Foundations of a Model and Modeling Perspective on Mathematics Teaching, Learning, and Problem Solving." In *Beyond Constructivism: Models and Modeling Perspectives on Mathematics Problem Solving, Learning, and Teaching*, edited by Richard Lesh and Helen Doerr, pp. 3–33. Mahwah, N.J.: Lawrence Erlbaum Associates, 2003.

―――. 2012. "Alternatives to Trajectories and Pathways to Describe Development in Modeling and Problem Solving." In *Mathematikunterricht im Kontext von Realität, Kultur und Lehrerprofessionalität*, edited by Werner Blum, Rita Borromeo Ferri, and Katja Maass, pp. 138–47. Wiesbaden, Germany: Springer, 2012.

Lesh, Richard, Marsha Landau, and Eric Hamilton. "Conceptual Models and Applied Mathematical Problem-Solving Research." In *Acquisition of Mathematics Concepts and Processes*, edited by Richard Lesh and Marsha Landau, pp. 263–343. New York: Academic Press, 1983.

Lesh, Richard, Tom Post, and Merlyn Behr. "Representations and Translations among Representations in Mathematics Learning and Problem Solving." In *Problems of Representations in the Teaching and Learning of Mathematics*, edited by C. Janvier, pp. 33–40. Hillsdale, N.J.: Lawrence Erlbaum, 1987.

Lesh, Richard, and Judith Zawojewski. "Problem Solving and Modeling." In *Second Handbook of Research on Mathematics Teaching and Learning*, edited by Frank K. Lester Jr., pp. 763–804. Charlotte, N.C.: Information Age Publishing, and Reston, Va.: National Council of Teachers of Mathematics, 2007.

Lobato, Joanne, and Eva Thanheiser. "Developing Understanding of Ratio as Measure as a Foundation for Slope." In *Making Sense of Fractions, Ratios, and Proportions: 2002 Yearbook of the National Council of Teachers of Mathematics*, edited by George W. Bright and Bonnie H. Litwiller, pp. 162–75. Reston, Va.: National Council of Teachers of Mathematics, 2002.

Marshall, Anne Marie, Alison Castro Superfine, and Reality S. Canty. "Star Students Make Connections." *Teaching Children Mathematics* 17, no. 1 (2010): 38–47.

Meyer, Margaret R. "Representation in Realistic Mathematics Education." In *The Roles of Representation in School Mathematics: 63rd Yearbook of the National Council of Teachers of Mathematics*, edited by Albert A. Cuoco and Frances R. Curcio, pp. 238–50. Reston, Va.: National Council of Teachers of Mathematics, 2001.

National Council of Teachers of Mathematics (NCTM). 2014. *Principles to Actions: Ensuring Mathematical Success for All*. Reston, Va.: NCTM, 2014

National Research Council. *Adding it Up: Helping Children Learn Mathematics*. Washington, D.C.: National Academy Press, 2001.

Pape, Stephen J., and Mourat A. Tchoshanov. "The Role of Representation(s) in Developing Mathematical Understanding." *Theory into Practice* 40, no. 2 (2001): 118–27.

Reys, Robert, Barbara Reys, Richard Lapan, Gregory Holliday, and Deanna Wasman. "Assessing the Impact of 'Standards'-Based Middle Grades Mathematics Curriculum Materials on Student Achievement." *Journal for Research in Mathematics Education* 34, no. 1 (2003): 74–95.

Senk, Sharon L., and Denisse R. Thompson, eds. *Standards-Based School Mathematics Curricula: What Are They? What Do Students Learn?* Mahwah, N.J.: Lawrence Erlbaum Associates, 2003.

Siegler, Robert, Thomas Carpenter, Francis Fennell, David Geary, James Lewis, Yukari Okamoto, Laurie Thompson, and Jonathan Wray. *Developing Effective Fractions Instruction for Kindergarten through 8th Grade: IES Practice Guide*. NCEE #2010-4039. Washington, D.C.: National Center for Education Evaluation and Regional Assistance, Institute of Education Sciences, U.S. Department of Education, 2010. whatworks.ed.gov/publications/practiceguides

Simon, Martin A., and Ron Tzur. "Explicating the Role of Mathematical Tasks in Conceptual Learning: An Elaboration of the Hypothetical Learning Trajectory." *Mathematical Thinking and Learning* 6, no. 2 (2004): 91–104.

Superfine, Alison Castro, Reality S. Canty, and Anne Marie Marshall. "Translation between External Representation Systems in Mathematics: All-or-None or Skill Conglomerate?" *Journal of Mathematical Behavior* 28, no. 4 (2009): 217–36.

Terwel, Jan, Bert van Oers, Ivanka van Dijk, and Pieter van den Eeden. "Are Representations to be Provided or Generated in Primary Mathematics Education? Effects on Transfer." *Educational Research and Evaluation* 15, no. 1 (2009): 25–44.

Thompson, Alba G., Randolph A. Philipp, Patrick W. Thompson, and Barbara A. Boyd. "Calculational and Conceptual Orientations in Teaching Mathematics." In *Professional Development for Teachers of Mathematics: 1994 Yearbook of the National Council of Teachers of Mathematics*, edited by Douglas B. Aichele and Arthur F. Coxford, pp. 79–92. Reston, Va.: National Council of Teachers of Mathematics, 1994.

Usiskin, Zalman P. "The Future of Fractions." *Mathematics Teaching in the Middle School* 12, no. 7 (2007): 366–69.

Van Den Heuvel-Panhuizen, Marja. "The Didactical Use of Models in Realistic Mathematics Education: An Example from a Longitudinal Trajectory on Percentage." *Educational Studies in Mathematics* 54, no. 1 (2003): 9–35.

Verschaffel, Lieven, Brian Greer, and Erik De Corte. "Whole Number Concepts and Operations." In *Second Handbook of Research on Mathematics Teaching and Learning*, edited by Frank K. Lester Jr., pp. 557–628. Charlotte, N.C.: Information Age Publishing, and Reston, Va.: National Council of Teachers of Mathematics, 2007.

Watanabe, Tad. "The Teaching and Learning of Fractions: A Japanese Perspective." *Teaching Children Mathematics* 12, no. 7 (2006): 368–74.

Webb, David C., Nina Boswinkel, and Truus Dekker. "Beneath the Tip of the Iceberg: Using Representations to Support Student Understanding." *Mathematics Teaching in the Middle School* 14, no. 2 (2008): 110–13.

Yackel, Erna, and Paul Cobb. "Sociomathematical Norms, Argumentation, and Autonomy in Mathematics." *Journal for Research in Mathematics Education* 27, no. 4 (1996): 458–77.

Yee, Sean P., and Jonathan D. Bostic. "Developing a Contextualization of Students' Mathematical Problem Solving." *Journal of Mathematical Behavior* 36 (2014): 1–19.

Zimba, Jason. "Examples of Structure in the *Common Core State Standards*' Standards for Mathematical Content." Unpublished manuscript (draft), July 6, 2011. http://ime.math.arizona.edu/2011-12/ccssatlas_2011_07_06_0956_p1p2.pdf

Chapter 4

Eliciting, Supporting, and Guiding the Math
Three Key Functions of the Teacher's Role in Facilitating Meaningful Mathematical Discourse

Megan Staples, *University of Connecticut, Neag School of Education*
Sherryl King, *Ellington Middle School, Ellington, Connecticut*

In this chapter, we examine the teaching-and-learning principle *facilitating meaningful mathematical discourse.* We begin by asking what is meant by *meaningful mathematical discourse* and what it means to *facilitate* such discourse. We then turn our attention to how teachers do this important work, including some of the challenges teachers face, and conclude with some suggestions for how teachers and districts might make progress toward having meaningful mathematical discourse become a daily event in their classrooms.

Facilitating Meaningful Mathematical Discourse: Getting Clear on Our Terms

What Is Meaningful Mathematical Discourse?

We focus on *meaningful mathematical discourse* as a discourse that is about *making mathematics reasonable in school* (Ball and Bass 2003). To clarify, discourse is not limited to spoken words but includes all mediums and methods that support communication and the expression and exchange of mathematical ideas, including diagrams, gestures, and other non-verbal signals that are part of how we convey and make meaning. That is to say, mathematical discourse is any form of communication that positions mathematics as a subject that makes sense, yielding insights when reasoning is used. It "sorts through" important ideas as students express ideas, clarify, and revise.

A meaningful mathematical discourse engages students with significant mathematics and targets a significant mathematical goal. The discussion can focus on concepts, procedures, problem-solving strategies, representations, or reasoning. The goal could be to compare definitions, develop a justification for why a strategy works, provide an argument to demonstrate whether a conjecture is true, determine how two different approaches can yield the same result, or identify when a particular strategy is more efficient than another (Chapin, O'Connor, and Anderson 2009; Kazemi and Hintz 2014). The meaningfulness of the discussion comes both from the significance of the mathematics and from the personal meaningfulness students ascribe as they generate ideas, are heard by others, consider others' viewpoints, and collectively develop new understandings.

Why Is Engaging Students in Meaningful Mathematical Discourse Important?

Engaging students in meaningful mathematical discourse promotes a range of desired learning outcomes (Ball and Bass 2003; Hiebert et al. 1997; NCTM 1989, 2000; NRC 2001). Mathematical discourse is a critical practice through which students develop mathematical communication and argumentation skills and the ability to critique the reasoning of others. The practice also supports students in developing a connected and strong understanding of mathematical concepts (Cross 2009; Kazemi and Stipek 2001; NRC 2001). Discourse is not an extension activity for students to engage in *after*

The classroom excerpt is from an NSF-funded project, Justification and Argumentation: Growing Understanding of Algebraic Reasoning (JAGUAR) (DRL 0814829). All names are pseudonyms. Opinions expressed are those of the authors and do not necessarily reflect those of funding agency.

they have learned content but should be part of the daily fabric of the mathematics classroom.

As students engage in meaningful mathematical discourse, they formulate ideas and present them to others, which creates opportunities for students to develop language to express ideas, represent evidence, and clarify their reasoning. They become increasingly proficient in articulating mathematical ideas and supporting them with mathematical arguments. These activities also offer opportunities for reflection and metacognition, two valuable practices that support learning and help students to solidify their thinking (NRC 2001).

As students experience sense-making and arrive at mathematical conclusions as a result of a classroom or group discussion, students begin to see themselves as thinkers, as people who can produce knowledge and who can do math. When engaged in meaningful mathematical discourse, the locus of authority in the classroom rests with the students and the discipline of mathematics, as validity and correctness are determined by the reasonableness of an argument or idea, and does not rest with the teacher or textbook (Hiebert et al. 1997). A shift in disciplinary authority has been connected with more productive beliefs about mathematics and its value (Boaler and Greeno 2000), high levels of student engagement (Boaler 1997; Engle and Conant 2002), and student perseverance (Boaler 1997). Furthermore, when students are involved with justification, reasoning, and expressing ideas, they learn to value the ideas and contributions of others as well as see the value of their own contributions (Boaler and Staples 2008; Nasir et al. 2014). These forces can disrupt status differences among students, which in turn promote more equitable participation (Cohen and Lotan 2014; Nasir et al. 2014) and may also support more equitable learning outcomes among students (Boaler and Staples 2008; Hiebert et al. 1997). As status differences shift and student participation increases, additional students have opportunities for "air time" and the classroom environment becomes increasingly responsive to students' thinking.

Finally, when students are engaged in mathematical discourse, teachers gain valuable insights into students' thinking. Discussions can provide valuable formative assessment data, revealing how students are making sense of information and reasoning about it in ways not afforded by students' written work. Student misconceptions are also frequently revealed and challenged during discussions, providing both teacher and student with useful information and opportunities to address and work through the misconception and enhance their learning (Hiebert et al. 1997; Hoffman, Breyfogle, and Dressler 2009).

What Is Facilitating?

The teaching practice highlighted in *Principles to Action: Ensuring Mathematical Success for All* is facilitating meaningful mathematical discourse. The term *facilitate* has many meanings and connotations. What does it mean for a teacher to facilitate meaningful mathematical discourse in the context of a mathematics classroom? The biggest challenge perhaps is to see what the teacher *is* doing (Chazan and Ball 1999), as facilitating can give the impression of a role that is "neutral" or unobtrusive, overseeing in a manner that does not impact the direction of the group or substance of the discussion. This type of facilitation is *not* what we mean when we describe a teacher as a facilitator of meaningful mathematical discourse. This hands-off vision of the role can lead to unproductive exchanges that fall short of being *mathematically meaningful* (Alfieri et al. 2011; Cross 2009; Nathan and Knuth 2003). Rather, when facilitating, the teacher plays a very active role—indeed multiple roles—toward the end of supporting meaningful mathematical discourse.

In our "active" definition, facilitating includes *guiding* as well as *supervising*. The nature of the teacher's guidance is critical for the productive organization of (or failure of) a discourse that engages students in meaning making, positions mathematics as reasonable, and builds the class's collective body of knowledge together. The supervisory role suggests that the teacher is responsible for coordinating the group, supporting productive interactions, and helping students do the work. A supervisor does not do the work for those under supervision but rather has the knowledge required to guide, troubleshoot, support, and bring out the best in a group. As Munter (2014) and others have pointed out, the teacher and students are mutually engaged, but the teacher is "a more knowledgeable partner who is responsible for ensuring that classroom mathematical practices come to resemble those of the discipline" (p. 590). Thus, although in some sense a co-participant, the teacher has unique responsibilities in supporting the group in attaining the desired goals.

The Teacher's Role in Facilitating Meaningful Mathematical Discourse

Having clarified what we mean by a meaningful mathematical discourse, we now consider the teacher's role in facilitating such discourse. What does it take to organize and engage students in meaningful mathematical discourse? The teacher's work to support meaningful mathematical discussions begins before the discussion takes place and includes identifying mathematical goals to pursue for the lesson and unit (chapter 1), selecting the task(s) for that lesson (chapter 2), establishing classroom norms, particularly those that support perseverance (chapter 7), and building relationships with students (Battey 2013), to identify a few. Necessarily, the exact work varies depending on the time of year, the newness of the content, the students' experience engaging in a math-talk community (Hufferd-Ackles, Fuson, and Sherin 2004), the instructional format (small group or whole class), and other factors. With this acknowledgment of the broader context, we focus on understanding the teacher's role *during* a meaningful mathematical discussion and address how teachers support meaningful mathematical discussions as they unfold.

Three Key Functions of the Teacher's Role

Drawing on frameworks and descriptions found in the research literature (e.g., Ball 1993; Bochicchio et al. 2009; Fraivillig, Murphy, and Fuson 1999; Hufferd-Ackles et al. 2004; Lampert 2001; Staples 2007), we describe the actions and decisions that a teacher makes to support meaningful mathematical discussions in terms of three key functions:

1. *Eliciting Student Thinking,* including providing opportunities for students to generate ideas and then share their ideas with the class;

2. *Supporting Student-to-Student Exchanges about Mathematical Ideas,* including establishing a common knowledge base from which to work; and

3. *Guiding and Extending the Math,* including pursuing common misconceptions and ensuring appropriate disciplinary norms to advance the learning of the class.

An overview of these three key functions, along with a brief description of each, is shown in figure 4.1. In this section, we clarify each function and describe "teacher moves" and strategies related to each function that have been shown to be useful in supporting meaningful mathematical discourse. Drawing from the extensive literature in this area, we give particular attention to teacher verbal discourse moves because what teachers say (and do not say) as discussions unfold significantly impacts the nature of the discussion and the degree to which it is mathematically meaningful to students.

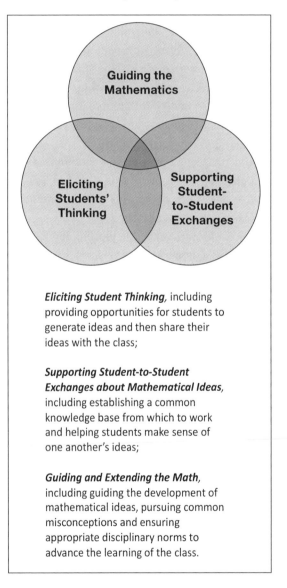

Eliciting Student Thinking, including providing opportunities for students to generate ideas and then share their ideas with the class;

Supporting Student-to-Student Exchanges about Mathematical Ideas, including establishing a common knowledge base from which to work and helping students make sense of one another's ideas;

Guiding and Extending the Math, including guiding the development of mathematical ideas, pursuing common misconceptions and ensuring appropriate disciplinary norms to advance the learning of the class.

Fig 4.1. Three key functions of the teacher's role in facilitating meaningful mathematical discourse

Because of space limitations, we emphasize one format—whole-class discussion—over others (e.g., pair work, small group discussions). We also give less attention to questioning and types of questions, as these topics are addressed extensively in chapter 5.

Eliciting. Students' reasoning is central to a meaningful mathematical discourse. Consequently, one of the teacher's most important functions is eliciting student thinking. This process starts with the teacher providing students time and space to generate ideas. This "thinking time," or wait time (Chapin, O'Connor, and Anderson 2009; Rowe 1986), allows students to think through a problem, form a strategy, and work on how they might express their ideas. Teachers can create further opportunities for students by using structures like quick writes, turn-and-talk, think-pair-share, or the use of hand signals by students to let the teacher know they have an idea and are ready to share.

Another aspect of eliciting student thinking is inviting students to share their ideas with the class. Note that such requests can be very open ("Who would like to share their answer to number 2?") or very specific ("I'm looking for different strategies for number 2. Who can show a numerical approach?"). Chapter 8 on the teaching practice of questioning includes strategies for how to effectively question and elicit students' thinking. One point we emphasize here is that the teacher's request may be more productive in eliciting student ideas if the teacher uses language that focuses on students' ideas and not the "right" answer (Hiebert et al. 1997; Humphreys and Parker 2015; Truxaw and DeFranco 2008). This feature relates back to the meaningfulness of the conversation and the shift of authority. For example, students may respond differently to the request, "Who can tell me the answer to Number 3 and how to do it?," versus the request, "Who can tell me what they got for Number 3 and how they approached it?" Both aim to elicit student ideas, but the latter phrasing implies that students are sharing their *thinking* in ways that might open up a conversation, whereas the former implies that the student's response is expected to be correct and might be subject to immediate evaluation.

A third consideration when eliciting student thinking is encouraging or supporting clear communication of ideas. The goal is, not perfect use of vocabulary or formal sentences, but rather clear enough expression of ideas so that both the teacher and other students can consider the contribution. To support student communication and develop these skills over time, teachers can provide students with a word bank of specific vocabulary or sentence frames, such as "I think the answer is . . . because . . . ," which help them to express ideas and articulate their thinking in an organized structure. Teachers also need to incorporate the use of visuals or manipulatives and opportunities for students to reference these as they describe their ideas. This aspect of the teacher's role overlaps with the next role, supporting student-to-student exchanges, as that work cannot be done if the student who is sharing does not present his or her idea in a sufficiently clear manner.

Supporting. The function of supporting student-to-student exchanges about mathematical ideas has two key aspects. First, the teacher must ensure that the ideas being worked on are accessible to the students in an ongoing manner, particularly as students contribute new ideas, some questions are resolved, and new questions are put on the table. Second, the teacher must manage, as needed, the student-to-student exchanges and turn taking as the discussion unfolds.

We focus first on accessibility. In a meaningful mathematical discussion, not only are student ideas elicited, but those ideas become a focus of the discussion. Students need support in attending to, making sense of, and commenting on one another's ideas. They also must be able to track the conversation over time as its focus shifts, new questions arise, and others are resolved. Teachers must monitor the discussion and act as needed to help students stay in a position where they can make sense of and contribute to a collective conversation.

To support this work, teachers can use a variety of strategies. A guiding principle for teachers is to ensure that ideas are represented publicly and with multiple opportunities for students to hear and make sense of an idea. Teachers can encourage students to come to the board or document camera (or other public space) to share and record calculations, tables, graphs, or other diagrams that support their reasoning or solution methods. Color coding visuals and restating key ideas are also useful ways to direct students' attention toward critical information.

By publicizing these elements, other students in the class have a better chance of being able to make sense of the shared strategy and offer their own thinking about it. In addition, these records are then available to be referenced later in discussion. Indeed, Ball and Bass (2003) argue that to engage students in mathematics in ways that centralize sense making and reasoning requires building public records, as discussions can only be supported on a base of public knowledge, which must be visible and shared.

The accessibility of the conversation, however, goes beyond what is happening in the present moment, or even that class period. For productive exchanges to occur, students must have a common ground (Clark 1996) or common knowledge (Barnes 1976; Edwards and Mercer 1987) as the basis of their communication. The common ground comprises those reference points that a student (or teacher) in the class can assume others in the class understand or can access and use meaningfully as they explain or share their ideas. For example, suppose the class is considering whether one can have an obtuse triangle that is also a right triangle. One strategy to publicize a contributing student's idea for others to consider is to have a student come to the board to record and "show" her thinking and the examples she has in mind. The teacher might also ask for some labeling or the use of a new color for the angle under consideration as right. But for this conversation to be a meaningful one that advances the class's knowledge, shared definitions of right and obtuse triangles need to be in play; otherwise, students will not be able to make sense of one another's ideas. For example, a student might reference "John's triangle" in sharing his own thought, which will support the discussion only if that is a common reference point that students can then refer to (mentally or otherwise) as they continue to work through ideas.

These types of supports help students to make sense of each other's ideas and ultimately to come to agreement. In general, teachers can encourage students to use agreed upon vocabulary or refer to a common diagram or example when explaining. Teachers can ask students to remind the class of the question being discussed, summarize the discussion so far, or restate the

different ideas being considered. By bringing attention back to established reference points, teachers help to ensure that students continue to be able to make sense of and contribute to the discussion (Staples 2007).

To further support student communication about mathematical ideas, teachers need discourse moves to help students hear, consider, and comment on one another's ideas. Chapin, O'Connor, and Anderson (2009) have developed a set of five talk moves, shown in figure 4.2, that are designed to support classroom discussions. These moves help publicize students' ideas and also help students attend to, make sense of, and build on one another's ideas.

1. Revoicing – Repeating what students have said and then asking for clarification

2. Repeating – Asking students to restate someone else's reasoning

3. Reasoning – Asking students to apply their own reasoning to someone else's reasoning

4. Adding on – Prompting students for further participation

5. Waiting – Using wait time

Fig. 4.2. Five productive talk moves. From Chapin, O'Connor, and Anderson (2009), pp. 12–17.

Revoicing and repeating are both important moves to publicize or establish an idea and help others access the idea, which increases the likelihood students will hear and make sense of an idea. Waiting after a student shares an idea is another form of wait time that supports the establishment of common ground, as students are provided the opportunity to consider and make sense of the contribution before being asked to respond to or use the idea.

Reasoning is a talk move that asks students to think about another student's idea or chain of reasoning and to consider whether or not they agree with the approach or idea and why. By doing so, students are prompted to make sense of another's idea and connect it with their own thinking. Adding on is another move that directs students to attend to another's idea, as it requests contributions that build on what has already been shared and potentially extends the mathematics. Each of these five talk moves positions the idea(s) already shared for further consideration by the class and offers opportunities for students to make sense of or comment on a peer's idea. Using the talk moves can help shift classroom discourse from sharing discussions, which can be supported by eliciting and publicizing student ideas, to collaborative discussions (Staples and Colonis 2007) where students work through ideas together, creating new understandings as a result of their conversations.

Guiding. A final function of the teacher's role in facilitating meaningful mathematical discussions is guiding and extending the math. That is, the teacher must guide the class's mathematical work during a discussion so that it advances and/or extends students' thinking and understanding. As a classroom discussion progresses, the teacher continually makes decisions regarding the direction of the lesson based on how it is unfolding with respect to her understanding of the discipline, her goals for the unit and lesson, her students' prior knowledge, and many other factors (Ball 1993; Chazan 2000; Lampert 2001). The teacher's listening skills are crucial here. She must hear students' contributions to monitor what they are wrestling with and where students are with their understanding. The students' contributions then inform her next moves as she decides how to productively support their continued engagement in a way that advances the class's mathematical work.

One challenge in facilitating a discussion is ensuring the mathematics is attended to with sufficient depth and rigor, which requires a teacher to decide when and how to step into the discussion (Rittenhouse 1998). These types of moves generally offer support for sustaining students' attention to an idea (particularly in the face of struggle) or advancing the discussion, by prompting students to consider new questions or content at a deeper level. While advancing the math, the moves also keep students "in the driver's seat."

More specifically, the teacher's work might include the following moves:

- Highlighting mathematically important aspects of student contributions for the class to further consider.

- Pressing students to offer mathematical reasoning

and arguments and not just explanations of their procedural steps. (See Kazemi and Stipek 2001 for a discussion of high-press versus low-press classroom environments.)

- Regarding "errors [as] opportunities to reconceptualize a problem and explore contradictions and alternative strategies" (Kazemi 1998, p. 411; see also Hoffman, Breyfogle, and Dressler 2009).

- Offering "information that students need in order to test their ideas or generate a counterexample" (Lobato, Clarke, and Ellis 2005, p. 110).

- Asking students to compare two or more methods (Fraivillig et al. 1999; Rathouz 2011) and/or explicitly prompting the use of multiple representations.

- Introducing a new example for consideration, strategically chosen to draw students' attention to some aspect of the mathematics.

These moves support students' mathematical work and do not take over the work or reduce the cognitive demand of the task (Stein, Grove, and Henningsen 1996).

While it is the ultimate goal for student ideas to drive the discussion and for students' mathematical reasoning to be the "judge" about correctness, there are also times when it is appropriate for the teacher to intervene more directly by telling (Chazan and Ball 1999; Lobato, Clarke, and Ellis 2005). Specifically, Lobato, Clarke, and Ellis (2005) conceptualized some forms of telling as initiating, where the teacher may, for example, summarize student work in a way that inserts new information, supplies a definition, or describes a new concept. More important than what the teacher says is the intention of the teacher's insertion. Lobato and colleagues assert that the purpose should be "to prompt coherence and sense-making." They further note that initiating is often followed by eliciting—"an action intended to ascertain how students interpret the information introduced by the teacher" (p. 111).

To illustrate, Lobato, Clark, and Ellis (2005) offer an example where students are working on the idea of steepness. The teacher detects potential misconceptions and offers ideas intended to clarify, as well as attune students to, commonalities across examples:

> One thing I want to say is that when we're talking about steepness we're talking about this slantiness. We're not

talking about whether it's harder to walk up it. They are definitely different ramps. You have to walk further on this one. . . . This one is higher. This one is longer. But there is something the same about them. (p. 128)

This kind of telling, or initiating, maintains students' authority and continues to position them as thinkers and doers of mathematics. The role of teachers at these moments—when students are satisfied with the depth and rigor (when the teacher is not) or are unsure of how to proceed further—is crucial. It is this type of guidance and structuring of students' attention to specific aspects of the mathematics that may make the key difference in whether the discussion is productive and meaningful and the degree to which it advances student learning (Alfieri et al. 2011; Cross 2009; Kazemi and Stipek 2001).

Table 4.1 offers a summary of the three functions of the teacher's role—eliciting student thinking, supporting student-to-student exchanges, and guiding and extending the math—with examples of teacher moves aligned to each. To help further illustrate these functions, we turn our attention to a classroom dialogue.

A Dialogue Is Worth a Thousand Words

A class of seventh-grade students is working on a hexagon patterns task as shown in figure 4.3. An excerpt from this lesson is shown in figure 4.4.

Table 4.1
Three sets of moves or strategies teachers can use as part of enacting each component of their facilitator role

Eliciting student ideas	Supporting student-to-student conversations and establishing common ground	Guiding and extending the mathematics
Providing students with time to think, generate, and work on expressing their ideas. (Quick Write, Think-Pair-Share, Turn-and-Talk, wait time) • "You have two minutes to talk, and at the end of that time, you need to be able to tell me who you agree with and why." Directly requesting students to share their ideas • "I'm looking for different strategies for number 2. Who can show a numerical approach?" Supporting clear communication • "I see you pointing and saying the corners. Let's make sure we know what you're referencing. Can you circle the corners you're talking about? And what's our mathematical word for those?" • "Lianne, as you explain, stand to the side so we can see your diagram and what you're referencing."	Ensuring a public space available to represent ideas • Small groups should have workspace in the middle of their table or desks • Teacher uses board or wall space carefully to record the main question, emerging ideas, and to focus the conversation Recording student ideas publically • "Come up and write your answer (thinking) on the board." • Use different colored markers to track different student ideas Encouraging students to engage and make sense of one another's ideas • "Vanessa, can you restate Felicia's idea in your own words?" • "Why do you think Albert chose to divide at this step?" Verbally recapping, or asking a student to recap, where the class is now with the ideas, and what they are still discussing	Prompting students to focus on particular aspects of the math, or to extend the mathematical thinking in a particular way: • "I'd like you two to compare your strategies." • "Hector just made a conjecture. Let's work on his conjecture as a class. That will get us into some other important mathematics." • "So we have the result. Now, why might that be true? Any thoughts?" Teacher inserts an idea for consideration to clarify or extend students' understandings • "From this discussion, I hear most agreeing it has to be an odd function, and some of you aren't sure yet. I'm going to draw a graph for you to consider. I want to know if this graph is odd as well, and why you think that." • "It sounds like we're not agreeing how to sort these objects because we're not agreeing on their definitions. Let's revisit the definitions and then come back to this."

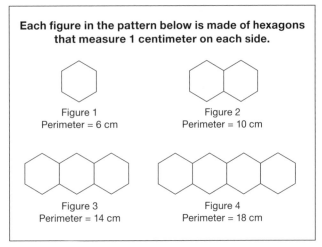

Each figure in the pattern below is made of hexagons that measure 1 centimeter on each side.

Figure 1
Perimeter = 6 cm

Figure 2
Perimeter = 10 cm

Figure 3
Perimeter = 14 cm

Figure 4
Perimeter = 18 cm

Fig. 4.3. Hexagon pattern task

In this excerpt, the class first considers the perimeter of a chain of four hexagons and then, using a particular method shared by a student, pursues the perimeter of a chain of ten hexagons. While the students drive much of this conversation, indicating a fairly mature math-talk community (Hufferd-Ackles et al. 2004), the teacher is still quite active, enacting each of the three role functions described above. Notice that the teacher does not do the mathematical work, however. In less mature communities the teacher enacts the same role functions but may need to do so in a different manner, such as in the example provided by Staples (2007, p. 16).

1. *Jackie* [*at board, pointing to a visual of four hexagons*]: Okay, well every time that you have one of these things, if it's *n* numbers, the middle ones will always have 4 and then these are going to be 5s. So I got 18.

2. *Ms. L*: So we all understand that? 18?

3. *Students*: Yeah.

4. *Ms. L*: No, do we all understand her strategy?

5. *Students*: Oh no. No.

6. *Ms. L*: No. Then, she is the presenter; you guys are the audience. Go ahead presenter, you're on.

7. *Sean*: How did you get the four?

8. *Jackie*: Well the 4 is the inside hexagons and then another 4 right here [*points to the second "interior" hexagon*] and then you have 5 on the ends [*points to the two "end" hexagons*].

9. *Cody*: So, what you are saying is all you did was 4 plus 4 plus 5 plus 5?

10. [*Jackie nods.*]

11. *Ms. L*: Okay [*addressing a student*], so go ahead, ask her how to find figure 10.

12. *Kate*: How did you find figure 10?

13. *Jackie*: Um, can I draw a picture?

14. *Ms. L*: Absolutely.

15. *Ms. L*: All right, while she is doing that up there and drawing it, why don't you try to use her strategy and find figure 10?

16. [*The teacher walks around the room, encouraging students to use Jackie's strategy. Jackie draws a chain of ten hexagons on the board and writes her calculations. After a minute, the teacher asks Jackie to explain.*]

17. *Jackie*: All right, well 8 right here [*pointing to the 8 "interior" hexagons of the chain that are not on the ends*], and then there is 4 on the [top and] bottom thing, so 8 times 4 equals 32, and then the ends there is 5 and then another 5, so plus 10 equals 42.

18. *Ms. L* [*to class*]: Does it work?

19. *Students*: Yeah.

20. *Ms. L*: Will it work for every single one?

21. *Students*: Yes.

22. *Ms. L* [*acknowledging a student*]: Do you have a question?

23. *Sean*: But for 100 it really wouldn't work, because you would have to draw 100 hexagons.

24. *Ms. L*: Okay, good question, would you have to draw them? What a good question. Would you have to draw it? Now Jackie, these guys over here used your method, too. Can they come up and support you and show how they don't need to draw it?

25. [*Jackie assents.*]

26. *Ms. L*: All right, let's do it.

Fig. 4.4. A classroom excerpt of a teacher facilitating meaningful mathematical discussions (edited for readability and anonymity)

We consider this an example of meaningful mathematical discourse, as the class is engaged in collaborative work, offering their ideas and attending to others' thinking, and making sense of significant mathematics. Looking more closely at the teacher's role in facilitating this meaningful mathematical discussion, let's begin with guiding the mathematics.

Line 4 is the teacher's first key move in guiding the class's mathematical work. She ascertains whether the class understands the presenter's strategy (beyond agreeing with the answer). Learning that the student's strategy is not well understood, in line 6 the teacher sets the agenda for the next part of the lesson–to understand Jackie's strategy for finding the perimeter of the hexagon chains.

In line 11, by encouraging a student to ask another student a question, the teacher moves the class to a consideration of a chain of 10 hexagons and, in line 15, asks the class to "use her strategy" to find the perimeter. This move further guides the class's mathematical work making sense of Jackie's approach, and we can see how this type of mathematical activity is setting the class up to consider the more general case. Line 23 is particularly interesting. The teacher hears a question that could lead to an important discussion about generalization: specifically, what kinds of strategies are general and can be used to determine perimeter for a hexagon chain of any length? She excitedly highlights it and invites another group to come up and share its work, which she indicates will help the class engage and ultimately answer the question. In this case, the teacher did not set the question herself to guide the math, but hearing a student question that was of import, gave weight to that and made it the focus of the conversation.

Some of the moves just discussed also support the other role components of eliciting students' ideas (e.g., lines 4) and supporting student exchanges (e.g., lines 6, 11, and 15). We also can see in this excerpt classroom norms as students seem comfortable and skilled at sharing and attending to each other's ideas as they question one another (lines 7 and 22).

Common Challenges and Productive First Steps: Supports for Making It Happen

Facilitating meaningful mathematical discourse is complex and challenging work. The research literature has documented the persistence of long-standing routines and discourse patterns of typical U.S. classrooms that run counter to engaging students in meaningful mathematical discourse and position mathematics as something to be directly transmitted and reproduced

(Jacobs et al. 2006; Stigler and Hiebert 1999). Making meaningful mathematical discourse a regular part of mathematics classes requires deliberate effort by classroom teachers and targeted support by districts. In this section, we highlight productive steps to advance this agenda, first at the classroom level and then at the district level.

Using Routines

One potentially productive approach for shifting teaching practice to better engage students in meaningful mathematical discourse involves teachers enacting new planning and classroom routines, or activity structures. Such routines provide a sequence of steps for part or all of a lesson to help create a context for meaningful mathematical discussions.

For example, Number Talks (e.g., Humphreys and Parker 2015; Parrish 2010) is a routine originally designed to support developing students' number sense and understanding of mathematical operations through sharing and discussing multiple approaches to a computational problem (e.g., 16×25). After think time, where the students signal the teacher when they have an approach, the teacher asks for student ideas (eliciting) and records these on the board (publicizing). As the teacher elicits and records, the teacher supports students in attending to and making sense of others' approaches. She then guides the subsequent discussion about the ideas. A discussion might focus on comparing two methods, raise questions about how students decomposed numbers, or revise and extend a student's method.

Other routines, such as the Launch-Explore-Summarize structure of *Connected Mathematics Project* (Lappan et al. 2009), the Five Practices routine (Smith and Stein 2011), the Talk Frame (Casa 2013; Williams and Casa 2011/2012), and Kazemi and Hintz's (2014) "targeted discussion" formats similarly create a context where students' generated ideas are used as the basis of the subsequent conversation. Routines provide a structure in which to have a meaningful mathematical discussion but will fall short if they become a forum for presenting one best way or allow students to serially report their approaches with no further discussion or connection (see *strategy reporting* versus *inquiry and argument* as patterns of interaction in Wood and Turner-Vorbeck [2001]).

Teaching New Practices to Students

Engaging in meaningful mathematical discourse may be just as new to students as to teachers. As students come together at the beginning of the year, they bring with them various conceptions of what math is and what it means to do math based on prior experiences. It is critical that teachers appreciate the extent to which they are asking students to engage with math in new ways—ways that require students to take risks—as they share ideas and try to work through ideas in a more public way than they have been asked to do before (e.g., Chazan 2000; Lampert 2001). Perhaps surprisingly, students who have been successful with more traditional models of instruction may be some of the strongest "resisters" of these changes, as their success and identity as a "good math student" may seem threatened.

Lampert (2001) offers an informative example of this paradox from her work with a fifth-grade class. She wanted to introduce the practice of revising as a way to support student sense making and engagement in authentic mathematical practices.

> Introducing *revising* . . . would require a change in how . . . students would typically think about what one does to study mathematics. It would probably also require some changes in what they thought about the roles of "smart" and less smart classmates. . . . I did not expect that my students would come to fifth grade knowing how to evaluate their own assertions or those of their peers in order to decide whether or not such assertions needed revising. Nor did I expect that they would see such evaluation and revision as activities that would contribute to their leaning. (Lampert 2001, p. 65)

This excerpt highlights the magnitude of the changes being asked of students and points to similarly daunting changes for teachers as they learn to do mathematics differently. Through Lampert's careful work with her class introducing new practices, she was able to expand students' individual and collective capacity to participate in a meaningful mathematical discourse.

Research studies have documented how teachers support the development of the class's capacity to participate in meaningful mathematical discourse and have found that teachers must deliberately introduce their students to new ways of working together, be explicit about how their participation in these new practices and formats supports their learning, and provide opportunities to negotiate the meanings of these new practices (Chazan 2000; Goos 2004; Hufferd-Ackles et al. 2004; Lampert 2001; Staples 2007). Going hand-in-hand with developing these practices, teachers must carefully establish classroom norms to support productive exchanges among students, such as the expectation that everyone must listen to each other, all students have the right to ask questions and share their thinking, and discussions are about mathematical ideas, not people (e.g., I'm critiquing the idea, not you). For detailed discussion and strategies, see Chapin, O'Connor, and Anderson (2009, 2014).

District-level Support

A critical component to supporting teachers as they strive to organize meaningful mathematical discourse is aligning the system. Pacing guides, teacher evaluation protocols, and curricular materials need to support and affirm pedagogies that centralize mathematical discussion. Similarly, student assessments must reach well beyond procedural skill to assess reasoning. Without such alignment, efforts to advance meaningful mathematical discourse in classrooms will not have a consequential impact. To undertake the challenge of shifting classroom culture and developing new pedagogical techniques, teachers need time, model resources, non-evaluative support, and opportunities to step back and reflect on how the discourse is developing in their classrooms. Teachers also need high quality resources to support their learning, reflection, and collaboration (such as published material), representations of practice (including videos), and access to and time with their local community of teachers (e.g., grade-level team or professional learning community). Specifying times that are protected and can be used for such learning-focused work is critically important as well, as teachers' days are busy and crowded with many important demands.

To support districts in monitoring their progress, Munter (2014) developed a set of protocols to help ascertain teachers' visions of high-quality mathematics instruction during implementation of district-level, multiyear reform. Though labor intensive, these protocols document teachers' changing visions and gauge the degree to which the vision of quality math teaching put forth from the district is being adopted consistently by teachers in the district. These and similar tools can be useful in supporting districts in designing and monitoring their efforts.

Concluding Remarks

Facilitating meaningful mathematical discourse is an essential goal if we are to support students' participation in mathematics, advance a view of mathematics as a connected whole, and develop students' conceptual understanding and proficiencies with key practices such as problem solving, argumentation, and communicating mathematically. Teachers play a multifaceted role requiring deep knowledge, pedagogical skill, and judgment. This work is challenging. Nevertheless, teachers, when supported, can take concrete, continual steps toward organizing this type of valued interaction in their classrooms. Though not prescriptive in nature, we hope this chapter provides a rationale, the beginning ideas, examples, and resources to undertake this important work.

References

Alfieri, Louis, Patricia J. Brooks, Naomi J. Aldrich, and Harriet R. Tenenbaum. "Does Discovery-Based Instruction Enhance Learning?" *Journal of Educational Psychology* 103, no. 1 (2011): 1–18.

Ball, Deborah L. "With an Eye on the Mathematical Horizon: Dilemmas of Teaching Elementary School Mathematics." *Elementary School Journal* 93, no. 4 (1993): 373–97.

Ball, Deborah L., and Hyman Bass. "Making Mathematics Reasonable in School." In *A Research Companion to Principles and Standards for School Mathematics,* edited by Jeremy Kilpatrick, W. Gary Martin, and Deborah Schifter, pp. 27–44. Reston, Va.: National Council of Teachers of Mathematics, 2003.

Barnes, David. *From Communication to Curriculum.* London: Penguin, 1976.

Battey, Daniel. "'Good' Mathematics Teaching for Students of Color and Those in Poverty: The Importance of Relational Interactions in Instruction." *Educational Studies in Mathematics* 82, no. 1 (2013): 125–44.

Boaler, Jo. *Experiencing School Mathematics: Teaching Styles, Sex and Setting.* Buckingham, United Kingdom: Open University Press, 1997.

Boaler, Jo, and James Greeno. "Identity, Agency, and Knowing in Mathematics Worlds." In *Multiple Perspectives on Mathematics Teaching and Learning*, edited by Jo Boaler, pp. 171–200. Westport, Conn.: Ablex Publishing, 2000.

Boaler, Jo, and Megan Staples. "Creating Mathematical Futures through an Equitable Teaching Approach: The Case of Railside School." *Teachers College Record* 110, no. 3 (2008): 608–45.

Bochicchio, Daniel, Shelbi Cole, Deborah Ostien, Vanessa Rodriguez, Megan Staples, Patricia Susla, and Mary Truxaw. "Shared Language." *Mathematics Teacher* 102, no. 8 (2009): 606–13.

Casa, Tutita M. "Capturing Thinking on the Talk Frame." *Teaching Children Mathematics* 19, no. 8 (2013): 516–23.

Chapin, Suzanne H., Catherine O'Connor, and Nancy Canavan Anderson. *Classroom Discussions: Using Math Talk to Help Students Learn, Grades K–6.* 2nd ed. Sausalito, Calif.: Math Solutions Publications, 2009.

———. *Classroom Discussions: A Teacher's Guide for Using Talk Moves to Support the Common Core and More, Grade K–6: A Multimedia Professional Learning Resource.* 3rd ed. Sausalito, Calif.: Math Solutions Publications, 2014.

Chazan, Daniel. *Beyond Formulas in Mathematics and Teaching: Dynamics of the High School Algebra Classroom.* New York: Teachers College Press: 2000.

Chazan, Daniel, and Deborah L. Ball. "Beyond Being Told Not to Tell." *For the Learning of Mathematics* 19, no. 2 (1999): 2–10.

Clark, Herbert. H. *Language Uses.* New York: Cambridge University Press, 1996.

Cohen, Elizabeth, and Rachel Lotan. *Designing Groupwork: Strategies for the Heterogeneous Classroom.* 3rd ed. New York: Teachers College Press, 2014.

Cross, Dionne I. "Creating Optimal Mathematics Learning Environments: Combining Argumentation and Writing to Enhance Achievement." *International Journal of Science and Mathematics Education* 7, no. 5 (2009): 905–30.

Edwards, Derek, and Neil Mercer. *Common Knowledge: The Development of Understanding in the Classroom.* London: Methuen, 1987.

Engle, Randi A., and Faith R. Conant. "Guiding Principles for Fostering Productive Disciplinary Engagement: Explaining an Emergent Argument in a Community of Learners Classroom." *Cognition and Instruction* 20, no. 4 (2002): 399–483.

Fraivillig, Judith, Lauren A. Murphy, and Karen C. Fuson. "Advancing Children's Mathematical Thinking in Everyday Mathematics Classrooms." *Journal for Research in Mathematics Education* 30, no. 2 (1999): 148–70.

Goos, Marilyn. "Learning Mathematics in a Classroom Community of Inquiry." *Journal for Research in Mathematics Education* 35, no. 4 (2004): 258–91.

Hiebert, James, Thomas Carpenter, Elizabeth Fennema, Karen C. Fuson, Diana Wearne, Hanlie Murray, Alwyn Olivier, and Piet Human. *Making Sense: Teaching and Learning*

Mathematics with Understanding. Portsmouth, N.H.: Heinemann, 1997.

Hoffman, Brittany L., M. Lynn Breyfogle, and Jason A. Dressler. "The Power of Incorrect Answers." *Mathematics Teaching in the Middle School* 15, no 4. (2009): 232–38.

Hufford-Ackles, Kimberly, Karen C. Fuson, and Miriam Ga-moran Sherin. "Describing Levels and Components of a Math-Talk Learning Community." *Journal for Research in Mathematics Education* 35, no. 2 (2004): 81–116.

Humphreys, Cathy, and Ruth Parker. *Making Number Talks Matter: Developing Mathematical Practices and Deepening Understanding, Grades 4–10.* Portland, Maine: Stenhouse, 2015.

Jacobs, Jennifer K., James Hiebert, Karen Bogard Givvin, Hilary Hollingsworth, Helen Garnier, and Diana Wearne. "Does Eighth-Grade Mathematics Teaching in the United States Align with the NCTM 'Standards'? Results from the TIMMS 1995 and 1999 Video Studies." *Journal for Research in Mathematics Education* 37, no. 1 (2006): 5–32.

Kazemi, Elham. "Discourse That Promotes Conceptual Understanding." *Teaching Children Mathematics* 4, no. 7 (1998): 410–14.

Kazemi, Elham, and Allison Hintz. *Intentional Talk: How to Structure and Lead Productive Mathematical Discussions.* Portland, Maine: Stenhouse, 2014.

Kazemi, Elham, and Deborah Stipek. "Promoting Conceptual Thinking in Four Upper-Elementary Mathematics Classrooms." *Elementary School Journal* 102, no. 1 (2001): 59–80.

Lampert, Magdalene. *Teaching Problems and the Problems of Teaching.* New Haven, Conn.: Yale University Press, 2001.

Lappan, Glenda, James T. Fey, William M. Fitzgerald, Susan N. Friel, and Elizabeth D. Phillips. *Connected Mathematics Curriculum 2.* Boston: Pearson Prentice Hall, 2009.

Lobato, Joanne, David Clarke, and Amy B. Ellis. "Initiating and Eliciting in Teaching: A Reformulation of Telling." *Journal for Research in Mathematics Education* 36, no. 2 (2005): 101–36.

Munter, Charles. "Developing Visions of High-Quality Mathematics Instruction." *Journal for Research in Mathematics Education* 45, no. 5 (2014): 585–636.

Nasir, Na'ilah S., Carlos Cabana, Barbara Shreve, Estelle Woodbury, and Nicole Louie. *Mathematics for Equity: A Framework for Successful Practice.* New York: Teachers College Press, 2014.

Nathan, Mitchell J., and Eric J. Knuth. "A Study of Whole Classroom Mathematical Discourse and Teacher Change." *Cognition and Instruction* 21, no. 2 (2003): 175–207.

National Council of Teachers of Mathematics (NCTM). *Curriculum and Evaluation Standards for School Mathematics.* Reston, Va.: NCTM, 1989.

———. *Principles and Standards for School Mathematics.* Reston, Va.: NCTM, 2000.

National Research Council. *Adding It Up: Helping Children Learn Mathematics.* Edited by Jeremy Kilpatrick, Jane Swafford, and Brad Findell. Washington, D.C.: National Academy Press, 2001.

Parrish, Sherry. *Number Talks.* Sausalito, Calif.: Math Solutions, 2010.

Rathouz, Margaret. "3 Ways That Promote Student Reasoning." *Teaching Children Mathematics* 18, no. 3 (2011): 182–89.

Rittenhouse, Peggy. "The Teacher's Role in Mathematical Conversation: Stepping In and Stepping Out." In *Talking Mathematics in School,* edited by Madelyn Lampert and Merrie L. Blunk, pp. 163–89. New York: Cambridge University Press, 1998.

Rowe, Mary Budd. "Wait Time: Slowing Down May be a Way of Speeding Up." *Journal of Teacher Education* 37, no. 1 (1986): 43–50.

Smith, Margaret Schwan, and Mary Kay Stein. *5 Practices for Orchestrating Productive Mathematics Discussions.* Reston, Va.: National Council of Teachers of Mathematics, 2011.

Staples, Megan. "Supporting Whole-Class Collaborative Inquiry in a Secondary Mathematics Classroom." *Cognition and Instruction* 25, no. 2 (2007): 161–217.

Staples, Megan, and Melissa Colonis. "Making the Most of Mathematical Discussions." *Mathematics Teacher* 101, no. 4 (2007): 257–61.

Stein, Mary Kay, Barbara W. Grove, and Marjorie Henningsen. "Building Student Capacity for Mathematical Thinking and Reasoning: An Analysis of Mathematical Tasks Used in Reform." *American Educational Research Journal* 33, no. 2 (1996): 455–88.

Stigler, James W., and James Hiebert. *The Teaching Gap.* New York: Free Press, 1999.

Truxaw, Mary P., and Thomas C. DeFranco, "Mapping Mathematics Classroom Discourse and Its Implications for Models of Teaching." *Journal for Research in Mathematics Education* 39, no. 5 (2008): 489–525.

Williams, Madelyn M., and Tutita M. Casa. "Connecting Class Talk with Individual Student Writing." *Teaching Children Mathematics* 18, no. 5 (2011/2012): 314–21.

Wood, Terry, and Tammy Turner-Vorbeck. "Extending the Conception of Mathematics Teaching." In *Beyond Classical Pedagogy: Teaching Elementary School Mathematics,* edited by Terry Wood, Barbara S. Nelson, and Janet Warfield, pp. 185–208. Mahwah, N.J.: Erlbaum, 2001.

Chapter 5

Repurposing Teacher Questions
Working toward Assessing and Advancing Student Mathematical Understanding

Marcy B. Wood, *University of Arizona*
Maggie Hackett, *Sunnyside Unified School District, Tucson, Arizona*

Effective teaching of mathematics uses purposeful questions to assess and advance students' reasoning and sense making about important mathematical ideas and relationships.

—Principles to Actions: Ensuring Mathematical Success for All, p. 35

Growing up in the Tucson desert, I (Maggie) was an indoor gal because it was too hot to play outside. I was fine; I had an active imagination, shelves full of books, and stuffed animals that took up more of my bed than I did. A favorite pastime was to line up my furry companions and play school. As their teacher, my job was to make sure they were paying attention, grade their homework, and ask lots and lots of questions.

I had not yet been to school, and I now wonder how this idea of teacher as inquisitor started. No doubt, it must have come from television programs and the books I so adored. There are endless examples of schooling in the media, and many of them feature teachers asking questions. One might even say that asking questions is a teacher's main job.

Our questions compel students to complete calculations, to share their solutions, and to recall key ideas. We use questions to check student understanding, to get particular ideas on the floor, and to encourage student participation. While well-intended, our questions do not always help our students reach our learning objectives. As much as 80 percent of teachers' questions focus on superficial mathematical information (Vacc 1993) or place the burden for mathematical thinking upon teachers' shoulders, giving the perception that student

learning is happening when, in reality, the teacher is doing the heavy lifting (Wood 1998).

In this chapter, we explore the teaching practice of posing purposeful questions. We begin by examining what is meant by purposeful questions. We then focus on challenges to posing more effective questions and suggest ways to repurpose our questions to better support mathematical learning.

What Is Meant by Purposeful Questions?

As discussed in chapters 4 and 7 of this book, two important goals for teaching are engaging students in meaningful mathematical discourse and encouraging productive struggle. As students persist in problem solving and in talking about mathematics, they develop strong understandings of mathematical ideas, learn argumentation skills and how to critique the reasoning of others, and begin to see themselves as mathematical people capable of succeeding at challenging tasks. There are many teaching moves that support these goals. However, one of the most effective and perhaps underused moves is posing questions that purposefully engage students in mathematical discussions.

Posing purposeful questions means asking questions that deepen students' understanding of mathematics while providing information about their mathematical thinking (NCTM 2000). For example, the question "How does that array relate to multiplication and division?" (NCTM 2014, p. 37) asks students to talk about mathematical structures and make connections among representations and operations. At the same time, the teacher learns what the student understands about the relationships among arrays, multiplication, and division.

These more productive questions ask students to do more than provide a short answer. They request explanations, reflections, connections, and justifications. For example, the question about arrays, multiplication, and division cannot be answered with one word or with a memorized definition of the term *array*. Instead, the question asks students to consider relationships they may have not yet articulated. As they respond, students reveal their thinking and make their ideas visible to their peers and the teacher, providing fodder for a rich discussion.

These questions reverse the usual flow of mathematical information. The teacher poses questions while the students explain and question their own and others' mathematical ideas. In the end, teachers listen more, talk less, and learn from their students. As a consequence, students talk more, listen more to other students, and teach themselves important mathematics.

The Questions We Tend to Ask

Asking these purposeful questions is not easy, as it requires that the teacher resist the urge to talk while also focusing on the overall mathematical purpose for the lesson. The teacher must determine what supports (if any) students need to extend their thinking and consider what more she might need to know about students' thinking in order to support their mathematical growth. One way to start posing more purposeful questions is to reflect upon our current questioning practices.

As we engage our students in mathematics, we frequently ask rapid-fire questions such as these: How much is 7 plus 14? What do I do next? Where should I write the 1? What is the answer? Or we ask sequences of questions and cherry-pick student answers as a way to funnel our students' responses and ideas toward a particular outcome or procedure (NCTM 2014). These questions and question sequences are well-intended and serve specific functions. They allow for student input in our lessons, and they control the flow of information so that all students are exposed to correct answers and efficient procedures. However, they demand limited mathematical effort from students.

For example, consider the teaching episode shown in table 5.1 (Fernandes 2010). Mr. M, the teacher, posed a sequence of questions that was satisfying and seemed productive. The questions helped his student, Carla, successfully complete several computations and arrive at a correct answer without stumbling over difficult mathematics. However, as we reviewed this lesson, we wondered about the flow of his questions.

We noticed that Mr. M's questions focused Carla's mathematical thinking on calculations and information in the problem. For example, on line 13, Mr. M asked Carla how many 5-inch squares it would take to fill the 50-inch side of the rectangle. Carla needed to translate this question into the appropriate mathematical procedure. However, she did not need to construct a solution strategy or determine the relationships between the square and the dimensions of the rectangle. In other words, Mr. M's sequence of questions funneled Carla's thinking and responses toward a correct answer. We appreciate Mr. M's support of Carla. However, his interventions starting on line 9 meant that Carla had fewer opportunities to do mathematics. Also, Mr. M had fewer opportunities to consider the range of Carla's mathematical understanding.

We wondered what might have happened if Mr. M had headed in a different direction beginning at line 9. Rather than ask how many squares would fit along the 100-inch side of the rectangle, he might have asked Carla how she could use the dimensions of the square to figure out how many squares it would take to cover the rectangle. This question would focus Carla on the big idea for the task, asking her to make sense of how to determine area. It would also place responsibility for the next step on Carla, encouraging her mathematical thinking. Finally, it would provide Mr. M with the opportunity to learn more about Carla's thinking.

Given that more challenging questions are better for student learning, why do so many of us engage in questions and questioning sequences that are more narrow and ask less from our students? John Smith (1996) argued that this kind of teaching practice—in which teachers' moves efficiently escort students through the teacher's procedural knowledge—arises from beliefs about the structure of mathematics and teachers' needs to feel effective in their work. Smith noted that many teachers (and others in society, including our students)

Table 5.1
Mr. M and Carla solve an area problem

Mr. M was a prospective teacher conducting a problem-solving interview with a sixth-grade student, Carla. He asked Carla to solve an area problem: How many square tiles, 5 inches on a side, does it take to cover a rectangular area that is 50 inches wide and 100 inches long? Carla had been staring at the problem for some time when Mr. M realized that she was unsure about what it meant for the square tile to be "5 inches on a side." We join them as Mr. M helped Carla make sense of the dimensions of the square tile.

Line	Speaker	Talk [*and Activity*]
1	*Mr. M:*	Here's the graph paper and let's pretend that this is a hundred inches long [*gesturing to the length of the graph paper*], and this is going to be fifty inches this way [*pointing to the width*]. So, this [*picking up a small paper square*] is one of the shapes you used on the other problem. So if that [*the paper square*] was a tile and it was five inches on each side, what would the measurement be on this side? [*pointing to one side of the paper square*]
2	*Carla:*	Five.
3	*Mr. M:*	How about this side? [*pointing to another side of the square*]
4	*Carla:*	Five.
5	*Mr. M:*	This side? [*pointing to another side of the square*]
6	*Carla:*	Five.
7	*Mr. M:*	And this side? [*pointing to another side of the square*]
8	*Carla:*	Five.
9	*Mr. M:*	It's five on all sides, right? So could we go ahead and, if this [*pointing to the length of the graph paper*] was a hundred inches long, can we put this on here? [*placing the square in the bottom left corner of the graph paper*] How many of these would it take [*moving the square up the graph paper and emphasizing this motion by tapping down on the table after each motion*] if it was a hundred inches?
10	*Carla:*	(*Doing the division on her paper*) Twenty!
11	*Mr. M:*	Twenty. Very good. So if it was fifty inches along this side [*indicating the graph paper*], is this side still five inches [*indicating the square*]? It didn't change, did it?
12	*Carla:*	No.
13	*Mr. M:*	So how many five inches, how many of these [*indicating the square*] would it take to go along this side if it is fifty?
14	*Carla:*	Ten!
15	*Mr. M:*	Ten. . . . So, how many will it take along this side? [*pointing to the length*] You just told me.
16	*Carla:*	Twenty.
17	*Mr. M:*	Twenty. [*pointing to the width*] How about this side?
18	*Carla:*	Ten.
19	*Mr. M:*	Ten. So how many would it take all together to fill it in?
20	*Carla:*	Um . . .
21	*Mr. M:*	And what are you going to do to figure that out?
22	*Carla:*	Twenty times ten. [*multiplying and writing 200*]

believe that school mathematics is a fixed body of knowledge that can be responsibly conveyed through clear definitions and demonstrations of procedures. In other words, our usual questioning sequences engage students in mathematical activity and ensure that they are exposed to important mathematical ideas. As teachers, we feel good because we covered the required content while our students successfully answered mathematical questions.

Smith (1996) argued that teachers can adopt more productive practices if these practices also support them in feeling effective as teachers. This requires that teachers (and others) shift their beliefs about the nature of mathematics. Rather than view mathematics as a fixed body of knowledge to be directly transmitted, teachers need to see mathematics as dynamic, growing, and created by people. For example, Mr. M seemed successful because he assisted Carla in quickly and correctly solving the problem. However, if Mr. M saw mathematics as a dynamic process of changing understandings, he might have focused on Carla's mathematical ideas. He then could evaluate his teaching based upon growth in Carla's mathematics as demonstrated by her articulation of her evolving ideas rather than upon her ability to follow his lead to reach a correct solution (Steinbring 1997). This more active vision of mathematics means that effective teaching is helping students engage in argumentation, justification, and deeper probing of mathematical ideas—mathematical moves supported by more purposeful questions.

Types of Questions

As we seek to ask more demanding questions, it is helpful to start by thinking about the different types of questions we might ask. *Principles to Actions* (NCTM 2014, pp. 36–37) summarizes four main types of questions:

* Gathering information—asks students to recall facts, definitions, or procedures

* Probing thinking—asks students to explain, elaborate, or clarify their thinking

* Making the mathematics visible—asks students to discuss mathematical structures and make connections among mathematical ideas and relationships

* Encouraging reflection and justification—asks students about deeper understandings of their reasoning and actions

These categories were gleaned from several questioning frameworks. One framework was developed by Jo Boaler and Karin Brodie (2004), who gathered and categorized teacher questions from three years of videotaped high school mathematics lessons. Also, James Hiebert and Diana Wearne (1993) generated categories of teacher questions by analyzing audiotaped lessons in six second-grade classrooms.

Each of these question types can be used to push student understanding of mathematics. However, some of these questions are less helpful than others. We tend toward questions that gather information, asking this kind of question 80 percent of the time (Vacc 1993). These questions, because they ask students simply to recall information, are the least effective in helping students learn mathematics. They are sometimes crucial to student learning—as when a student might need a reminder of a useful definition or when the teacher wants to be sure students understand the context of a problem. However, as we seek to be more sophisticated in our questions, we should try to ask many more questions from the other three categories.

In our work with teachers, we found that the most difficult category of questions is "making the mathematics visible." An initial reading of this phrase might suggest that these questions literally ask students to make mathematical objects something someone can see. For example, the questions Can you show 3/4 on a number line? and How can you represent this in a different way? ask students to display mathematical objects. While these questions may be entirely appropriate in certain circumstances, they fail to get at the metaphorical purpose of this category of questions: to uncover or reveal important mathematical ideas or concepts otherwise obscured by the problem and its context.

Questions that make mathematics visible ask students to articulate their current understanding of mathematical concepts and also to draw verbal (and perhaps visual) connections to prior learning. For example, in the area problem in table 5.1, Mr. M might have asked why the problem emphasized linear measurements when the task was about area. This question might have helped Carla gain a deeper understanding of the relationships between linear and area measurements and allowed Mr. M to better assess Carla's understanding of measurement. Other questions that make the mathematics visible include these: How does your equation relate to this graph? What connections do you see between Maria's idea and Jaquan's solution? and What does this fraction representation show that this other fraction representation does not? As students respond to these questions, it becomes possible for students and teachers to see problems and gaps in student understanding, making it possible to take steps to clarify concerns (Hull, Balka, and Miles 2011).

As you work toward asking more demanding questions, you might consider what types of questions you ask most frequently. If you find yourself asking questions that gather information (e.g., What is 5 times 7?), see if you can stop yourself and instead pose questions that ask for students' ideas (e.g., Why is multiplying helpful here? What other way could you show that?). You might also preplan questions, anticipating how students might respond to tasks and what questions will help them connect to the overall goal for the lesson. We recommend Margaret S. Smith and Mary Kay Stein's book *5 Practices for Orchestrating Productive Mathematics Discussions* (2011) for additional support in planning purposeful questions.

Beyond the First Question: Sequences of Questions

What you ask for your first question turns out to be less important than how you work with the subsequent responses. When teachers follow initial questions with requests for explanations and connections to ideas, students talk more about their ideas and make richer mathematical connections (Webb et al. 2014). As we shift toward questions that purposefully invite sense making, we have to ask ourselves what question sequences we typically use and how those sequences support students in exploring challenging mathematical ideas.

Known-Information Questioning Sequences

Teachers ask question sequences that fall into two main categories depending upon whether the teacher is look-ing for a specific answer (resulting in known-information question sequences) or is exploring what students understand (information-seeking question sequences) (Mehan 1985). In the first category, known-information question sequences, teachers are testing the students' knowledge or are interested in using student responses to get particular information on the floor. These sequences involve information already known to the teacher (and perhaps also known to students), such as a mathematical definition or result of a calculation.

Known-information question sequences can be both more and less helpful in advancing and assessing student learning. Sometimes, known-information sequences help support student learning by highlighting critical aspects of a problem. For example, Kara Jackson and her colleagues (2012) noted the importance of discussing key contextual features of a task, key mathematical ideas, and common vocabulary. If a problem involves raising money from a dance marathon, students will need to make sense of what a dance marathon is (a contextual feature) and understand certain vocabulary (such as initial amount and rate). As a teacher asks questions about these things, she is likely to use known-information questions.

Mr. M engaged in a helpful sequence of known-information questions in the first seven lines of his conversation with Carla. While these questions demanded little mathematical effort from Carla, they were important for Carla's understanding of the task. Carla had stared at the problem for some time and seemed stuck. Mr. M's questions helped her make sense of an essential piece of the task: the dimensions of the square tile. We suspect that, after responding to these questions, Carla could have continued with the problem on her own. Thus, known-information question sequences have a place in meaningful mathematical discourse, as they can help clarify important ideas and remind students of essential information.

Fooled by Funneling

However, these known-information question sequences can become problematic if they are the only sequences we use or when we ask them in moments where students can benefit from talking about their mathematical ideas. One especially compelling, and therefore problematic, type of known-information question sequence is called *funneling* (Wood 1998). Funneling sequences draw heavily upon student responses, so they seem to be student-centered. However, rather than exploring student ideas, these sequences funnel student responses toward a specific outcome.

The funneling sequence frequently starts with an incorrect or otherwise undesirable student response. Rather than probe the thinking behind this response, the teacher asks a question that leads the student toward a correct answer. Through a sequence of low-level questions (much like Mr. M's questions in table 5.1, lines 9–21), the teacher builds from student responses to direct, or funnel, students step-by-step toward the correct answer.

Scenario A in table 5.2 illustrates a funneling sequence. In this scenario, the teacher used her questions to funnel Danielle's responses toward the statement that 3/9 was equivalent to 2/6. In line 10A, she directed Danielle to draw a representation of 3/9. Instead, the teacher might have asked Danielle how she could learn more about 2/6 and 3/9. Danielle's response to this question might have provided the teacher with information about Danielle's understanding of equivalency. Similarly, in line 11A, Danielle seemed to realize something new; but in line 12A, the teacher described the important features of Danielle's drawing rather than ask for Danielle's new thinking. Then, in line 14A, the teacher funneled Danielle toward the correct statement that the two fractions were equivalent.

At first glance, this funneling sequence seemed quite effective, as Danielle efficiently arrived at the correct answer. However, Danielle's thinking was limited to drawing (line 11A), noticing particular features pointed out by the teacher (line 13A), and providing a statement that the fractions were equivalent. In this funneling sequence, the teacher (and Britney) lost the opportunity to learn about Danielle's thinking, and Danielle lost the opportunity to talk through and push on her ideas. Also, because Britney had no role in this conversation, she lost the opportunity to talk through and perhaps elaborate her ideas, while Danielle lost the opportunity to see Britney as a source of mathematical sense making. Thus, while this funneling sequence may have been efficient, the cost to student learning was quite high.

Funneling questions are satisfying because students are responding and the mathematical talk is moving in the teacher's desired direction. However, a sequence that uses this type of question can be problematic, as it does not truly explore student thinking. It also does not induce students to justify their thinking or connect their ideas to those of others (NCTM 2014). Instead, students forgo mathematical sense-making to focus on generating the response desired by the teacher (Wood 1998). While it is important to connect to our learning objectives, we want to notice when our questions make those connections for the students rather than allowing them to work toward their own conclusions.

To summarize, known-information question sequences can play an important role in learning. However, they can also detract from learning when they take the place of questions that focus on student, rather than teacher, ideas. Known-information questions can limit opportunities for students to explore alternative strategies or explain mathematical ideas (Mok, Cai, and Fung 2008). Also, as students work to respond with the answer the teacher is seeking, they pay less attention to mathematical reasons for their responses (Steinbring 1997). Because teachers feel pressed to move students quickly through material, they can find it difficult to justify a slower pace that focuses on student thinking. However, any time saved by using known-information questioning sequences does not make up for the learning lost when students focus on a teacher's intentions rather than on their own mathematical ideas.

Information-Seeking Question Sequences

In information-seeking question sequences, teachers' questions seek information about student thinking that is not already known to the teacher (or to the students). These question sequences encourage students to share ideas, allowing teachers to learn about students' mathematical understandings. Teachers can then adjust their teaching to better support their students. These question sequences also enable students to generate new meanings for themselves, allowing the students to learn mathematics with greater understanding (Wood 1998). Finally, these questions help students clarify the mathematics at hand so that the class can understand particular nuances.

One particular information-seeking questioning sequence is the *focusing* sequence. Terry Wood (1998)

Table 5.2
Fraction scenarios

A fictionalized fourth-grade class was working on finding equivalent fractions. Britney and Danielle were finding equivalent fractions for 2/6. Britney's answer was 3/9. Danielle's answer was 1/3. They compared their answers.

Line	Speaker	Talk [*and Activity*]
1	*Danielle*:	I don't think 3/9 [*Britney's answer*] is right.
2	*Britney*:	Yes, it is—3/9 is the same as 2/6. Both 2/6 and 3/9 are equivalent to 1/3.
3	*Danielle*:	I know they are both equivalent to 1/3, but we weren't supposed to find fractions that were equivalent to 1/3. We were supposed to find fractions equal to 2/6.
4	*Teacher*:	[*after watching this interaction*] How are you two doing?
5	*Danielle*:	We have different answers. I say it's 1/3, and Britney says it's 3/9.

Scenario A:

6A	*Teacher*:	Interesting. Why do you say Britney is wrong, Danielle?
7A	*Danielle*:	Because 3/9 is not the same as 2/6.
8A	*Teacher*:	It's not? Well, let's see. Can you show me 2/6?
9A	*Danielle*:	Yes. [*She points to rectangle partitioned into 6 parts with 2 shaded parts.*]
10A	*Teacher*:	OK. Right under that representation, let's draw the same-sized whole, but let's show 3/9.
11A	*Danielle*:	[*Draws a second rectangle showing 3/9 and compares the two representations.*] Oh.
12A	*Teacher*:	Do you see how 3/9 takes up the same space in the representation as 2/6?
13A	*Danielle*:	Yeah.
14A	*Teacher*:	So what does that mean?
15A	*Danielle*:	They're equivalent?
16A	*Teacher*:	Correct! There is more than one equivalent fraction for 2/6, so you are both correct. Good job, girls. Move on to the next problem.

Scenario B

6B	*Teacher*:	Interesting. Why do you say Britney is wrong, Danielle?
7B	*Danielle*:	Because 3/9 is not the same as 2/6.
8B	*Teacher*:	And, Britney, why do you say you are correct?
9B	*Britney*:	I think I am correct because 2/6 and 3/9 are both equivalent to 1/3.
10B	*Teacher*:	Tell me more about that.
11B	*Britney*:	Well, I know in my head, I've memorized that 2/6 is equivalent to 1/3. Also, I know that a "big one" fraction of 2/2 can make 1/3 into 2/6. [*In this class, "big one" fraction means that students find a fraction equivalent to one whole and multiply this by the original fraction to find an equivalent fraction. In this case, 2/2 is the "big one" fraction.*] So then I started thinking what else is equivalent to 1/3, and I used the "big one" fraction of 3/3 and I got 3/9.
12B	*Teacher*:	Danielle, what questions do you have for Britney?
13B	*Danielle*:	But you can't use a "big one" fraction for 2/6 and get to 3/9. That's why they aren't the same.
14B	*Britney*:	But they are—if they both are the same as 1/3, then they have to be the same as each other.
15B	*Teacher*:	You are doing some important thinking about generating equivalent fractions using "big one" fractions. So far, our class has only used "big one" fractions to find *one* equivalent fraction from another. But Britney is proposing that you can use two different "big one" fractions to prove that 2/6 is equivalent to 1/3 *and* that 3/9 is equivalent to 1/3. I want you two to wrestle with this question. If 1/3 is equivalent to 3/9 because of the "big one" fraction 3/3 [*she points to the 3/3 in Britney's work*] and 1/3 is equivalent to 2/6 because of the "big one" fraction 2/2 [*she points to the 2/2 in Britney's work*], are 2/6 and 3/9 equivalent to each other? I would like for you to explain this to the class when we wrap up.

described *focusing* as an interaction pattern in which the teacher asks students to explore or elaborate student ideas. The teacher questions build on student thinking and press students to deepen the mathematical connections within that idea. For example, the teacher may ask students how they know their mathematical conjecture is always true. This question could be followed by others that encourage students to consider different ways to test conjectures or what variations on their conjecture might lead to more mathematical insights.

Focusing sequences are similar to funneling sequences in that the teacher has a mathematical objective in mind. However, when a teacher uses focusing questions, she highlights student ideas with potentially rich mathematical implications. Her questions demand mathematical thinking from students rather than definitions or calculations. Also, focusing questions do not point students toward a particular solution but instead position students to grapple with important mathematical ideas that they do not yet fully understand.

Scenario B in table 5.2 demonstrates a focusing sequence. The teacher did not try to lead Danielle toward a statement about the equivalence. Instead, the teacher invited each student to explain her thinking (lines 6B and 8B). The teacher also asked Britney to share more about her thinking (line 10B). Rather than evaluate Britney's explanation, the teacher invited Danielle to ask Britney questions, allowing Danielle to clarify her thinking by asking Britney for specific details. Finally, the teacher ended by focusing Danielle and Britney on the critical aspect of Danielle's confusion—whether you can use two different "big one" fractions to prove equivalence. The teacher's questions did not funnel Danielle to the right answer but instead used her ideas to present an important mathematical question. The teacher did not explicitly address Danielle's undesirable understanding of fractions. Instead, she provided Britney and Danielle with a clear, yet open-ended, task that might help both students (and perhaps the class) better understand equivalent fractions.

Wood and colleagues (2006) noted another particularly effective information-seeking questioning sequence they called *exploring methods*. In this questioning sequence, the teacher asks students for several different strategies for solving a problem. As students present their strategies, the teacher asks questions that

require further explanation, clarification, and reasoning. The teacher also invites other students to ask their own questions. As a result, more students have opportunities to participate and engage in mathematical thinking. (See Hintz and Kazemi 2014 or Kazemi and Hintz 2014 for specific examples of how to engage a whole class in strategy sharing.)

Information-seeking questions do not need to be a surprise or kept secret from students. One fourth-grade teacher posted three main questions: Would your strategy always work? Can you justify your answer? Is there another way to get your answer? The teacher drew attention to these questions at the start of the task so that they were at the forefront in students' minds as they worked. Not only did this strategy remove the mystery of what the teacher would ask, it subtly broadened the students' thinking beyond solving the problem.

As a final note, getting students to respond to purposeful questions with thoughtful answers requires more than simply asking these kinds of questions. Student responses are guided by beliefs about appropriate mathematical activity. These beliefs, or sociomathematical norms, arise over time through mathematical interactions. The teacher's questions and responses to student answers are an essential piece of establishing sociomathematical norms that encourage reflection, justification, and reasoning (Yackel and Cobb 1996). Thus, as teachers shift to more purposeful questions, they must be persistent and patient, as it may take some time for students to understand and take up these new sociomathematical norms.

Other Purposes for Questions

While the primary purposes for questions vary from gathering known information to asking questions that allow students to discuss mathematical structures, there are secondary, but equally important, reasons teachers might ask questions.

Linking Mathematics to Life

Teacher questions may ask students to consider how mathematical ideas are connected to real-world applications. Links between the real world and mathematics support students in learning more mathematics as they draw from their knowledge of the real world to support their mathematical thinking (e.g., Torrez-Velasquez and Lobo 2004). For example, when a teacher asks a young student to figure out how many wheels are on four tricycles, the student can use her knowledge of tricycles to solve the problem.

Several researchers have also noted that real-world links enable students to see how math is already present in their own worlds, helping students understand that math surrounds them, that they are already successful in using mathematics, and that mathematics is a tool for critiquing and making sense of their worlds (e.g., Peterson 2005; Simic-Muller, Turner, and Varley 2009). For example, when students claimed that their school was more crowded than others, their teacher asked them what information and measurements they would need to show that a size difference existed between their building and neighboring schools (Turner and Font Strawhun 2007). Posing purposeful questions that explore inequities can be powerful tools for engaging students in mathematics, while also empowering students to address social justice concerns.

Getting Everyone to Participate

Even when we ask probing mathematical questions that elicit student ideas, our questions may not engage each student in thinking about and talking about mathematics. Some students may be reluctant to participate or may be actively excluded from conversations. We need to ensure that our questioning strategies provide all students with ways into conversations and opportunities to voice their ideas.

In Project Challenge, Suzanne Chapin and Catherine O'Connor (2007) documented significant gains in mathematics achievement for students in classrooms where teachers focused on engaging each student in reasoning and expressing ideas. Chapin and O'Connor described four teacher talk moves that can create classroom norms of respect and equal access to participation. First, teachers (and students) can *revoice* a student's ideas and verify accuracy ("Carla, I heard you say . . . . Is that right?"). Teachers can ask another student to *repeat* what the first student said ("Gregg, can you tell me what Lisa said?"). Teachers can also ask students if they *agree* with the other's ideas ("What do you think about Leticia's claim? Does her idea make sense to you?"). Finally, teachers can *invite other*

students to add ideas ("Does anyone have anything to add?"). These moves open opportunities to engage in mathematical thinking and are important strategies for purposefully increasing mathematical talk. These ideas were unpacked in chapter 4, which focused on discourse.

Victoria Hand (2012) noted the need for teachers to ask questions that provide more information about student participation. For example, rather than assume that off-task students are procrastinating or avoiding work, teachers might listen to student talk and then ask questions that acknowledge student concerns while also shifting students toward the mathematical task. While these questions may not be mathematical, they can be essential for supporting students in participating in mathematics and in helping teachers learn more about their students.

Outcomes of Posing Purposeful Questions

Benefits from the Teacher's Point of View

Purposeful questioning provides teachers an opportunity to really *hear* what students are thinking. When teachers ask purposeful questions, the responses help them monitor student mathematical thinking (Franke et al. 2009). Students might reveal naïve conceptions, or they might make a connection to a previous lesson. These understandings, which might not surface in a closed questioning environment, may be revealed in response to the kinds of productive questions we have described above.

For example, in table 5.2, scenario A, in which the teacher primarily funneled Danielle toward a correct answer, it was unclear whether Danielle understood why 2/6 was equivalent to 3/9 or whether she would be able to apply the teacher's visual strategy to future problems. Conversely, in scenario B, the teacher provided the opportunity for the students to share their mathematical thinking and reasoning through the use of focusing questions. Danielle's response revealed that she relied on the strategy of using a "big one" fraction to create equivalent fractions and that she struggled to extend that understanding beyond an algorithm. The teacher also learned more about Britney's work with fractions: that she could readily recall some equivalent fractions and that she was comfortable using the "big one" fraction strategy to generate more fractions.

Finally, listening to student responses informed the teacher's instructional moves as she decided to explore Britney's solution and Danielle's disagreement as part of a whole-class discussion. This move created opportunities for the class to engage in higher-level mathematics (Franke et al. 2009). In future conversations with Danielle, the teacher might emphasize aspects of Danielle's ideas that were mathematically desirable and ask her questions that could provide her opportunities to push her thinking.

Benefits from the Students' Points of View

Students also experience significant benefits from purposeful questioning. Their thinking becomes more explicit as they articulate their processes and reasoning. When teachers ask questions that help students attend to each other's ideas, students build a more complete mathematical understanding (Chapin and O'Connor 2007; Webb et al. 2014). Also, purposeful questioning makes the students, rather than the teacher, the doers of the mathematics. Finally, with the use of purposeful questioning, student thinking becomes the lesson content, allowing students to learn from their ideas rather than trying to make sense of the teacher's thinking.

Interestingly, despite an innate inquisitive nature, students may be satisfied with relatively superficial solutions. Amy Martino and Carolyn Maher (1999) studied teacher and student interactions in third- and fourth-grade classrooms. They found that students initially used random methods to solve a problem and then moved to trial and error or guess and check to finalize their solutions. The students did not naturally seek to build justification or proof for their calculations. Instead, teacher questions were required to push students into explanations, clarifications, justifications, and, ultimately, more sophisticated solution strategies. Thus, teacher questions play a critical role in engaging students more deeply in mathematical thinking.

Benefits from the English Language Learners' Points of View

Purposeful questions demand more of students, especially students who are learning to speak English. When answering purposeful questions, English language learners (and other students) cannot simply repeat vocabulary or offer numerical answers. Instead, they must explain their mathematical thinking and make sense of others' ideas. While this work can be challenging, it is essential work for ELL students, as it provides rich opportunities to develop not only mathematical ideas but also to gain more proficiency in complex communication in English.

In Judit Moschkovich's 1999 study of one classroom of ELL students, she noted two strategies that supported students in participating in mathematics discussions. One strategy involved asking students to clarify aspects of their reasoning by requesting more information. Another involved probing students' talk to uncover their mathematical meanings. By asking these purposeful questions, teachers can support ELL students in bringing their ways of talking and their resources to the mathematical discussion, enriching the conversation for all.

Conclusion

If we want students to move beyond correct answers and mastering procedures, we have to create classroom environments that support explanations and explorations of mathematical ideas. Purposeful, student-focused questioning is one important tool for creating these understanding-oriented classroom spaces. Taking on purposeful questioning is quite challenging, as it requires the beliefs that students learn best when they construct knowledge through talk and that classroom time is well spent on the learning that comes when students talk about their ideas. However, the substantial learning outcomes for everyone in the classroom (teachers and students alike) make it worth the time investment of using purposeful questions.

References

Boaler, Jo, and Karin Brodie. "The Importance, Nature and Impact of Teacher Questions." In *Proceedings of the 26th Annual Meeting of the North American Chapter of the International Group for the Psychology of Mathematics Education*, vol. 2, edited by Douglas E. McDougall and John A. Ross, pp. 773–81. Toronto: Ontario Institute for Studies in Education of the University of Toronto, 2004.

Chapin, Suzanne H., and Catherine O'Connor. "Academically Productive Talk: Supporting Students' Learning in Mathematics." In *The Learning of Mathematics: Sixty-ninth Yearbook of the National Council of Teachers of Mathematics*, edited by W. Gary Martin and Marilyn Strutchens, pp. 113–39. Reston, Va.: NCTM, 2007.

Fernandes, Anthony. "A Study of Mathematics Preservice Teachers Learning about English Language Learners through Task-Based Interviews and Noticing." Unpublished data set. 2010.

Franke, Megan L., Noreen M. Webb, Angela G. Chan, Marsha Ing, Deanna Freund, and Dan Battey. "Teacher Questioning to Elicit Students' Mathematical Thinking in Elementary School Classrooms." *Journal of Teacher Education* 60, no. 4 (2009): 380–92.

Hand, Victoria. "Seeing Culture and Power in Mathematical Learning: Toward a Model of Equitable Instruction." *Educational Studies in Mathematics* 80, no. 1–2 (2012): 233–47.

Hiebert, James, and Diana Wearne. "Instructional Tasks, Classroom Discourse, and Students' Learning in Second-Grade Arithmetic." *American Educational Research Journal* 30, no. 2 (1993): 393–425.

Hintz, Allison, and Elham Kazemi. "Talking about Math." *Educational Leadership* 72, no. 3 (2014): 36–40.

Hull, Ted H., Don S. Balka, and Ruth Harbin Miles. *Visible Thinking in the K–8 Mathematics Classroom*. Thousand Oaks, Calif.: Corwin Press, 2011.

Jackson, Kara J., Emily C. Shahan, Lynsey K. Gibbons, and Paul A. Cobb. "Launching Complex Tasks." *Mathematics Teaching in the Middle School* 18, no. 1 (2012): 24–29.

Kazemi, Elham, and Allison Hintz. *Intentional Talk: How to Structure and Lead Productive Mathematical Discussions*. Portland, Maine: Stenhouse Publishers, 2014.

Martino, Amy M., and Carolyn A. Maher. "Teacher Questioning to Promote Justification and Generalization in Mathematics: What Research Practice Has Taught Us." *Journal of Mathematical Behavior* 18, no. 1 (1999): 53–78.

Mehan, Hugh. *Learning Lessons: Social Organization in the Classroom*. Cambridge, Mass.: Harvard University Press, 1979.

———. "The Structure of Classroom Discourse." In *Handbook of Discourse Analysis, Volume 3: Discourse and Dialogue*, edited by Teun A. Van Dijk, pp. 119–31. London: Academic Pres, 1985.

Mok, Ida Ah Chee, Jinfa Cai, and Agnes Tak Fong Fung. "Missing Learning Opportunities in Classroom Instruction: Evidence from an Analysis of a Well-Structured Lesson on Comparing Fractions." *Mathematics Educator* 11, no. 1/2 (2008): 111–26.

Moschkovich, Judit. "Supporting the Participation of English Language Learners in Mathematical Discussions." *For the Learning of Mathematics* 19, no. 1 (1999): 11–19.

National Council of Teachers of Mathematics (NCTM). *Principles and Standards for School Mathematics*. Reston, Va.: NCTM, 2000.

———. *Principles to Actions: Ensuring Mathematical Success for All*. Reston, Va.: NCTM, 2014.

Peterson, Bob. "Teaching Math across the Curriculum." In *Rethinking Mathematics: Teaching Social Justice by the Numbers*, edited by Eric Gutstein and Bob Peterson, pp. 9–15. Milwaukee, Wis.: Rethinking Schools Publication, 2005.

Simic-Muller, Ksenija, Erin E. Turner, and Maura C. Varley. "Math Club Problem Posing." *Teaching Children Mathematics* 16, no. 4 (2009): 206–12.

Sims, Linda. "Look Who's Talking: Differences in Math Talk in U.S. and Chinese Classrooms." *Teaching Children Mathematics* 15, no. 2 (2008): 120–24.

Smith, John P., III. "Efficacy and Teaching Mathematics by Telling: A Challenge for Reform." *Journal for Research in Mathematics Education* 27, no. 4 (1996): 387–402.

Smith, Margaret S., and Mary Kay Stein. *5 Practices for Orchestrating Productive Mathematics Discussions*. Reston, Va.: National Council of Teachers of Mathematics, 2011.

Steinbring, Heinz. "Epistemological Investigation of Classroom Interaction in Elementary Mathematics Teaching." *Educational Studies in Mathematics* 32, no. 1 (1997): 49–92.

Torres-Velasquez, Diane, and Gilberto Lobo. "Culturally Responsive Mathematics Teaching and English Language Learners." *Teaching Children Mathematics* 11, no. 5 (2004): 249–55.

Turner, Erin E., and Beatriz T. Font Strawhun. "Posing Problems That Matter: Investigating School Overcrowding." *Teaching Children Mathematics* 13, no. 9 (2007): 457–63.

Vacc, Nancy Nesbitt. "Implementing the 'Professional Standards for Teaching Mathematics': Questioning in the Mathematics Classroom." *Arithmetic Teacher* 41, no. 2 (1993): 88–92.

Webb, Noreen M., Megan L. Franke, Marsha Ing, Jacqueline Wong, Cecilia H. Fernandez, Nami Shin, and Angela C. Turrou. "Engaging with Others' Mathematical Ideas: Interrelationships Among Student Participation, Teachers' Instructional Practices, and Learning." *International Journal of Educational Research* 63 (2014): 79–93.

Wood, Terry. "Alternative Patterns of Communication in Mathematics Classes: Funneling or Focusing." In *Language and*

Communication in the Mathematics Classroom, edited by Heinz Steinbring, Maria Bartolini Bussi, and Anna Sierpinska, pp. 167–78. Reston, Va.: National Council of Teachers of Mathematics, 1998.

Wood, Terry, Gaye Williams, and Betsy McNeal. "Children's Mathematical Thinking in Different Classroom Cultures." *Journal for Research in Mathematics Education* 37, no. 3 (2006): 222–55.

Yackel, Erna, and Paul Cobb. "Sociomathematical Norms, Argumentation, and Autonomy in Mathematics." *Journal for Research in Mathematics Education* 27, no. 4 (1996): 458–77.

Chapter **6**

Teaching to Build Procedural Fluency

Jennifer M. Bay-Williams and Amy Stokes-Levine, *University of Louisville*

Few topics in mathematics education are more debated than the meaning and the teaching of procedures and concepts in the K–grade 12 mathematics curriculum. However, there is a strong consensus about the desired outcome: procedural fluency. *Principles to Actions: Ensuring Mathematical Success for All* (NCTM 2014) explains how this might be accomplished in the teaching of procedures:

> Build Procedural Fluency from Conceptual Understanding: Effective teaching of mathematics builds fluency with procedures on a foundation of conceptual understanding so that students, over time, become skillful in using procedures flexibly as they solve contextual and mathematical problems. (p. 42)

Notice the language related to procedural fluency found within this statement: fluency, flexibility, skill, procedures, and understanding. Research on this topic, similarly, uses these terms and others. In addition, the words surrounding procedures are not synonymous, nor are they used the same way by different researchers or educators. Therefore, we begin this chapter with a discussion of word choice related to procedures and concepts and the nuances within that vocabulary; then we will clarify what is meant in this teaching practice by procedural fluency. The role of conceptual understanding in achieving procedural fluency is paramount in determining how we might teach to reach this outcome. Research provides significant insights into student development of procedural and conceptual knowledge, suggesting that, as a field, we should move away from the chicken-and-egg "which comes first" debate to a dialogue that focuses on how they might best support each other. A number of teaching strategies have been found to do just that: support procedural fluency with

a foundation of conceptual understanding. We discuss these in the second part of this chapter.

What Are Procedural Fluency and Conceptual Understanding?

To begin, we explore what *procedural fluency* and *conceptual understanding* mean. We must be precise and intentional in the terminology we use around these critical learning goals before we can make sense of the research related to effective instructional approaches to developing procedural fluency.

Procedural Fluency

The word *procedural* is often used as a modifier for a variety of nouns related to computation (see fig. 6.1). These terms are often used interchangeably, and yet

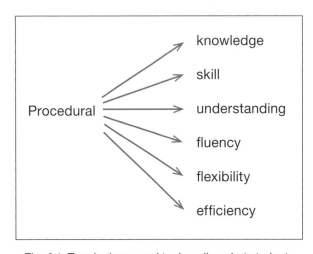

Fig. 6.1. Terminology used to describe what students know about procedures

they have different meanings. The commonly used definition of *procedural knowled*ge is Hiebert and Lefevre's (1986): knowing "step-by-step how to complete tasks" (p. 6). Star (2005) argued that such a definition of procedural knowledge is limiting, implying that there is one way (an algorithm) that can be known. He suggested that procedural knowledge might be at a superficial level but could also be at a deep level, "associated with comprehension, flexibility, and critical judgment" (p. 408). *Procedural skill,* rather than being about the knowledge a student might have, typically refers to the way in which students use their knowledge and has historically been used to refer to accurate, smooth, and rapid execution of mathematical procedures with no attention to comprehension, flexibility, or strategy selection (Hiebert and Grouws 2007). Until recent years, researchers based their evaluation of effective teaching practices and student learning through the lens of these less comprehensive definitions of procedural knowledge and skill (Brophy 1988; Hiebert and Grouws 2007; Star 2005). *Procedural understanding*, by contrast, refers to knowing both *how* to complete an algorithm and *why* an algorithm works.

Procedural fluency, the goal for all students, is more than procedural skill or understanding. Students who demonstrate procedural fluency have the deep knowledge described above and apply that knowledge in carrying out procedures flexibly, accurately, efficiently, and appropriately (Kilpatrick, Swafford, and Findell 2001; NGA Center and CCSSO 2010; Russell 2000). A careful look at procedure-related standards within the Common Core State Standards for Mathematics clearly indicates that fluency is something more than mastering the standard algorithm, which speaks to the layered components of fluency. For example, consider two standards from third and fourth grade on multidigit addition.

> 3.NBT.A.2 *Fluently* add and subtract within 1000 *using strategies* and *algorithms* based on place value, properties of operations, and/or the relationship between addition and subtraction. (p. 24) [italics added]

> 4.NBT.B.4 *Fluently* add and subtract multi-digit whole numbers *using the standard algorithm*. (p. 29) [italics added]

To be fluent with addition and subtraction within 1000, a student is to use strategies *and* algorithms (including the standard algorithm). Strategies are different than algorithms (Fuson and Beckmann 2012–13; NGA Center and CCSSO 2010). Strategies are "purposeful manipulations that may be chosen for specific problems, may not have a fixed order, and may be aimed at converting one problem into another," while algorithms are a "set of predefined steps for a class of problems" (NGA Center and CCSSO 2010, p. 85). The goal for students, then, is to be fluent in using strategies (e.g., counting up to benchmarks or skip counting on a number line) and algorithms other than the standard algorithm (e.g., partial sums), as described in the grade 3 standard, as well as efficiently and accurately using the standard algorithm, as described in the grade 4 standard. Importantly, these standards are additive. Students do not graduate to the standard algorithm, never again to use the other strategies and algorithms they learned; rather, the standard algorithm is added to the repertoire of strategies, any one of which may be the most efficient strategy given the values in the problems.

"Being fluent" is a component of fluency but is not equivalent to fluency. *Fluent* typically means accurate and quick. *Fluency* is more comprehensive than being able to solve a problem with speed and accuracy. For example, the rule of thumb is that to be fluent with basic facts students should be able to respond to a particular fact correctly within three seconds (either because they know it by memory or they apply a mental strategy quickly). However, fluency also includes a component of efficiency. *Efficiency* refers to both speed (implementing a strategy or algorithm quickly) and appropriate strategy selection (one that can quickly get to the answer). Consider an efficient way to solve $506 - 398 =$ _____. A counting up strategy, for example, might count up from 398 to 400, then up 100 to 500, and then up 6 more to 506. For this example, this counting up strategy is quicker than the standard algorithm. A different problem, such as $559 - 488 =$ _____, may be efficiently solved with either a counting up strategy or the standard algorithm.

Procedural flexibility means knowing multiple procedures and using them appropriately to solve a range of problems (Baroody and Dowker 2003; Kilpatrick, Swafford, and Findell 2001; Star 2005). Flexibility includes strategy selection as well as the ability to modify strategies (or algorithms) to fit the numbers in

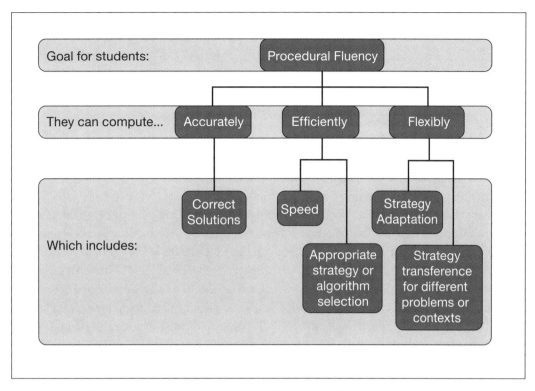

Fig. 6.2. Components of procedural fluency and their interrelationships

a given problem (Blöte, Van der Burg, and Klein 2001; Rittle-Johnson, Star, and Durkin 2012). In the last example (559 – 488), the student might use the counting up procedure (count up 12, then 50, then 9 for a sum of 71), or he might find a solution using an algorithm process, such as adding 12 to both values to preserve equivalence and make the problem easier to solve (571 – 500 = 71).

In figure 6.2, we provide a graphic intended to illustrate the nesting of components and terminology used in describing procedural fluency. This figure helps to illustrate the difference between superficial and deep procedural knowledge. A student with superficial knowledge may know only one procedure and be able to execute it with speed and accuracy, whereas a student with deep knowledge knows multiple strategies and algorithms and strategically deploys and adapts them as warranted by the situation.

Bloom's (revised) taxonomy (Anderson and Krathwohl 2001) can also provide a useful lens for thinking about a continuum of procedural fluency. Bloom's taxonomy was, in fact, designed to describe levels of expertise required to achieve a measurable student outcome. Fan and Bokhove (2014) describe a cognitive

model for learning algorithms adapted to three levels, modeled after Bloom's taxonomy. See figure 6.3.

Level 1: Knowledge and Skills—knowing the steps and carrying them out in a straightforward situation [Bloom's Level: Remember]

Level 2: Understanding and Comprehension—knowing why a procedure works and applying it to a complex situation [Bloom's Levels: Understand, Apply, Analyze]

Level 3: Evaluation and Construction—comparing different algorithms, judging the efficiency of an algorithm, constructing new algorithms (strategies), and generalizing [Bloom's Levels: Evaluate, Create]

Fig. 6.3. A cognitive model for learning algorithms

Fan and Bokhove explain that lower levels support higher levels and vice versa. Comparing these levels to the components of procedural fluency in figure 6.2, a few components coincide with level 1 (e.g., accurate use of an algorithm), while other skills align more closely with level 2 (e.g., using a strategy), and still others with level 3 (e.g., selecting an appropriate strategy, adapting a strategy). In other words, procedural fluency reflects the highest levels of Bloom's (revised) taxonomy.

Conceptual Understanding

What is conceptual understanding? In research, the definition of *conceptual knowledge* focuses on *connected* knowledge: "mental connections among mathematical facts, procedures, and ideas" (Hiebert and Grouws 2007, p. 380), "a network in which the linking relationships are as prominent as the discrete pieces" (Hiebert and Lefevre 1986, p. 4), and "concepts of a domain and their interrelations" (Schneider, Rittle-Johnson, and Star 2011, p. 1). Similarly, the term *conceptual understanding* is defined as the comprehension of mathematical concepts, operations, and relations (Kilpatrick, Swafford, and Findell 2001). Star (2005) argued that while concept implies connected knowledge, "knowledge of a concept is not necessarily rich in relationships" (p. 407). Conceptual knowledge, like procedural knowledge, can be placed on a continuum from limited and superficial levels of understanding to deep and connected knowledge (de Jong and Ferguson-Hessler 1996; Star 2005).

A review of the meanings of procedural fluency and conceptual understanding underscores three important points. First, teachers need clarity of language to be clear about learning outcomes for students. Second, both types of knowledge (procedural and conceptual) can be either superficial or deep; the goal for both is deep understanding, such as Bloom's higher-level learning outcomes. Baroody, Feil, and Johnson (2007) explained that "adaptive expertise, for one, unites the notions of deep conceptual knowledge, deep procedural knowledge and flexibility" (p. 120). Third, comprehension is paramount for developing deep knowledge in both areas and must be the focus of teaching procedural fluency.

Planning for Procedural Fluency and Conceptual Understanding

Establishing the language and expectations for learning procedures and concepts provides the foundation for instructional design. For example, should concepts be taught prior to procedures? This question has launched significant debate and has been a central component of the rhetoric of the math wars (Sowder 1998; Star 2005). Research can help us better understand how to sequence instruction, as well as how to ensure we are developing procedural fluency. Each is briefly discussed here.

Sequencing Instruction of Concepts and Procedures

Should instruction of concepts precede instruction on procedures? There is evidence that an initial focus on conceptual understanding and relationships can strengthen procedural knowledge (e.g., Griffin 2005; Hiebert and Grouws 2007). These studies primarily focused on classrooms that developed conceptual understanding prior to developing procedural knowledge, and the results indicated that students demonstrated greater conceptual understanding and an equitable level of procedural knowledge, compared to their peers in classrooms that focused primarily on procedural knowledge.

Conversely, one might ask whether procedures could or should precede concepts; stated differently, "Does procedural knowledge support or inhibit the development of conceptual understanding?" Research is less clear on this point. Some studies suggest that, once students have learned procedures, they are less likely to understand the meaning or the reasoning behind them (Hiebert 1999; Pesek and Kirshner 2000), and the learning of facts or procedures (i.e., using drill and timed tests without connections to conceptual understanding) can lead to math anxiety (Boaler 2014; Isaacs and Carroll 1999). Other studies have found that procedural knowledge supports the development of conceptual knowledge (e.g., Canobi 2009; Schneider, Rittle-Johnson, and Star 2011). For example, Canobi (2009) found that well-structured practice problems lead to improvements in seven- and eight-year-old students' abilities to describe key concepts.

Flexibility has long been a goal in developing procedural fluency and, as indicated above, requires a high level of cognition. Students who have procedural flexibility are more likely to use or adapt existing procedures when faced with unfamiliar problems *and* have a greater conceptual understanding (Blöte, Van der Burg, and Klein 2001; Carpenter et al. 1998). Schneider, Rittle-Johnson, and Star (2011) studied the relationships between procedural knowledge, conceptual knowledge, and procedural flexibility and found that procedures support concepts (and vice versa); this was true regardless of the extent of prior knowledge a student had in either type of knowledge. Importantly, they found that both conceptual and procedural knowledge independently contributed to student development of procedural flexibility. In other words, procedural flexibility requires both conceptual and procedural knowledge (regardless of the order in which they were acquired).

What might appear to be mixed results regarding whether a procedures-first approach hurts or helps students may actually be explained by the way in which procedures are defined in the research and taught in the interventions (Star 2005, 2007). Superficial measures or rote instruction of procedures (see level 1 of Fan and Bokhove's cognitive model for learning algorithms, shown in figure 6.3) may not support the development of conceptual understanding, while higher levels of procedural knowledge may have a positive impact on conceptual knowledge.

There is a growing body of evidence that instruction on procedures and concepts should be iterative (e.g., Canobi 2009; Rittle-Johnson and Koedinger 2009; Rittle-Johnson, Schneider, and Star 2015) and explicitly connected (e.g., Fuson, Kalchman, and Bransford 2005; Hiebert and Grouws 2007; Osana and Pitsolantis 2013). Fuson and colleagues (2005) suggested that multiple strategies should be presented with attention to why they work, the relative efficiency and reliability of each, and a "conceptual ladder that helps students move in a connected way" to more efficient and abstract strategies (p. 232). As Schneider and colleagues (2011) wrote:

> Hence, instruction focusing on only one of the two kinds of knowledge is not desirable. Conceptual knowledge may help with the construction, selection, and appropriate execution of problem-solving procedures. At the same time, practice using procedures may help students develop and deepen understanding of concepts. Both kinds of knowledge are intertwined and can strengthen each other over time. (p. 10)

For example, as students explore ratios, they explore contexts that are multiplicative comparisons (as well as contexts that are not multiplicative). As they continue to study ratios and proportions using various strategies (e.g., informal reasoning, bar diagrams, ratio tables,

equations), they develop a stronger understanding of the concepts related to proportional reasoning. As they consider different ways they can set up a proportion or a ratio table, they strengthen their procedural knowledge. Across these days and weeks of instruction, the teacher is able to select goals, tasks, and questions that focus on both conceptual and procedural knowledge. The instructional strategies shared in the next section provide specific, effective ideas for developing conceptual and procedural knowledge in an iterative way, and for making those connections explicit.

Rush to Fluency: An Oxymoron

Developing procedural fluency is complex and takes time. The phrase "rush to fluency" has been coined to mean a rush to executing a standard algorithm. The concern in the rush to a standard algorithm is that students have insufficient time to develop deep conceptual or procedural understanding. In reality, rushing to a single algorithm limits or even prevents students' opportunities to develop conceptual understanding *and* procedural fluency. Fluency, as described above, requires knowing and understanding a variety of strategies and algorithms (being fluent), being able to judge the repertoire to determine which one best fits the problem given (efficiency), and, finally, being able to adapt the selected strategy to fit the problem (flexibility). These level 3 cognitive processes take time to develop (Baroody and Dowker 2003; LeFevre et al. 2006; Osana and Pitsolantis 2013; Schneider et al. 2011).

A rush to fluency is particularly troubling as it relates to basic fact fluency. Fluency with basic facts also involves flexibility, efficiency, accuracy, and appropriate strategy application. Baroody, Bajwa, and Eiland (2009) described a three-phase developmental model wherein students move from counting to reasoning strategies to automaticity. A rush to fluency can neglect students' development of reasoning strategies. Going too quickly from counting to automaticity results in children memorizing facts in the short term but falling back on counting when they are unable to recall facts in the long term (Baroody 2006; Henry and Brown 2008). Timed tests also undermine the development of fluency. First, timed tests only measure accuracy. Some argue they are a measure of efficiency, but it is impossible to know whether students selected an efficient strategy for each fact. Second, timed tests may have damaging psychological effects, causing math anxiety in young children (Ashcraft 2002; Boaler 2014; Ramirez et al. 2013).

With basic facts and other computation, students need time to develop strategies and algorithms. Embedded in the development of strategies and algorithms must be the opportunity for appropriate practice. Once students have learned a strategy, they need to practice it to develop efficiency (speed) with that strategy. But recall that efficiency also requires strategy selection. Therefore, students also need opportunities to practice selecting a strategy. For example, with basic facts, students may learn "near doubles" and "make 10" strategies for sums within 20, and then practice their facts with a focus on which strategy fits which facts. "Practice that follows substantial initial experiences that support understanding and emphasize 'thinking strategies' has been shown to improve student achievement with single-digit calculations" (NRC 2001, p. 193). Students need time to develop fluency, but time spent solely on level 1 practice will not result in this skill. Strategic instructional decisions must focus on all components of fluency as well as make strong links between concepts and procedures. The instructional approaches described in the next section provide opportunities to practice procedures in ways that focus on all aspects of procedural fluency.

Instructional Approaches to Develop Procedural Fluency

In this section, we share three instructional approaches that have been effective in developing students' procedural fluency building upon a foundation of conceptual understanding. We use the term instructional *approach* to refer to a way a teacher might instruct students, avoiding the term *strategy* because it is used throughout this chapter to describe how a student might solve a problem. While many more instructional approaches exist, the three described below have been shown to support the development of procedural fluency with a foundation of conceptual understanding. For each we share the *concept* of the approach and some *procedures* for implementing it.

1. Focus on Why and When

Critical to developing fluency is knowing the purpose for algorithms and understanding why they work—in other words, knowing *why* a strategy works and therefore *when* it might be the best choice of strategies. Posing purposeful questions (e.g., "when" and "why" questions) serves to "make the mathematics more visible and accessible for student examination and discussion" (NCTM 2014, p. 41). There are several instructional approaches that focus students' attention on when and why a strategy or algorithm works; in other words, the focus is on a teleological understanding of a procedure (Star 2005). *Teleological understanding* means knowledge beyond a sequenced list of steps, addressing the reasoning or intent behind the purpose of each step in a procedure, the qualifying task conditions that are needed, as well as the limitations of a procedure (Star 2002). Procedural knowledge taught in this way advances what is typically surface knowledge toward deep knowledge and is a basis for developing student flexibility (Star 2005). Teleological understanding raises the level of cognition to level 2 (comprehension and application), a higher level than focusing solely on level 1 (procedural steps).

The *concept* of this instructional approach is to address mathematical procedures themselves on a conceptual level so that students are exposed to procedures as relational components rather than rote steps of a standard algorithm. The *procedure* is to discuss attributes of selected algorithms or stategies, including their goals and limitations. For example, consider the subtraction problem discussed above, $506 - 498 = \underline{}$. A counting up strategy could be selected to find the difference between the two values. Key questions for a strategy discussion include the following:

Why was this strategy selected?

When is this strategy a good one to use?

Students may have chosen to count up because 498 is close to a benchmark (500) or because 506 and 498 are close together. For other values (e.g., $1245 - 437$) these attributes do not apply, so counting up is not an efficient approach. Students must learn, then, that a limitation of counting up is that it does not work efficiently under all conditions. Focusing on purpose and understanding is useful when students are first introduced to a strategy or procedure, as well as when working through practice problems and unfamiliar nonroutine tasks. Notice the iterative process between conceptual and procedural knowledge at work in this example. Deciding when to take away or when to find the difference (two options for procedures) depends on knowing that subtraction can be a separation situation (take away) or a comparison situation (difference).

Students benefit from considering options for solving a problem before they attempt to solve it. For example, when presented a task such as $4(x + 1/2) - 6 = 10$, discuss the purpose or goal of adding 6 first versus the goal of distributing the multiplication of 4 first. Such a discussion helps students decide which order may best fit a similar problem—in other words, deciding when they might use a certain approach. Strategizing about which operation to apply first communicates to students that they can make decisions on how to solve a problem based on the numbers or variables rather than assuming that the same process fits all problems of a particular type.

Additionally, by conceptually addressing operations during procedural application, students may deepen their comprehension of operation relatedness. Consider solving $4 \times 2\frac{1}{3}$ with a focus on teleological understanding. This focus might include a discussion of what options could be used to solve this problem.

$$\left(4 \times 2\right) + \left(4 \times \frac{1}{3}\right)$$

$$\left(1 \times 2\frac{1}{3}\right) + \left(3 \times 2\frac{1}{3}\right)$$

$$4 \times \frac{7}{3}$$

For each of these first steps, teachers might ask questions like these: Does this represent an equivalent expression? Why? Why would a student choose this as the first step? When might this first step be an efficient way to solve a (multiplication of fractions) problem? Each of these questions strengthens students' conceptual understanding and procedural flexibility.

Presenting worked examples is also an effective instructional approach to help students understand and solve problems (Renkl 2014; Star and Verschaffel 2017). Looking at worked examples focuses attention on students' mathematical thinking, a key aspect to equity-based teaching, because it attends to students' prior knowledge and mathematical identities. Worked examples provide an opportunity for students to verbalize their thinking by talking, writing, or drawing the steps they used (or someone else used) in solving a problem, practices found to have a significant positive impact on students with difficulties in mathematics (Gersten and Clarke 2007). Additionally, worked examples help students become aware of and address their own misconceptions, especially when tasks include self-explanation prompts (McGinn, Lange, and Booth 2015). Figure 6.4 provides an example of a worked example. Notice that these prompts encourage students to talk through the steps and logic of the problem on their own by asking *why* questions rather than *what* questions.

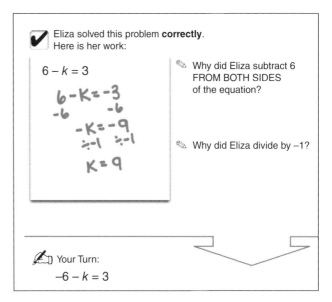

Fig. 6.4. Worked examples can help students understand when and why a strategy might work.
From McGinn, Lange, and Booth (2015, p. 28). Reprinted with permission from *Mathematics Teaching in the Middle School*, copyright 2015, by the National Council of Teachers of Mathematics. All rights reserved.

Worked examples can and should include correct solutions and incorrect solutions. One routine that focuses on a common error or misconception is "My Favorite No: Learning from Mistakes" (see the Teaching Channel video https:www.teachingchannel.org/videos/class-warm-up-routine). Every student solves the same problem on a note card; the teacher collects the worked problems, sorts correct and incorrect solutions, and

Nathan's Solution

$5(y + 1) = 3(y + 1) + 8$

$5y + 5 = 3y + 3 + 8$	*Distribute*	_____	
$5y + 5 = 3y + 11$	*Combine*	_____	
$2y + 5 = 11$	*Subtract*	_____	*on both*
$2y = 6$	*Subtract*	_____	*on both*
$y = 3$	*Divide*	_____	*on both*

Patrick's Solution

$5(y + 1) = 3(y + 1) + 8$

$2(y + 1) = 8$	*Subtract*	_____	*on both*
$y + 1 = 4$	*Divide*	_____	*on both*
$y = 3$	*Subtract*	_____	*on both*

Fig. 6.5. Tasks used for comparing solution strategies.
Adapted from Rittle-Johnson, Star, and Durkin (2009).

identifies one solution from the incorrect pile that addresses a common error or misconception. The teacher reproduces this solution for the class to see and analyze, first focusing on what is correct about the process, then asking what is incorrect. Focusing attention on understanding what steps are correct and incorrect (and why) helps students consider task conditions, choice of strategy, and why particular steps were taken to solve it.

Strategizing steps prior to solving problems and *analyzing steps* after a problem has been solved (i.e., worked examples) provide rich opportunities for students to consider why and when a procedure will work, and they help students develop flexibility and appropriate strategy selection, two aspects of procedural fluency.

2. Compare Procedures and Problems

Research on improving student achievement suggests that mathematics flexibility and conceptual understanding can be increased when students are asked to make comparisons (Fuson 2005; Rittle-Johnson and Star 2009; Rittle-Johnson, Star, and Durkin 2009, 2012; Star et al. 2015). Comparison tasks are cognitively higher level tasks, falling within Bloom's (revised) taxonomy under "Analysis" and within Fan and Bokhove's (2014) cognitive model for learning algorithms at level 3, Evaluation and Construction (see fig. 6.3).

The *concept* of comparing procedures and problems comprises presenting alternative task conditions or solutions so that students can judge the correctness and efficiency of the selections (without necessarily solving the problems themselves). The *procedure* for this approach is to invite students to compare problem types or problem solution methods (Rittle-Johnson, Star, and Durkin 2009; Star et al. 2015). Figure 6.5 shows two solution methods for comparison.

Students are asked to describe differences and identify problem features that would need to be true in order to solve the problem in the way Patrick solved the problem. For students with some prior knowledge of the strategies, comparing two strategies side-by-side is more effective than looking at one strategy and then another (Rittle-Johnson, Star, and Durkin 2009).

Making comparisons is effective even for novice students when adjustments are made to explore limited material within a lesson (Rittle-Johnson, Star, and Durkin 2012). Practice sets can be designed strategically to look for patterns and make generalizations through comparing (Blanton 2008). In so doing, students are gaining conceptual insights into the algorithms they are using and strengthening their number sense. A set of multiplication problems might be created to support the informal strategies discussed above (see fig. 6.6).

1.	$9 \times 13 =$
2.	$10 \times 13 =$
3.	$10 \times 17 =$
4.	$12 \times 17 =$
5.	$11 \times 42 =$
6.	$10 \times 42 =$
7.	$8 \times 42 =$
8.	Explain how #1 compares to #2.
9.	Explain how #3 could help you solve #4.
10.	Describe a general strategy you can use when multiplying a number by 9.

Fig. 6.6. A problem set that lends itself to connecting procedures and concepts

Other suggestions for incorporating comparing opportunities in the classroom include—

- comparing multiple examples of the same approach applied to different problems,

- studying strategies independently before comparing different strategies, and

- comparing a new strategy to a known strategy.

In any case, comparisons should be introduced early in instruction, as early as the same day a procedure is introduced. Waiting even a day to ask students

to make comparisons may diminish student reflection as well as increase student preference toward particular solution methods, decreasing their flexibility (Rittle-Johnson, Star, and Durkin 2012). Finally, sharing multiple solution strategies at the end of a lesson as a "showcase" can quickly turn into a show-and-tell with little higher-level thinking. The showcase of strategies sets up the opportunity for strategy comparison, but the teacher must pose questions that focus students' attention on similarities and differences across solutions in order for students to reason at high levels about the strategies (NCTM 2014).

3. Making Connections Explicit

Making connections explicit is a well-established way to support conceptual understanding and procedural fluency (Baker et al. 2014; Fuson 2005; Hiebert and Grouws 2007; Osana and Pitsolantis 2013). Similar to the two previous instructional approaches, making connections requires higher-level thinking, focusing on comprehension and even generalization (levels 2 and 3 in the cognitive model for learning algorithms, fig. 6.3). The *concept* here is to make connections among mathematical objects, including symbols, physical representations, and real examples (contexts). The *procedure* is to use coherent, structured, and connected discussions of the relevant mathematical skills and concepts.

One approach uses physical models to illustrate the meaning behind mathematical symbols (NCTM 2014; Osana and Pitsolantis 2013). For instance, drawing a rectangle portioned into three equal parts and shading one of the portions, locating $1/3$ on a number line, illustrating $1/3$ with fraction pieces, or finding $1/3$ of a set of cubes can help students connect their internal concept of the value "one-third" to its external symbolic notation, $1/3$. These connections can later provide support for making sense of multiplication. For example, the equation presented earlier, $4 \times 2 1/3$, can be illustrated with any of the tools listed here, and many others. Comparing the visual representations for the problem can aid in generalizing the meaning of the operation. Additionally, different strategies or algorithms using the same tool can be discussed and compared.

Finally, use contexts or story situations to provide relevance and prompt students to gauge whether the solution is reasonable (Osana and Pitsolantis 2013).

Context can convert a rote exercise (level 1) into an understanding or generalizing cognitive activity. For instance, consider the following story situation (based on Davis 2005):

> A gym with operating expenses of $700 a day that sells tickets to a basketball game for $3.50 per person might have a profit model such as $p = -700 + 3.5x$. How many ticket sales does the school need in order to make $200?

Asking students to solve or graph the equation can be a rote process, but asking students to consider the context as central to solving the problem can reinforce conceptual and procedural connections (Davis 2005). For example, ask students to connect each step of their procedure to the context of the problem. An answer may look like this:

> I would need to add $700 to $200 because the number of tickets sold must cover both the operational cost and the desired profit. This totals to $900. I would then need to split the money into equal ticket portions. Because each ticket costs $3.50, I divide $3.50 into $900 and that's how many tickets need to be sold.

Attention to symbols, physical models, and situations builds connections between concepts and procedures and illustrates the connections between the two knowledge types. Attending explicitly to concepts and making connections can happen in highly structured, teacher-centered environments as well as less-structured, student-centered environments (Heibert and Grouws 2007).

Summary

The NCTM teaching practices described in *Principles to Actions* are interdependent. Without the identification of mathematical goals that focus on level 2 and level 3 of Fan and Bokhove's (2014) cognitive model of algorithm development (fig. 6.3), students will not develop deep procedural or conceptual knowledge. Without the careful selection of tasks that promote reasoning, students will not have opportunities to understand and compare strategies nor consider the most efficient approach, based on the problem's features. And without questions that focus on salient features of an algorithm, students will not create a well-developed network of ideas.

This teaching practice, building procedural fluency from conceptual understanding, focuses teaching on the importance of both procedures and concepts. Importantly, the student outcome for procedural fluency and conceptual understanding is higher-level cognition. Rote, step-by-step procedures should not be juxtaposed with deep conceptual understanding; rather, rote procedures should be measured against the components of fluency as shown in figure 6.2, with instructional effort focused on the robust and interdependent aspects of fluency. Conceptual understanding provides a foundation from which a higher level of cognition and complexity can occur. Teaching approaches that focus on identifying purpose, comparing strategies, and making explicit connections support the iterative and interrelated development of procedural fluency and conceptual understanding.

References

Anderson, Lorin W., and David R. Krathwohl, eds. *A Taxonomy for Learning, Teaching, and Assessing: A Revision of Bloom's Taxonomy of Educational Objectives.* New York: Longman, 2001.

Ashcraft, Mark H. "Math Anxiety: Personal, Educational, and Cognitive Consequences." *Current Directions in Psychological Science* 11 (2002): 181–85.

Baker, Scott, Geva Esther, Michael J. Kieffer, Nonie Lesaux, Sylvia Linan-Thompson, Joan Morris, C. Patrick Proctor, Randi Russell, Russell Gersten, Joseph Dimino, Madhavi Jayanthi, Kelly Haymond, and Rebecca Newman-Gonchar. *Teaching Academic Content and Literacy to English Learners in Elementary and Middle School: Educator's Practice Guide.* WhatWorks Clearinghouse NCEE 2014-4012. Washington, D.C.: Institute of Education Sciences, U.S. Department of Education, 2014.

Baroody, Arthur J. "Why Children Have Difficulties Mastering the Basic Number Combinations and How to Help Them." *Teaching Children Mathematics* 13, no. 1 (2006): 22–31.

Baroody, Arthur J., Neet Priya Bajwa, and Michael Eiland. "Why Can't Johnny Remember the Basic Facts?" *Developmental Disabilities Research Reviews* 15, no. 1 (2009): 69–79.

Baroody, Arthur J., and Ann Dowker, eds. *The Development of Arithmetic Concepts and Skills: Constructing Adaptive Expertise.* Mahwah, N.J.: Erlbaum, 2003.

Baroody, Arthur. J., Yingying Feil, and Amanda R. Johnson. "An Alternative Reconceptualization of Procedural and Conceptual Knowledge." *Journal for Research in Mathematics Education* 38, no. 2 (2007): 115–31.

Blanton, Maria L. *Algebra in the Elementary Classroom: Transforming Thinking, Transforming Practice.* Portsmouth, N.H.: Heinemann, 2008.

Blöte, Anke W., Eeke Van der Burg, and Anton S. Klein. "Students' Flexibility in Solving Two-Digit Addition and Subtraction Problems: Instruction Effects." *Journal of Educational Psychology* 93, no. 3 (2001): 627–38.

Boaler, Jo. "Research Suggests That Timed Tests Cause Math Anxiety." *Teaching Children Mathematics* 20, no. 8 (2014): 469–73.

Brophy, Jere. "Research on Teacher Effects: Uses and Abuses." *Elementary School Journal* 89, no. 1 (1988): 3–21.

Canobi, Katherine H. "Concept-Procedure Interactions in Children's Addition and Subtraction." *Journal of Experimental Child Psychology* 102, no. 2 (200): 131–49.

Carpenter, Thomas P., Megan L. Franke, Victoria Jacobs, Elizabeth Fennema, and Susan B. Empson. "A Longitudinal Study of Invention and Understanding in Children's Multidigit Addition and Subtraction." *Journal for Research in Mathematics Education* 29, no. 1 (1998): 3–20.

Davis, Jon D. "Connecting Procedural and Conceptual Knowledge of Functions." *Mathematics Teacher* 99, no. 1 (2005): 36–39.

De Jong, Ton, and Monica G. M. Ferguson-Hessler. "Types and Qualities of Knowledge." *Educational Psychologist* 31, no. 2 (1996): 105–13.

Fan, Lianghuo, and Christian Bokhove. "Rethinking the Role of Algorithms in School Mathematics: A Conceptual Model with Focus on Cognitive Development." *ZDM* 46, no. 3 (2014): 481–92.

Fuson, Karen C., and Sybilla Beckmann. "Standard Algorithms in the Common Core State Standards." *NCMS Journal of Mathematics Education* 14, no. 2 (2012–13): 14–30.

Fuson, Karen, C., Mindy Kalchman, and John D. Bransford. "Mathematical Understanding: An Introduction." In *How Students Learn Mathematics in the Classroom*, edited by M. Suzanne Donovan and John Bransford, pp. 217–56. Washington D.C.: National Academy of Sciences, 2005.

Gersten, Russell, and Benjamin S. Clarke. "Effective Strategies for Teaching Students with Difficulties in Mathematics: NCTM Research Brief." Reston, Va.: National Council of Teachers of Mathematics, 2007. http://www.nctm.org/uploadedFiles/Research_and_Advocacy/research_brief_and_clips/Research_brief_02_-_Effective_Strategies.pdf

Griffin, Sharon. "Fostering the Development of Whole-Number Sense: Teaching Mathematics in the Primary Grades." In *How Students Learn Mathematics in the Classroom,* edited by M. Suzanne Donovan and John Bransford, pp. 257–308. Washington D.C.: National Academy of Sciences, 2005.

Henry, Valerie J., and Richard S. Brown. "First-Grade Basic Facts: An Investigation into Teaching and Learning of an Accelerated, High-Demand Memorization Standard." *Journal for Research in Mathematics Education* 39, no. 2 (2008): 153–83.

Hiebert, James. "Relationships between Research and the NCTM Standards." *Journal for Research in Mathematics Education* 30, no. 1 (1999): 3–19.

Hiebert, James, and Douglas A. Grouws. "The Effects of Classroom Mathematics Teaching on Students' Learning." In *Second Handbook of Research on Mathematics Teaching and Learning*, edited by Frank K. Lester Jr., pp. 371–404. Charlotte, N.C.: Information Age Publishing, and Reston, Va.: National Council of Teachers of Mathematics, 2007.

Hiebert, James, and Patricia Lefevre. "Conceptual and Procedural Knowledge in Mathematics: An Introductory Analysis." In *Conceptual and Procedural Knowledge: The Case of Mathematics*, edited by James Hiebert, pp. 1–27. Hillsdale, N.J.: Erlbaum, 1986.

Isaacs, Andrew C., and William M. Carroll. "Strategies for Basic-Facts Instruction." *Teaching Children Mathematics* 5, no. 9 (1999): 508–15.

Kilpatrick, Jeremy, Jane Swafford, and Bradford Findell, eds. *Adding It Up: Helping Children Learn Mathematics.* Washington, D.C.: National Academy Press, 2001.

LeFevre, Joanne, Brenda L. Smith-Chant, Lisa Fast, Sheri-Lynn Skwarchuk, Erin Sargla, Jesse S. Arnup, and Deepthi Kamawar. "What Counts as Knowing? The Development of Conceptual and Procedural Knowledge of Counting from Kindergarten through Grade 2." *Journal of Experimental Child Psychology* 93, no. 4 (2006): 285–303.

McGinn, Kelly M., Karin E. Lange, and Julie L. Booth. "A Worked Example for Creating Worked Examples." *Mathematics Teaching in the Middle School* 21, no. 1 (2015): 26–33.

National Council of Teachers of Mathematics (NCTM). *Principles to Actions: Ensuring Mathematical Success for All.* Reston, Va.: NCTM, 2014.

National Governors Association Center for Best Practices (NGA Center) and Council of Chief State School Officers (CCSSO). *Common Core State Standards for Mathematics.* Washington, D.C.: NGA Center and CCSSO, 2010. http://www.corestandards.org

Osana, Helen P. and Nicole Pitsolantis. "Addressing the Struggle to Link Form and Understanding in Fractions Instruction." *British Journal of Educational Psychology* 83, no. 1 (2013): 29–56.

Pesek, Dolores D., and David Kirshner. "Interference of Instrumental Instruction in Subsequent Relational Learning." *Journal for Research in Mathematics Education* 31, no. 5 (2000): 524–40.

Ramirez, Gerardo, Elizabeth A. Gunderson, Susan C. Levine, and Sian L. Beilock. "Math Anxiety, Working Memory, and Math Achievement in Early Elementary School."

Journal of Cognition and Development 14, no. 2 (2013): 187–202.

Renkl, Alexander. "Learning from Worked Examples: How to Prepare Students for Meaningful Problem Solving." In *Applying Science of Learning in Education: Infusing Psychological Science into the Curriculum*, edited by Victor Benassi, Catherine E. Overson, and Christopher M. Hakala, pp. 118–30. Society for the Teaching of Psychology, 2014. http://teachpsych.org/ebooks/asle2014/index.php

Rittle-Johnson, Bethany, and Kenneth Koedinger. "Iterating between Lessons on Concepts and Procedures Can Improve Mathematics Knowledge." *British Journal of Educational Psychology* 79, no. 3 (2009): 483–500.

Rittle-Johnson, Bethany, Michael Schneider, and Jon R. Star. "Not a One-Way Street: Bidirectional Relations between Procedural and Conceptual Knowledge of Mathematics." *Educational Psychology Review* 27, no. 4 (2015): 1–11.

Rittle-Johnson, Bethany, and Jon R. Star. "Compared with What? The Effects of Different Comparisons on Conceptual Knowledge and Procedural Flexibility for Equation Solving." *Journal of Educational Psychology* 101, no. 3 (229): 529–44.

Rittle-Johnson, Bethany, Jon R. Star, and Kelley Durkin. "The Importance of Prior Knowledge when Comparing Examples: Influences on Conceptual and Procedural Knowledge of Equation Solving." *Journal of Educational Psychology* 101, no. 4 (2009): 836–52.

———."Developing Procedural Flexibility: Are Novices Prepared to Learn from Comparing Procedures?" *British Journal of Educational Psychology* 82, no. 3 (2012): 436–55.

Russell, Susan Jo. "Developing Computational Fluency with Whole Numbers." *Teaching Children Mathematics* 7, no. 4 (2000): 154–58.

Schneider, Michael, Bethany Rittle-Johnson, and Jon R. Star. "Relations among Conceptual Knowledge, Procedural Knowledge, and Procedural Flexibility in Two Samples Differing in Prior Knowledge." *Developmental Psychology* 47, no. 6 (2011): 1525–38.

Sowder, Judith T. "What Are the 'Math Wars' in California All About? Reasons and Perspectives." *Mathematically Sane: Promoting the Rational Reform of Mathematics Education.* 1998. http://faculty.tarleton.edu/brawner/coursefiles/579/Math%20Wars%20in%20California.pdf

Star, Jon. R. "Re-'Conceptualizing' Procedural Knowledge in Mathematics." 2002. http://www.eric.ed.gov/contentdelivery/servlet/ERICServlet?accno=ED472948.

———. "Research Commentary: Reconceptualizing Procedural Knowledge." *Journal for Research in Mathematics Education* 36, no. 5 (2005): 404–11.

Star, Jon R., Anne Foegan, Matthew R. Larson, William G. McCallum, Jane Porath, Rose Mary Zbiek, Pia Caronongan, Joshua Furgeson, Betsy Keating, and Julia Lyskawa. *Teaching Strategies for Improving Algebra Knowledge in Middle and High School Students: Educator's Practice Guide.* What Works Clearinghouse NCEE 2015-4010. Washington, D.C.: Institute of Education Sciences, U.S. Department of Education, 2015. https://ies.ed.gov/ncee/wwc/PracticeGuide/20

Star, Jon R., Martina Kenyon, Rebecca M. Joiner, and Bethany Rittle-Johnson. "Comparing Pays Off!" *Mathematics Teacher* 103, no. 8 (2010): 608–12.

Star, Jon R., and Lieven Verschaffel. "Providing Support for Student Sense Making: Recommendations from Cognitive Science for the Teaching of Mathematics." In *Compendium for Research in Mathematics Education*, edited by Jinfa Cai, pp. 292–307. Reston, Va.: National Council of Teachers of Mathematics, 2017.

Chapter 7

Key Questions to Guide Teachers in Supporting Productive Struggle in Learning Mathematics

Blake E. Peterson, *Brigham Young University*
Rina Viramontes, *Chaparral Middle School, Chaparral, New Mexico*

In the 1995 video study conducted as part of the Trends in Mathematics and Science Study (TIMMS), instruction in the United States was described as "learning terms and practicing procedures" (Stigler and Hiebert 1999, p. 27). A typical eighth-grade lesson consisted of discussing a previous day's homework, a teacher explanation of a new topic, and students practicing modeled procedures. Four years later, the 1999 TIMSS video study found little had changed in teacher practice even though many observed teachers described changes in their teaching. This routine was similar to what was seen in American classrooms for decades and continues to be apparent in classrooms across the country (Hiebert 2013). The common practice of having students practice procedures that have been explicitly modeled for them is in stark contrast to the teaching that is described in *Principles to Actions: Ensuring Mathematical Success for All* (NCTM 2014), which states:

> Effective teaching of mathematics consistently provides students, individually and collectively, with opportunities and supports to engage in productive struggle as they grapple with mathematical ideas and relationships. (p. 48)

Because this advocated teaching practice is so different from what the TIMSS studies found in U.S. classrooms, the goal of this chapter is to discuss some research that clarifies productive struggle, why it is valuable, and how teachers can support it.

We note that, when seeking to improve the proficiency of students, there is a tendency to focus on the "characteristics of the teacher, not methods of instruction" (Hiebert and Grouws 2007, p. 377). This belief leads to a focus on teacher quality—courses taken, workshops attended, scholastic aptitude—to improve

teaching rather than focusing on the actual teacher practice. Research, however, has failed to find a clear connection between teacher quality and student performance (e.g. Harris and Sass 2011; Wayne and Youngs 2003). Thus, we will center our discussion of supporting productive struggle on *teaching* (the methods of instruction) and not the *teacher* (quality of the teacher). With that focus on teaching, we encourage teachers to develop a "plan to learn about teaching by studying targeted instructional activities and their effects" (Heibert and Stigler 2004, p. 14). The ideas about supporting productive struggle we will discuss in this chapter can function as the targeted instructional practices that teachers can study.

What Is Productive Struggle?

When thinking about the idea of "supporting productive struggle in learning mathematics" (NCTM 2014, p. 48), one might wonder what is meant by "struggle." In general, struggle means one is contending with an opposing force or task or problem that initially may seem beyond his/her capability. In mathematics, struggle occurs when students are asked to solve a problem for which there is no clear path to a solution, requiring them to connect ideas or strategies in a new way. The recommendation to allow students to struggle does not mean that teachers should give students a set of unreasonably difficult mathematics problems to solve, however. Rather, students need to be given opportunities to wrestle with mathematical situations that are problematic to them but within their reach (Hiebert and Wearne 2003). For example, when middle school students who know how to find the areas of rectangles and triangles but not of more complex shapes are given the task shown in figure 7.1, they will experience struggle because there is no clear path to a solution.

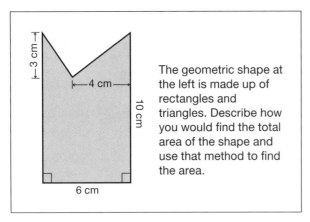

The geometric shape at the left is made up of rectangles and triangles. Describe how you would find the total area of the shape and use that method to find the area.

Fig. 7.1. Example of a middle school task that will likely engage students in struggle

What makes some struggles productive while other struggles are just frustrating? We identify three questions a teacher could ask to determine if the struggle is productive:

1. Is the mathematics or task within reach?

2. Is the mathematics central?

3. Are the students employing sense making?

Is the mathematics or task within reach? Hiebert and Grouws (2007) claimed that teachers need to pose tasks "that are within reach" of the students (p. 387). Tasks within reach of the students are those within a student's zone of proximal development (Vygotsky 1978), which means the students may not be able to solve the task independently but can solve it with the assistance of peers or questions from the teacher. The task shown in figure 7.1 is within reach of the students because it builds on concepts that they understand (areas of rectangles and triangles) but requires them to put those ideas together in a new way.

Is the mathematics with which the students are wrestling central? If the mathematics is not central to the mathematical learning goals of the lesson, then it is not a productive struggle, and the teacher should step in to redirect the students toward mathematics that is central. For example, in a middle school lesson on pro-

portional reasoning, a student was stuck on dividing 7 by 12 because an error in computation yielded an incorrect answer of 0.5083. In this case, it is not necessary to let the student persist in struggling because division is not the goal in this lesson. Instead, the teacher could point out the location of the error and ask the student to redo the computation (or perhaps even provide the correct result without asking the student to redo the computation).

Are the students employing sense making? If the mathematics or task is within the students' reach and is central to the lesson, then this third question should be considered. Hiebert and Grouws (2007) described productive struggle as occurring when "students expend effort to make sense of mathematics, to figure something out that is not immediately apparent" (p. 387). Expending effort on something that is not immediately apparent captures the idea of struggle, and sense making is an indicator of productivity. Warshauer (2011) made a similar claim about the productive nature of struggle being tied to the students' reasoning and sense making.

Next, we will mention some cases of unproductive struggle and some steps that could be taken to help them be more productive. Some indicators that a struggle may not be productive occur when students' frustration level is high enough that they are unwilling to persist, which is commonly caused by one of two things: the problem is not within their reach or the students are not accustomed to such cognitive work. The former case can be resolved by more carefully selecting or adapting tasks to ensure they are within the students' zone of proximal development (Vygotsky 1978). Of course, care needs to be taken not to underestimate our students' capabilities. We have often heard teachers express doubts in students' abilities to complete complex tasks for which they have not been shown a procedure, yet we find that students never fail to impress us if given the opportunity.

In the latter case, when students are not accustomed to such cognitive work and are expressing frustration, teachers who need to offer support should be careful to maintain the cognitive demand of the task (Stein et al. 2009). Lowering the cognitive demand happens when the "problematic aspects of the task become routinized . . . by specifying explicit procedures . . . to perform." In other words, emphasis shifts "from meaning, concepts or understanding to correctness or completeness of the answer" (Stein et al. 2009, p. 16). Teachers often step in to help because they think frustration and lack of immediate success are indicators that they have failed their students. We feel strongly that all of us, as mathematics teachers, need to stop doing what is easy (stepping in to rescue) and do what is right (giving students the time or space to become independent, self-reliant problem solvers). When we step in to rescue, we communicate to students that they are not able to solve the problems they have been given. Conversely, "effective teachers have high expectations for their students," which influence students' "opportunities and motivation for learning" (Kilpatrick, Swafford, and Findell 2001, p. 9).

We have described what teachers should not do when students are stuck and resistant to struggle because they are not accustomed to such cognitive work, and now we offer some suggestions of what a teacher *can* do to support students in this situation. Part of the solution is for teachers to pose purposeful questions (NCTM 2014) that encourage students to consider a valuable connection or to reflect on what they have done so far. More detail about what a teacher can do when students are stuck will be discussed later in this chapter.

In summary, productive struggle occurs when students are given complex mathematics problems that are focused on underlying concepts. These problems are accessible to the students because the mathematics is within their reach and they have the tools to solve them. However, the problems are complex enough that there are no clear paths to the solutions. As students intellectually engage with the problems, they bump into mathematical concepts related to the goals of the lesson, and the students persist as they reason and try to make sense of the problem. For an example, consider the following scenario from Ms. Viramontes' classroom. As you read the scenario, look for the characteristics of productive struggle outlined above:

• •

In a unit on three-dimensional geometry, the students explored the volumes of a rectangular prism, triangular prism and a cylinder, with a focus on a "layering

strategy." The "layering strategy" allows the students to make connections to the formula $V = Bh$ because they can think of each layer as having the same number of cubes as the area of the base B. Students were not given any formula, but rather their task was to find the volume of the three different types of prisms. The class had a discussion about what volume meant, and they came to a consensus that it was the amount of space it takes to fill a three-dimensional object, measured in cubic units. In the class discussion of the triangular prism, some students saw the triangular prism as $1/2$ of the rectangular prism yielding the expression

$$\frac{lwh}{2}$$

(see fig. 7.2a). Other students saw the triangular prism as a shape with a triangular base, which gave rise to the expression

$$\left(\frac{1}{2}lw\right)h$$

(see fig. 7.2b).

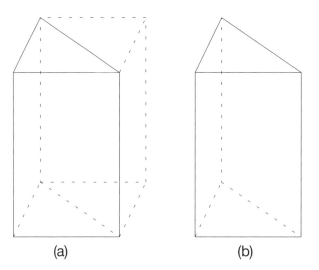

(a)   (b)

Fig. 7.2. Half of a rectangular prism (a) compared to a prism with a triangular base (b)

On the next day, they were shown a standardized test reference sheet that listed the volume of a prism as $V = Bh$ with no explanation of the formula's origin. It was in the context of the students resolving the equations they had generated with the one they had been given that the following discussion occurred between two students and Ms. Viramontes (referred to as "Ms. V" in the dialogue).

Ms. V: You [*student 1*] and your partner [*student 2*] have different formulas for finding the volume of a triangular prism. Can you explain each one to me?

Student 2: $V = Bh$. You find the area of the base and multiply it by the height.

Student 1: $V = (1/2)Bh$. You have to do $1/2$ area of the base times the height.

Student 2:   But you are already doing $1/2$ when you find the area of a triangle.

Student 1:   That's why you have to put the $1/2$, because it is a triangle.

Student 2:   But B represents the area of the base.

Student 1:   Yes, so you have to find half of that.

Ms. V: Student 1, so you are saying that you need to find the area of the base and then find half of that?

Student 1:   Yes.

Ms. V: Can you show me?

[*Student 1 correctly finds the volume, but starts with the incorrect formula $V = (1/2)Bh$ and then writes a correct one, $V = (1/2)lwh$, underneath.*]

Student 2:   You don't need the $1/2$ in front of the B because the B stands for the area of the base. So, it should look like this:

$$V = Bh$$
$$V = \frac{1}{2}lwh$$

Student 1:   But we both got the same answer, so it works.

Ms. V: Student 1, what does this base look like?

Student 1:   It is the base of a rectangular prism, because you multiply the l times w to get the area of the base. Then, you multiply it by $1/2$, since it is a triangle.

Student 2:   But the base of a triangular prism is not a rectangle; it is a triangle.

Student 1:   That's why.

Ms. V: Student 1, can you show me the formula for the volume of a cylinder?

Student 1:   The formula is

$$V = Bh$$
$$V = \pi r^2 h$$

Ms. V: So what does B represent here?

Student 1:   The area of the base.

Ms. V: What is the base?

Student 1:   A circle. Oh, I see; the B stands for area of whatever the Base is. OK, I get it now.

• •

In this example of productive struggle, it is clear that reconciling student-generated equations for volume with a standard form volume equation is within reach of the students because it begins with student work, and yet it is a struggle because there is no clear path to a solution. The goal of the previous day's lesson was to generate equations for the volume of prisms and cylinders, and the struggle is centered on that goal, so the mathematics remains central. In addition, the focus of the task is on reasoning and sense making about the underlying concept of volume and not on the procedure of computing volume.

In addition to the nature of the task and the struggle, this example also provides insight into teacher moves to support productive struggle. In this example, six of the seven teacher comments are questions. The initial questions ask the students to articulate their thinking, allowing the teacher to gain a better understanding of that thinking. Ms. Viramontes then restates what she understands the student thinking to be. Finally, she asks the students to consider the equation for the volume of a cylinder to nudge the students to make connections between the different representations of the volume equations.

What Are the Benefits of Having Students Productively Struggle?

There are several benefits to having students engage in productive struggle as they solve mathematics problems. We will talk about five benefits found in the literature: (1) a sense of accomplishment; (2) knowledge and understanding; (3) high achievement; (4) improved achievement; and (5) mastery and long-term retention.

A Sense of Accomplishment

We will first discuss teachers' self-efficacy or sense of accomplishment and how that might get in the way of students' productive struggle. Next, we discuss students experiencing a sense of accomplishment through productive struggle. Because teachers often believe their actions are directly related to student learning, they do things that facilitate students' immediate success and thus have evidence of their successful teaching. Asking students to solve problems with which they might struggle undercuts students' immediate success and can lead the teacher to believe that he has not been successful. This thinking leads teachers to avoid activities where students struggle or might be frustrated because it negatively impacts the teacher's self-efficacy (M. Smith 2000; J. Smith 1996). In order to maintain positive self-efficacy, many teachers prescribe ways of solving problems and they avoid open-ended tasks. Dewey (1926) claimed that such an approach imposes "intellectual blinders upon pupils" (p. 206). Thus, these teacher actions might allow teachers to feel better about themselves and their teaching, but they may undermine how the students feel about their learning. We agree with Weinert, Schrader, and Helmke (1989) that "the activity and cognitive orientation of the learners are as important as the activities and the behaviors of the teachers" (p. 899).

As we think about the benefits of students engaging in productive struggle and consider the orientations of the learner, we turn to a perspective of Pólya. An emphasis in his book, *How to Solve It* (1945), is for students to maintain ownership of the problems they solve. He said, "The teacher should help, but not too much and not too little, so that the student shall have a reasonable share of the work" (p. 1). He drew this conclusion based on his many years of experience as a mathematics professor at Stanford University. The preface of Pólya's book states,

> A great discovery solves a great problem but there is a grain of discovery in the solution of any problem. Your problem may be modest; but if it challenges your curiosity and brings into play your inventive faculties, and if you solve it by your own means, you may experience the tension and enjoy the triumph of discovery. Such experiences at a susceptible age may create a taste for mental work and leave their imprint on mind and character for a lifetime. (Pólya 1945, p. 17)

The experience of persisting through a struggle allows students to feel the "triumph of discovery" and a sense of accomplishment.

Knowledge and Understanding

One of the purposes of grappling with a task—as opposed to mimicking a procedure—is to gain a deeper understanding of the mathematics being investigated. Dewey (1929) suggested that knowledge is the result of answering a question, disposing of a difficulty, clearing up confusion, making coherence out of an inconsistency, or mastering a perplexity. He claimed that the process of transforming a problematic situation into a resolved one is what yields knowledge. We view this transforming process as a product of persisting in a productive struggle with a high-cognitive demand task (Stein et al. 2009). In addition to knowledge acquisition, the persistence of solving problems develops, extends, and enriches mathematical understandings (Hiebert and Wearne 2003).

High Achievement

It is well known that on international mathematics achievement tests, some countries are consistently top scoring (Stigler and Hiebert 1999, 2009). These results give rise to questions about the nature of instruction in those top scoring countries. Hiebert and Stigler (2004) videotaped mathematics lessons in seven countries and analyzed the teaching in each of those countries, paying particular attention to the similarities and differences of the teaching in the high-achieving countries as compared to lower-achieving countries. For example, they examined the nature of the problems given to the students. The two categories of problems focused on "relationships that can be constructed among the mathematical facts, procedures and ideas" (p. 13) and on practicing procedures. They found variation among high-achieving countries in the frequency of presenting problems that focused on relationships in that more such problems were presented in the United States than in some of these same countries.

However, there was great consistency among those countries in how problems were implemented. About 50 percent of the time, "students studied the connections and relationships embedded in the problems." In the United States, however, less than 1 percent of these conceptual problems were implemented in this way (Hiebert and Stigler 2004, p. 12). Thus, we see that the type of problems implemented during instruction may not be common in high-achieving countries, but the way in which problems are implemented is common. Stigler and Hiebert (2009) further elaborated on this idea by saying that it was "the *engagement of students in active struggle with core mathematics concepts and procedures*" (p. 34, emphasis in original) that was common among high-achieving countries but not evident in the United States. The U.S. teachers "almost always stepped in and did the work for the students or ignored the conceptual aspect of the problem when discussing it" (Hiebert and Stigler 2004, p. 12). In other words, teachers did not allow students to productively struggle with the problem they had been given. They scaffolded the problems by breaking them down into smaller subtasks that students could successfully complete (M. Smith 2000). We will argue later that it is the very process of breaking down complex problems that the students need to learn, and that when the teacher does that mental work, it only gives the illusion that the students can solve the original complex problems.

Another example of high achievement being related to productive struggle is found in a study done by Hiebert and Grouws (2007). They conducted a review of the research on how teaching affects learning and found two features of teaching that positively influenced student conceptual understanding of mathematics. One of those features was teaching focused on important mathematical concepts. The second feature was "the engagement of students in struggling or wrestling with important mathematical ideas" (Hiebert and Grouws 2007, p. 387). One of the benefits of this struggle is that it facilitates conceptual learning because students are forced to make sense of the new ideas with which they are struggling in the context of what they already know. This process enables them to make new connections and restructure their existing knowledge (Hiebert and Grouws 2007).

Improved Achievement

In this section, we elaborate on some of the results of the research done by Carol Dweck, where she defines a *fixed mindset* as a belief "that intelligence or math and science ability is simply a fixed trait" and a growth mindset as a belief that intellectual "abilities can be developed" (Dweck 2008, p. 2). Those students with a growth mindset also see intelligence as "malleable" (Blackwell, Trzesniewski, and Dweck 2007, p. 247). We argue that supporting productive struggle facilitates a growth mindset, which, in turn, has been linked to improved achievement.

One of the connections between these different mindsets and productive struggle is that a student's mindset influences the student's willingness to persevere. When students with a fixed mindset face a challenging problem, they fear it might reveal their lack of intelligence. Thus, they believe in a "futility of effort" (Blackwell, Trzesniewski, and Dweck 2007, p. 247) because "effort was necessary only for those who lacked ability and was, to boot, likely to be ineffective for them" (Dweck 2008, p. 4). On the other hand, students with a growth mindset saw the "utility of effort" (Blackwell, Trzesniewski, and Dweck 2007, p. 247) when working on challenging problems because "they believe that effort promoted ability and that was effective regardless of your current level of ability" (Dweck 2008, p. 4).

In one study of the effects of mindset on students' mathematics performance, Blackwell and colleagues (2007) surveyed a group of entering seventh-graders to determine whether they had a fixed or growth mindset. Although the two groups were comparable at the beginning of seventh grade, Blackwell and colleagues evaluated these students' math achievement through eighth grade and found that their math achievements diverged as they progressed through the eighth grade, with the growth mindset students' achievement increasing and the fixed mindset students' achievement decreasing over the two-year period.

This group of researchers next studied whether students' mindsets can be changed to have a similar impact on achievement. Blackwell and colleagues (2007) randomly split 91 seventh graders into two groups with comparable characteristics, including similar representations of students with growth and fixed mindsets.

Both groups participated in one workshop a week for eight weeks, with four of the workshops being identical. The experimental group spent four workshops learning that intelligence is malleable, "you can grow your intelligence," and "learning makes you smarter" (Blackwell, Trzesniewski, and Dweck 2007, p. 255), while the control group learned about memory in four of the eight workshops. Initially both groups of students had similar math achievement; but after the intervention, students taught about the growth mindset had a clear increase in achievement, while the fixed mindset group did not. Achievement improved for all students with a growth mindset, and achievement gaps between males and females narrowed as did the achievement gap between black and white students when they had a growth mindset (Dweck 2008).

Having a growth mindset is not common among U.S. parents. In a study of families, cultures, and schools, Stevenson and Stigler (1992) found a U.S. belief that success in mathematics is based on natural ability, while the Asian belief (i.e., in Japan, China, and Taiwan) is that mathematical success is based on effort. U.S. parents of a struggling child commonly say, "My son or daughter isn't doing well because I wasn't good at math either"—a fixed mindset. Connected with these U.S. beliefs is the perception that "errors are a possible precursor to failure" (Stevenson and Stigler 1992, p. 17), so they should be avoided. This fear of failure in the American culture is a clear obstacle to students' willingness to persist and struggle. Asian teachers and students, on the other hand, "regard mistakes as an index of what still needs to be learned. They expect that with persistence and effort, people eliminate errors and eventually make the correct response" (Stevenson and Stigler 1992, p. 17). Parents of struggling Asian students are more likely to say the child needs to work harder if he is not doing well in mathematics—clearly a growth mindset.

We have previously documented that Asian countries perform well on international studies and now have established that parents, students, and teachers in these countries possess a growth mindset. We have also established that students who possess a growth mindset see the benefits of productive struggle and have higher achievement. Thus, we have evidence that if we teach students about a growth mindset, they will see the util-ity of effort and thus be more willing to productively struggle. This, in turn, will influence their mathematics achievement.

Some may think that because a growth mindset seems to be inherent in the culture, getting students to adopt this mindset is not possible. However, Lewis (1995) establishes that many of the cultural behaviors seen in Japan are explicitly taught in the schools. Thus, it is reasonable to believe that efforts in U.S. schools to teach students about a growth mindset toward mathematics could have a broader cultural impact.

Mastery and Long-Term Retention

A common characteristic of struggle is that students do not know what strategy or algorithm to use to solve a problem. As described earlier, the common model of teaching in the United States is for teachers to do an example of a certain type of problem and then have the students solve many of the same type of problems. In this case, the students do not experience any struggle in deciding which strategy to use. This idea of doing many of the same types of problems is referred to as "massed practice" (Brown, Roediger, and McDaniel 2014). By contrast, when students solve a mix of problems, this is called "interleaved practice" (Brown, Roediger, and McDaniel 2014). The struggle in solving problems in the interleaved practice situation is not about executing a procedure; rather, it is about deciding which procedure to use. This is analogous to being given a high-cognitive demand task for which there is not a clear path to a solution. The struggle is deciding what strategy one might use to solve the problem.

Brown and colleagues (2014) illustrated the benefits of interleaved practice by describing a study of the batting practice of college baseball players. One group of players did massed practice of hitting fifteen curveballs, fifteen fastballs, and fifteen changeups. The second group experienced interleaved practice of randomly thrown pitch types. During batting practice, the players doing massed practice outperformed those doing interleaved practice. However, in game situations, those who had done interleaved practice were the better performers. Brown and colleagues (2014) concluded, "It is one skill to hit a curveball when you know a curveball will be thrown; it is a different skill to hit a curveball when you don't know it's coming. Baseball players need to build the latter skill, but they often practice the former" (p. 81). Similarly, students can get good at solving quadratic equations using factoring if they know all of the problems they are given lend themselves to that strategy, but it is a different skill to solve a quadratic equation when you do not know the most efficient strategy for each problem. Rather than just performing rote execution of strategies, mathematics students need to become adept at knowing which strategy to use, which can be accomplished by giving them tasks where they need to struggle because there is no clear path to a solution.

The above argument presented by Brown and colleagues (2014) supports the claim that "research shows unequivocally that mastery and long-term retention are much better if you interleave practice than if you mass it" (p. 50). Because problems where the path to the solution is not known can be construed as a type of interleaved practice, we offer this example to suggest another benefit of students experiencing productive struggle as they work on high-cognitive demand mathematics tasks.

Ways of Supporting Students in Productive Struggle

Up to this point, we have defined what we mean by productive struggle and what we see as some of the benefits of this type of struggle. Along the way, there have been a few suggestions regarding how one might support productive struggle, but we now elaborate on those ideas. A first step in supporting students is to reorient teachers and students to their roles in student learning. Likewise, we will talk about some specific things teachers can do during instruction to support productive struggle.

Rethinking Teaching

We first talk about ways that teachers can reorient their approaches to teaching. Rather than viewing struggle as something to be avoided, it should be viewed as a natural part of the learning process. Teachers often view their instructional success according to the ease with which students are able to execute procedures. As Smith (2000) points out, this "mooring" of teacher success needs to change. Her ideas for new moorings, outlined

in *Principles to Actions* (*PtA*) (NCTM 2014, p. 49), are a solid basis for the reorientation that needs to occur.

Another part of a teacher's reorientation will be to consider her own beliefs about students experiencing productive struggle and measure them against the productive and unproductive beliefs listed in figure 7.3. *PtA* outlines general productive and unproductive beliefs about teaching and learning mathematics (NCTM 2014, p. 11). In figure 7.3, we offer a set of unproductive beliefs and a set of productive beliefs related specifically to supporting productive struggle.

In addition to addressing beliefs about the practice of supporting productive struggle, teachers also need to reorient themselves in their approaches to improving practice. Hiebert and Stigler (2004) offer three suggestions to change practice in ways that will impact student achievement. We adapt their suggestions to focus on the practice of supporting productive struggle as follows: make a regular time commitment to study the practice of supporting productive struggle, with a focus on carefully planning and reflecting on lessons; study clear examples of teaching that supports productive struggle; and analyze student work to better understand ways students are seeing the mathematics and adjust methods of supporting productive struggle accordingly (Hiebert and Stigler 2004, p. 13).

We see the first suggestion of careful planning as particularly helpful in learning to support productive struggle. Selecting and creating tasks that are within the reach of students while simultaneously encouraging sense making about central mathematics will take time, but the most critical part of planning is tied to the third suggestion: anticipating student thinking. As teachers anticipate how students may think about a given task, they can identify places where they believe students will struggle and plan the kinds of questions they can ask without lowering the cognitive demand. This emphasis on student thinking as part of planning is particularly helpful because research suggests that when teachers focus on students' mathematical thinking, it is a basis for their practice to evolve (Franke et al. 1998).

Establishing Norms: Explicitly Teaching Students about Struggle

Once teachers are committed to the idea of students having opportunities to struggle with high-cognitive

Unproductive Beliefs	Productive Beliefs
When students are frustrated and do not experience success immediately it tells me that I have failed (M. Smith 2000).	I need to help students understand that "confusion is something you go through, not a permanent state of being" (Carter 2008, p. 136).
Students need direct demonstration in order to learn, so I need to provide clear explanations (J. Smith, 1996).	I need to give the students the opportunity to solve problems on their own and give them the sense of efficacy that comes with taking charge of their own learning (Pólya 1945).
Parents believe that my job is to make doing mathematics easy for students because "a good teacher … helps students learn in a smooth and effortless way" (Hiebert and Wearne 2003, p. 6).	I need to challenge my students and allow them to struggle in order for them to learn mathematics deeply (Hiebert and Wearne 2003).
If I scaffold a task by breaking it down into small subtasks, students will learn to solve problems like the original task (M. Smith 2000).	If I let my students struggle to figure out which strategy to use (Brown, Roediger, and McDaniel 2014) and how to break a task down, they will become confident in their approach to problems of all types.
Tests show which of my students are good at math and their potential (Dweck 2008).	A brain is like a muscle and only gets stronger when it is pushed to do difficult things. My students can, with effort, improve in mathematics. Tests do not define my students (Dweck 2008).
I shouldn't make my students struggle because they are afraid of challenges, making mistakes, and that it will reveal their intellectual limits (Dweck 2008).	My students will learn that failure isn't something to be avoided, it "is a manifestation of learning and exploration" (Catmull 2014, p. 109).
If my students struggle to solve problems, they will blame the teacher and parents will complain to the administrators.	Once my students are acclimated to the expectations of problem solving and productive struggle, they will appreciate the autonomy these struggles provide (Boaler 2002).
When my students are stuck, I need to step in and show them the steps so they can learn the procedure for getting answers.	Telling my students the answer does not help them learn; in fact, it stops their learning (Carter 2008).
If my students "are allowed to make errors, it's the errors that they will learn" (Brown, Roediger, and McDaniel 2014, p. 90).	If my students realize that errors are a natural part of learning, they can see mistakes as "turning points along the path to mastery" (Brown, Roediger, and McDaniel 2014, p. 91).

Fig. 7.3. Unproductive and productive beliefs about supporting productive struggle

demand tasks, they should explicitly talk with their students about struggle being a natural part of learning. These conversations with students about productive struggle should not be viewed as a one-and-done lesson; they need to be ongoing throughout the school year. Conversation topics could include how we view struggle and mistakes, the importance of persistence, the growth mindset, and the different stages of problem solving. Having these recurring discussions with students is a fairly straightforward action that every teacher can take to support students' attitudes and the struggles they face when doing mathematics.

Mistakes are portals for learning. One of the reasons students are resistant to being asked to struggle is their fear of mistakes or failure. Good tasks deliberately do not have a clear path to a solution, which causes the struggle but also contributes to a fear of making mistakes. Brown, Roediger, and McDaniel (2014) claim that struggle is part of learning and mistakes are part of that struggle. People who have experienced struggle are more willing to take on difficult problems and "tend to see mistakes not as failures but as lessons . . . along the path to mastery" (p. 91).

In his exposition about supporting creativity at Pixar Animation Studios, CEO Ed Catmull describes the common reaction to challenges or new situations: "Failure is bad; failure means you didn't study or prepare; failure means you slacked off or—worse!—aren't smart enough to begin with. Thus, failure is something to be ashamed of" (Catmull and Wallace 2014, p. 108). A fear of failure may cause some people to avoid situations where they can fail because they fear that a failure in such situations might reveal their fixed intelligence—a fixed mindset. Those who have a fear of failure expend mental energy worrying about making mistakes and thus use up working memory that should be used to solve the problem at hand (Brown, Roediger, and McDaniel 2014). A positive spin that can be placed on mistakes or failure is treating them as "a manifestation of learning and exploration. If you aren't experiencing failure, then you are making a far worse mistake: You are being driven by desire to avoid it" (Catmull and Wallace 2014, p. 109). Society and students must be taught that mistakes and failure are a natural part of learning, and it is through productive struggle that deep understanding occurs. One of the challenges in positioning mistakes as a natural part of learning mathematics is that students only see the carefully planned solutions that teachers share with them. If teachers are more open about the mistakes they made when preparing the solution, then students are more likely to believe that from mistakes and "struggle does clarity emerge" (Catmull and Wallace 2014, p. 152).

Another way to influence students' views of mistakes as being an integral part of learning is by the way we assess students. Too often, assessment emphasizes "the evaluation of student achievement" (NCTM 2014, p. 89), which will lead students to fear mistakes. Alternatively, students need opportunities to work on problems that will not be graded, and their thinking—correct or incorrect—will be the object of class discussions. When students engage in productive struggle, mistakes often occur, and it is through discussions of those mistakes that learning can occur. Because mistakes are sites for learning, students should be taught to identify mistakes by giving them opportunities to critique their own and each other's work rather than waiting for the external evaluation of the teacher.

In the example discussed previously, the student's incorrect equation $V = (1/2)Bh$ for the volume of a triangular prism allowed Ms. Viramontes to discuss the meaning of the various components of the equation with those students. The student's mistake became a site for learning for other students in the classroom. In such cases, the value of the mistake should be acknowledged to reiterate the norm that mistakes are a natural part of learning.

Persistence has value. Whether learning mathematics, mastering a musical instrument, or improving an athletic skill, persistence in doing the activity is necessary. Ralph Waldo Emerson once wrote, "That which we persist in doing becomes easier to do, not that the nature of the thing has changed, but that our power to do has increased." A related statement by Confucius says, "Achievement consists of never giving up. . . . If there is no dark and dogged will, there will be no shining accomplishment; if there is no dull and determined effort, there will be no brilliant achievement" (quoted in Stevenson and Stigler 1992, p. 97). These two statements are messages that could be communicated to students before they ever engage with a task to encourage their persistence and are the beginning of establishing the norm of persistence in the face of struggles.

The idea of persistence is a common theme in NCTM's *Principles and Standards for School Mathematics* (2000) and is usually associated with problem solving. The document claims that if students do problem solving in mathematics, they "acquire ways of thinking, habits of persistence and curiosity, and confidence in unfamiliar situations that will serve them well outside the mathematics classroom" (NCTM 2000, p. 52). One way that teachers can "nurture persistence" in problem solving is by the nature of problems they pose to students, as "good problems can inspire the exploration of important mathematical ideas" (NCTM 2000, p. 182).

In addition to the NCTM documents, the idea of persistence is evident in the Common Core State Standards for Mathematics. In fact, the first mathematical practice is "Make sense of problems and persevere in solving them" (NGA Center and CCSSO 2010, p. 9). With these national documents calling for teachers to encourage students to persist and persevere, one may wonder how this can be done in a culture where students give up if a problem takes more than a minute to solve. As mentioned earlier, we believe that students should be explicitly taught the value of persistence, and this should be a regularly heard mantra in classrooms where productive struggle is expected and supported. These conversations will help shape the attitudes of the students and the norms in the classrooms.

Intelligence is malleable—a growth mindset. A third, interrelated message that needs to be reiterated often is about a growth mindset. We have already discussed the benefits of students having a growth mindset and the fact that they can develop such a mindset. Along with explicitly teaching students not to fear mistakes and the value of persistence, we offer some ideas that can be shared with students to help them develop a growth mindset. Simple conversations about these ideas can move students away from a fixed mindset toward a growth mindset (Blackwell, Trzesniewski, and Dweck 2007).

Many believe that those who are very successful in their field were born with natural ability or are some kind of genius—a fixed mindset. However, "genius often appears to be developed over time through focused, extended effort" (Dweck 2008, p. 3). Gladwell (2008) highlights this phenomenon when he reported

that the Beatles, who are considered musical geniuses, had an estimated 1200 live performances before their explosive success in 1964. Similarly, Bill Gates, who is considered a computer genius, had programmed for thousands of hours before he started his first computer software company in his early twenties. In both cases, much of their success can be attributed to "focused, extended effort"—a growth mindset (Dweck 2008, p. 3).

The second idea that can be shared with students is that "intelligence can be altered through training" (Dweck 2008, p. 3). In fact, the brains of people or animals that regularly face challenges are physiologically different and more developed than the brains of those who do not face challenges (Mindset Works 2014). Thus, when students are given opportunities to productively struggle, their brains will physically change.

A third idea to develop a growth mindset is for teachers and parents to praise the process (such as effort or strategy) and not intelligence. In fact, praise that focuses on intelligence can have a negative impact on student achievement and motivation (Mueller and Dweck 1998). If students experience failure after they have been praised for intelligence, they are less persistent and show less enjoyment in working on tasks. Conversely, students praised for effort show more enjoyment, greater persistence, and better performance when working on tasks (Mueller and Dweck 1998). Cangelosi (2007) talks about the dangers of labeling students as being "smart" or "good at math" because when they experience a failure, they have not lived up to that label and self-esteem suffers. If praise of students is used, it should be focused on desirable behaviors such as effort or engagement and not on the students themselves (Hattie and Timperley 2007). Some contrasting examples of praising the process instead of praising the person are shown in figure 7.4.

Problem solving is a process. We have mentioned several ways to talk explicitly with students about struggle: mistakes are sites for learning, persistence has value, intelligence is malleable. "Praising the process" is something that will play out while students are struggling or engaged in the problem-solving process. This process of problem solving should be discussed early in

Instead of Praising the Person	Try Praising the Process
Great job! You must be smart with dividing fractions.	Great job! You must have worked really hard to solve those fraction division problems.
See, you are good with similar triangles. You got an A on your last test.	You really studied for your similar triangles test and your improvement shows it.
You got it! I told you that you were smart.	I like the way you tried all kinds of strategies on that problem until you finally got it.
You are such a good student!	I love how you stayed engaged with the problem and kept your concentration. That's great!

Fig. 7.4. The do's and don'ts of praise. Adapted from Mindset Works (2015).

the school year but revisited when students are engaged in the process.

Carter (2008) taught her first-grade students that when there was a mismatch between their current understanding and new ideas, they were experiencing disequilibrium (Piaget 1970). When students realized they were experiencing disequilibrium, they were able to express their confusion and move on because they saw it as a natural part of learning. They had been given "permission to struggle" (Carter 2008, p. 136).

In a similar way, if students had a better understanding of the problem-solving process, they could be more precise in identifying where they are stuck and be better able to push through the struggle because "the general struggle is made more specific and appears more manageable to the students" (Warshauer 2011, p. 93). One common way to break down problem solving is through Pólya's four steps (1945): understand the problem; devise a plan; carry out a plan; and look back. In her study of productive struggle in middle school mathematics classrooms, Warshauer (2011) identified four places where students typically struggle: getting started; carrying out the process; giving a mathematical explanation; and expressing misconceptions and errors. The "getting started" and "carrying out the process" locations of struggle in Warshauer's research are similar to Pólya's "understand the problem" and "carry out the plan," respectively. When students are asked to provide a mathematical explanation, they often need to reflect or "look back" on the strategy they have used and justify why it worked. Thus, we see this as a third area of overlap between Warshauer's research and Pólya's four-step problem solving. Because of the overlap between places where students struggle (Warshauer, 2011) and Pólya's problem-solving steps, we believe that explicitly

teaching students how to use Pólya's steps will give them the tools and language to assist them in talking about and pushing through their struggles.

Moving Forward with Supporting Productive Struggle

Once teachers and students have been reoriented in their approaches to situations of struggle, teachers can move forward in selecting complex tasks that are within the reach of students, are focused on central mathematics, and encourage sense making. Sometimes, a misconception exists that good tasks must take a full class period or extend across several days, and thus the struggle must also persist across these longer time frames. We stress that there is not an ideal time length for a struggle to be productive; whether or not struggle is productive is based on the level of engagement rather than the duration.

Finally, we discuss the challenge of knowing the appropriate amount of scaffolding that should be used to support students when they are struggling with a task. We could attempt to prescribe a procedure for doing this, but that would be not only difficult but also contrary to the philosophy that learning, for teachers as well as students, is about engaging in experiences where we make our own connections. Thus, we will provide a few suggestions that can act as guidelines when facing a decision about the nature of the support to provide students.

We use Pólya's steps as a framework to provide a set of questions a teacher could ask students who are struggling. We believe, over time, students could begin to ask themselves the same set of questions to move through a struggle on their own:

Understand the problem

- What is the problem asking you to do?

- Are there any terms in the problem with which you are unfamiliar?

- Can you state the problem in your own words?

Devise a plan

- What strategies have you considered? (e.g., solve a simpler problem, guess and test, look for a pattern, or draw a picture [Pólya 1945])

- What are the pros and cons of that strategy?

- What are the attributes of the problem that suggested you should use the strategy you selected?

- What are some other tools or representations you could use?

Carry out the plan

- How did you implement the strategy you chose?

- What problems did you run into when you tried that strategy?

Look back

- Does the solution make sense?

- Do you think there is a more efficient way to solve this problem?

- How is this problem's solution or strategy related to other problems you have solved?

We believe questions such as these serve two purposes: They encourage students to reflect on what they have done and where they are going, and they allow the teacher to understand where the students are in the problem-solving process. Questions meeting the first purpose may help students move forward on their own, while questions for the second purpose provide the context for the teacher to ask further questions directly related to what the student needs without removing ownership of the problem. For example, once Ms. Viramontes had asked questions to understand how the students were seeing the equations $V = (1/2)Bh$ and $V = Bh$ in the vignette, she was better positioned to ask a question about the volume of a cylinder and thus allow the students to make the necessary connections between the different representations.

Williams and Baxter (1996) discuss similar teacher moves to be used when students "get stuck." They describe how Ms. H encouraged a student to explain how he solved the problem using his own words because it would help him understand it better—a form of looking back. This request is indicative of the scaffolding Ms. H provided about behaviors that would help the students' learning. Other examples of this scaffolding occurred when she encouraged peers to ask questions such as these: "What seems hard about the problem? Can you explain that? I'm still having trouble understanding your thinking" (p. 30).

As teachers, we may be uncomfortable watching students struggle and may step in too quickly to alleviate the student anxiety, which also robs students of "opportunities to discover and make progress on their own" (Stein, Grover, and Henningsen 1996, p. 480). We encourage teachers who are facing this dilemma to ask the three questions about productivity discussed earlier in the chapter: Is the mathematics or task within reach?; Is the mathematics central?; and Are the students employing sense making? If the struggle appears to be productive, the questions related to the problem-solving process could be asked to help students move forward or to guide the teacher in the kind of support they can offer.

We offer one caveat as you consider the above questions and situations. We are not saying that you should never step in and offer direct instruction, nor are we saying that students must be the ones to articulate all of the key mathematical points. We are saying that there are likely more situations in your current classrooms where you could say less and allow students to struggle, and thus learn, more. We believe the questions about productivity outlined earlier will provide guidance as to when those situations might occur.

Conclusion

In this chapter, we have described what is meant by affirming that students should experience productive struggle when doing mathematics. We described what we believe are some of the benefits of having students learn mathematics by placing them in situations where they would struggle, as opposed to situations where teachers try to remove all challenges by stepping in whenever students get stuck. Finally, we described some strategies that might be helpful in supporting students in their productive struggle. We believe that the most beneficial strategies are those related to changing the beliefs of teachers and students, because all other strategies will fall short if all parties don't believe that struggle is worthwhile. We also feel that this focus to explicitly talk about struggle and the beliefs surrounding it is the most direct way to begin to support productive struggle.

References

Blackwell, Lisa S., Kali H. Trzesniewski, and Carol Sorich Dweck. "Implicit Theories of Intelligence Predict Achievement across an Adolescent Transition: A Longitudinal Study and an Intervention." *Child Development* 78, no. 1 (2007): 246–63.

Brown, Peter C., Henry L. Roediger III, and Mark A. McDaniel. *Make It Stick.* Cambridge, Mass.: Belknap Press of Harvard University Press, 2014.

Cangelosi, James S. *Classroom Management Strategies: Gaining and Maintaining Students' Cooperation.* Hoboken, N.J.: John Wiley & Sons, 2007.

Carter, Susan. "Disequilibrium and Questioning in the Primary Classroom: Establishing Routines That Help Students Learn." *Teaching Children Mathematics* 15, no. 3 (2008): 134–37.

Catmull, Ed, and Amy Wallace. *Creativity, Inc: Overcoming the Unseen Forces That Stand in the Way of True Inspiration.* New York: Random House, 2014.

Dewey, John. *Democracy and Education: An Introduction to the Philosophy of Education.* New York: Macmillan, 1926.

Dewey, John. *The Quest for Certainty: A Study of the Relation of Knowledge and Action.* New York: Minton, Balch, and Company, 1929.

Dweck, Carol S. *Mindsets and Math/Science Achievement.* New York: Carnegie Corporation of New York Institute for Advanced Study, 2008.

Franke, Megan Loef, Thomas Carpenter, Elizabeth Fennema, Ellen Ansell, and Jeannie Behrend. "Understanding Teachers' Self-Sustaining, Generative Change in the Context of Professional Development." *Teaching and Teacher Education* 14, no. 1 (1998): 67–80.

Gladwell, Malcolm. *Outliers: The Story of Success.* New York: Little Brown and Company, 2008.

Harris, Douglas N., and Tim R. Sass. "Teacher Training, Teacher Quality and Student Achievement." *Journal of Public Economics* 95, no. 7 (2011): 798–812.

Hattie, John, and Helen Timperley. "The Power of Feedback." *Review of Educational Research* 77, no. 1 (2007): 81–112.

Hiebert, James. "The Constantly Underestimated Challenge of Improving Mathematics Instruction." In *Vital Directions for Mathematics Education Research,* edited by Keith R. Leatham, pp. 45–56. New York: Springer, 2013.

Hiebert, James, and Douglas A. Grouws. "The Effects of Classroom Mathematics Teaching on Students' Learning." In *Second Handbook of Research on Mathematics Teaching and Learning,* edited by Frank K. Lester, Jr., pp. 371–404. Charlotte, N.C.: Information Age, and Reston, Va: National Council of Teachers of Mathematics, 2007.

Hiebert, James, and James W. Stigler. "A World of Difference." *Journal of Staff Development* 25, no. 4 (2004): 10–15.

Hiebert, James, and Diana Wearne. "Developing Understanding through Problem Solving." In *Teaching Mathematics through Problem Solving: Grades 6–12,* edited by Harold L. Schoen and Randall I. Charles, pp. 3–13. Reston, Va: National Council of Teachers of Mathematics, 2003.

Kilpatrick, Jeremy, Jane Swafford, and Bradford Findell, eds. *Adding It Up: Helping Children Learn Mathematics.* Washington, D.C.: National Academy Press, 2001.

Lewis, Catherine C. *Educating Hearts and Minds: Reflections on Japanese Preschool and Elementary Education.* Cambridge, U.K.: Cambridge University Press, 1995.

Mindset Works. *Brainology Curriculum Guide for Teachers: Introductory Unit.* Mindset Works, 2014. https://www.mindsetworks.com/

Mindset Works. "Do's and Don'ts of Praise." mindsetkit.org. 2015. https://www.mindsetkit.org/topics/praise-process-not-person/dos-donts-of-praise

Mueller, Claudia M., and Carol S. Dweck. "Praise for Intelligence Can Undermine Children's Motivation and Performance." *Journal of Personality and Social Psychology* 75, no. 1 (1998): 33.

National Council of Teachers of Mathematics (NCTM). *Principles and Standards for School Mathematics.* Reston, Va.: NCTM, 2000.

———. *Principles to Actions: Ensuring Mathematical Success for All.* Reston, Va.: NCTM, 2014.

National Governors Association Center for Best Practices (NGA Center) and Council of Chief State School Officers (CCSSO). *Common Core State Standards for Mathematics.* Washington, D.C.: NGA Center and CCSSO, 2010. http://www.corestandards.org.

Piaget, Jean. *Science of Education and the Psychology of the Child.* Translated by D. Coltman. New York: Orion Press, 1970.

Pólya, George. *How to Solve It: A New Aspect of Mathematical Method.* Princeton, N.J.: Princeton University Press, 1945.

Smith, John P., III. "Efficacy and Teaching Mathematics by Telling: A Challenge for Reform." *Journal for Research in Mathematics Education* 27, no. 4 (1996): 387–402.

Smith, Margaret Schwan. "Reflections on Practice: Redefining Success in Mathematics Teaching and Learning." *Mathematics Teaching in the Middle School* 5, no. 6 (2000): 378–86.

Stein, Mary Kay, Barbara W. Grover, and Marjorie Henningsen. "Building Student Capacity for Mathematical Thinking and Reasoning: An Analysis of Mathematical Tasks Used in Reform Classrooms." *American Educational Research Journal* 33, no. 2 (1996): 455–88.

Stein, Mary Kay, Margaret S. Smith, Marjorie Henningsen, and Edward A. Silver. *Implementing Standards-Based Mathematics Instruction: A Casebook for Professional Development.* 2nd ed. New York: Teachers College Press, 2009.

Stevenson, Harold, and James W. Stigler. *The Learning Gap: Why Our Schools Are Failing and What We Can Learn from Japanese and Chinese Education.* New York: Touchstone, 1992.

Stigler, James W., and James Hiebert. *The Teaching Gap: Best Ideas from the World's Teachers for Improving Education in the Classroom.* New York: Simon and Schuster, 1999.

———. "Closing the Teaching Gap." *Phi Delta Kappan* 91, no. 3 (2009): 32–37.

Vygotsky, Lev. "Interaction between Learning and Development." *Readings on the Development of Children* 23, no. 3 (1978): 34–41.

Warshauer, Hiroko Kawaguchi. "The Role of Productive Struggle in Teaching and Learning Middle School Mathematics." PhD diss., University of Texas at Austin, 2011.

Wayne, Andrew J., and Peter Youngs. "Teacher Characteristics and Student Achievement Gains: A Review." *Review of Educational Research* 73, no. 1 (2003): 89–122.

Weinert, Franz E., Friedrich-W. Schrader, and Andreas Helmke. "Quality of Instruction and Achievement Outcomes." *International Journal of Educational Research* 13, no. 8 (1989): 895–914.

Williams, Steven R., and Juliet A. Baxter. "Dilemmas of Discourse-Oriented Teaching in One Middle School Mathematics Classroom." *Elementary School Journal* 97, no. 1 (1996): 21–38.

Chapter 8

Eliciting and Using Evidence of Student Thinking
Giving Students Voice

Dana C. Cox, *Miami University*
Judy Meicenheimer and Danette Hickey, *Maude Marshall Elementary School, Oxford, Ohio*

●　●　●　●　●　●　●　●　●　●　●　●　●　●　●　●　●　●

Mrs. Hickey: You've each had some time to figure out which holds more water: the flower vase or the red plastic cup. Tell me what you think.

Nathan: The plastic cup wins over the vase. I tried it, and the cup wins!

Anjou: Nope. They are the same. They both hold it.

Wyatt: That's silly. They can't be the same. The vase is so tall, and the cup isn't very tall at all. Just look at it! The vase wins.

Mrs. Hickey: You each think something different! I need to hear more about what you are thinking. Why don't you each tell me one more thing about how you know which holds more so that we can compare our ideas?

Nathan: [*shouting, happily*] If you fill up the cup and dump it into the vase, it makes a flood all over the table! That means it wins because it holds more.

Anjou: But if you fill up the vase and dump it into the cup, the cup can hold it all. The same water in the vase fits in the cup.

Wyatt: Can I try dumping the water? I think I have an idea.

●　●　●　●　●　●　●　●　●　●　●　●　●　●　●　●　●　●

In the vignette above, Mrs. Hickey explores the concept of volume with a small group of first-grade students. The students were trying to decide which vessel held more: a red plastic cup or a tall and narrow flower vase. Before they began the exploration at the water table, Mrs. Hickey asked the whole class to predict which held more, and the students were unanimous that the flower vase was much "bigger" (and therefore held more) than the cup. In the discussion that followed, students began to use comparison words such as *taller*, *wider*, *straighter*, and *curvier* to compare the size and shape of the vessels. They arranged the vessels next to each other in a variety of ways to see how the heights, widths, and base areas compared. It was in this context that Mrs. Hickey invited the students to explore the question at the water table in small groups, and it was at the conclusion of this water play that the conversation above unfolded.

By inviting all three students to share their mathematical thinking, Mrs. Hickey saw that the three students had reached different conclusions based on their play, even if the rationale for those conclusions was a bit mysterious. For example, what did Nathan mean by "wins," and what did Anjou mean by "it"? A follow-up conversation is necessary to uncover the meaning behind the students' descriptions in order to use their thinking to inform instruction.

Principles to Actions: Ensuring Mathematical Success for All (NCTM 2014) states that "effective mathematics teaching elicits evidence of students' current

The authors would like to acknowledge the Dovetail Group for their support in thinking about what it means to have voice and to listen to others. Particularly, we would like to thank Suzanne Harper and Beatriz D'Ambrosio for providing guidance and a critical ear as we prepared our manuscript.

mathematical understanding and uses it as the basis for making instructional decisions" (p. 53). What it means to elicit and use students' mathematical thinking in instruction, however, depends on teachers' perceptions of the roles students and teachers play in the classroom. First, we describe what we mean by *listening for students' mathematics.* Second, we share strategies for planning and enacting instruction that values a multiplicity of ideas, along with how to elicit, respond to, and extend student thinking in the classroom. Specifically, we describe how to orchestrate moments where students engage mathematically, how to help students make their thinking public, and how to help students (and ourselves!) make connections between their thinking, classmates' thinking, and our own thinking. We conclude by acknowledging and addressing two key tensions in teaching, time and testing, that are affected by a decision to elevate the importance of student thinking in the math classroom.

Listening for Students' Mathematics

Lampert and Cobb (2003) defined two stances teachers might take toward student participation. When taking an *acquisition* stance, teachers expect students to master a set of mathematical processes and facts specified for them by outside authorities. This perspective has been called *listening for mathematics* (Davis 1997). In contrast, when taking a *participatory* stance, teachers help students participate in an increasingly competent way in "mathematical practices that have been developed over a period of centuries and that constitute students' intellectual inheritance" (Lampert and Cobb 2003, p. 237), a perspective called *listening to students* (Davis 1997). Taking one stance or the other leads to different motives for how teachers listen to what students have to say and how they shape their responses. In this section, we seek to join these two perspectives by describing our interpretation of a third option—*listening for students' mathematics* and incorporating their thinking into instruction. To make the case for this third option, we first describe the other two options in more detail.

Listening for Mathematics

In the conversation about volume described above, a teacher with an acquisition stance who is listening for mathematics might tell students which of the two containers has the larger volume and demonstrate using the water table, because the teacher's goal is for students to develop a predetermined notion of volume from this exercise. From an acquisition stance, the motive for soliciting students' ideas is to determine what mathematical knowledge a student has acquired and to evaluate the quality of that knowledge with the purpose of providing confirmation or remediation for the student. Student responses are compared to an idealized sense of what mathematics should be and should sound like and are declared right or wrong. Here, we *listen for* an expected mathematical response.

However, this sort of evaluative listening limits what we are able to hear (Davis 1997). For example, we may limit our view of what students know to a select set of expected responses. Furthermore, what we are able to notice, what we choose to notice, and how we interpret what we see and hear depend greatly on who we are as individuals, including our experiences, our education, our beliefs, and our cultural backgrounds (Jacobs, Lamb, and Philipp 2010). In other words, teachers "hear through" their own personal and social resources (Even and Wallach 2004). This complicates the act of listening for mathematics, as we have to consider not only what students say but also how we interpret those messages.

People often over- or under-hear what students say, hearing more or less of what we expect to hear than what students actually say. For instance, a teacher may over-hear a student whom she perceives as extremely competent, assuming when that student says that a rectangle has two short sides and two long sides that she really knows a rectangle can have four sides of the same length. On the other hand, a teacher may under-hear a student who struggles to smoothly articulate her thinking when he listens for key words and forms a response before the student has finished talking. As teachers, we may even assume that the student does not really understand the mathematical ideas and may interrupt or take over the explanation rather than giving voice to the student. Furthermore, we may be prone to biased hearing, which occurs when we attribute more or less mathematical reasoning to a student on the basis of what we know from previous encounters, achievement, or affect (Even and Wallach 2004). Racial, gender, and class bias are also present and complicate our ability to encounter students as individuals outside of stereotypes or generalizations (Baron, Tom, and Cooper 1985).

Elbow (1986) describes evaluative listening as coming from a place of methodological doubt. By that, he means that we listen with an ear to uncover inconsistencies, bad reasoning, and weakness in arguments. This is not to say we are only listening for errors; rather, sometimes we listen to make sure they do not exist. In this way, we use doubt as a tool of scrutiny or as a means to assign value to students' thinking. The value we eventually assign is connected to complex power structures in the classroom (see Gutiérrez 2013).

Listening to Students

To return to the opening vignette, a teacher with a participatory stance who is listening to students might invite students to explain their reasoning or demonstrate their thinking at the water table. Similarly, the teacher might invite other students to ask questions of those who have shared ideas, because the teacher's goal is to induct students into the practice of mathematics; the students are the mathematicians. Here, we are not listening for a particular response but listening to students to uncover the "sparks of rightness" (Harkness 2009, p. 244) that exist if we are willing to help them clarify their assumptions. Finding (or unpacking) the meaning requires what Davis (1997) referred to as interpretive listening.

When we start with the assumption that students have valid reasons for their ideas and commit to setting aside our own mathematical understandings in order to uncover the meaning and logic in students' ideas, even if we cannot imagine what it might be (Duckworth 1987), we are applying methodological belief (Elbow 1986). While *doubting* assumes that the logic of the teacher is correct, *believing* assumes that the logic of the student can also make sense. This is what Morrow-Leong (2016) means when she advocates using a "what's right" lens as part of an evidence-centered assessment strategy. In this way, listening is understood from a participatory stance. In *listening to* students, we create a space for making conjectures, forming and critiquing arguments, making connections, and promoting a culture of student reasoning and mathematical autonomy.

Listening for Students' Mathematics

Although one might think of listening for mathematics and listening to students as polar opposites, it is more productive to think of them on a continuum where the teacher's role is to balance the tensions that arise from going too far to one extreme or the other. For instance, taking only an acquisition stance could lead to rote learning and a lack of enjoyment of mathematics, while taking only a participatory stance does not address the need to focus on specific mathematical content that students need to learn in order to be successful in the next grade or course.

Although there is tension, it is possible to listen with one ear *for* mathematics and, with the other, listen *to* students (Davis 1997). The solution is in listening for students' mathematics and using their thinking to frame instruction. The teacher who listens for students' mathematics is one who "integrates the voice of the discipline and the voices of children as she defines her inner voice in making sense of learners' understanding" (D'Ambrosio 2004, p. 137). Davis (1997) called this form of listening *hermeneutic listening*, which he defined as working alongside students to negotiate meaning and being willing to "interrogate the taken for granted and the prejudices that frame our perceptions and actions" (p. 370). When we listen to students in this way, we engage in inquiry alongside our students, and it is not only students who emerge changed; our beliefs about mathematics, teaching, and learning can change as a result of these interactions with student thinking (Ambrose 2004; D'Ambrosio and Campos 1992; Fisher et al. 2014; Knapp and Peterson 1995; Vacc and Bright 1999).

The act of listening for students' mathematics requires at the outset a commitment to setting aside our own mathematics and picking up that of our students as if it were our own; we agree to centralize the mathematics being shared by students and relinquish control over the evaluation of those ideas, and we do not engage or act on our own desires about what we wish students would say or ways they would say it. While a good lesson begins with expectations about what mathematics students will encounter, in the moment of listening we leave behind all expectations about what students *should* know or say. This requires that we view student thinking as more than just right or wrong, which can be a challenging habit to break (see Crespo 2000; Even and Tirosh 1995). It certainly raises the question of what to do when student reasoning diverges from our more standardized notion of "good mathematics" in the course of a lesson.

Planning and Enacting Instruction That Values Multiplicity of Ideas

Listening for students' mathematics requires teachers to seek out and nurture the multiplicity of mathematical ideas in the classroom, and much deliberate work goes into planning and enacting such lessons. In this section, we describe actions that teachers can take when planning to make use of student thinking and actions that teachers can take during instruction to elicit and use student thinking productively.

The first key element of planning is identifying specific and strategic instructional goals, then selecting mathematical tasks that align with these goals. (See chapter 1 for more about identifying goals and chapter 2 for more details about selecting tasks.) Once the tasks are selected, it is important to anticipate the mathematics that students might share about the task (Smith and Stein 2011). Learning trajectories (sometimes called projections or progressions) are tools that help with both planning and anticipation.

Learning trajectories describe a known developmental progression of students' reasoning based on research on student learning (Clements and Sarama 2004). A learning trajectory, then, stands in contrast to the way mathematical learning is often planned, which is through the dissection of a topic from a mathematical perspective (considering prerequisite skills, for instance). While the notion of trajectory might bring up connotations of a one-dimensional path that must be followed strictly, trajectories are intended to be more holistic. A trajectory should be less like a pacing guide and more like an orienting document that helps us see

where students are coming from and where they are going. Consequently, there are often multiple paths through a trajectory. See "Progressions Documents for Common Core Math Standards" (IME 2007) for examples of learning trajectories for various topics, as well as chapter 1 for more details on learning trajectories.

Using a trajectory to inform instruction entails designing instructional tasks that are intended to engender the type of thinking identified at various points on the trajectory and then using the trajectory to anticipate possible student responses and ways of thinking. However, no trajectory will allow us to anticipate fully all student thinking that may emerge; so trajectories need to be used flexibly (Doerr 2006), and instruction needs to be responsive to the thinking students demonstrate. Trajectories are not intended to be used as yardsticks to measure whether or not students are on the "right" path. Rather, teachers should anticipate that students will travel a multitude of paths and must learn to interpret what students say and to assess how a lesson is evolving, and then use that interpretation for both short-term and long-term instructional decisions about how to braid those paths together.

Eliciting, Responding to, and Extending Student Thinking

Making Student Thinking Public

Once the lesson is under way, it is necessary to elicit and make students' thinking public, for both their teacher and their peers to consider. Smith and Stein (2001) recommend that teachers monitor student thinking during individual and small-group work time in order to deliberately select and sequence student work to share during whole-class discussion. As part of monitoring, the teacher listens and observes as students solve a problem to get a sense of the strategies being used. By setting the expectation that students create records of their process of thinking through a task, the teacher can move around the room and capture a big picture of available ideas. Gaining this big picture allows the teacher to know what mathematical ideas and representations will likely emerge during discussion and to consider what support or even dissonance to supply. In this work, "teachers must consider how to interpret and respond to what students say, draw, build, or write, as well as attend to the absence of specific evidence" (NCTM 2014, p. 54).

As the teacher invites particular students to share their ideas or encourages students to volunteer, the multiplicity of ideas creates an opportunity for cognitive conflict. The power is not in just one student sharing an example of thinking but in sharing and comparing multiple solutions and recognizing mathematical connections across solutions (Doerr 2006). Bray (2013) identifies two essential classroom conditions for productive cognitive conflict: the active engagement of students in unpacking the mathematics behind the conflict, and public discussion of these ideas so that key mathematical concepts are emphasized. Supporting students as they make their mathematics visible and public is important and requires careful consideration. (See chapter 4 for examples of effective facilitation of such discussions.)

Responding to and Extending Student Thinking

"Effective teaching involves finding the mathematics in students' comments and actions, considering what students appear to know in light of the intended learning goals and progression, and determining how to give the best response and support to students on the basis of their current understandings" (NCTM 2014, p. 56). While there is value in cultivating correct or logical mathematical thinking in class, there is also value in instances of unexpected mathematics. Whether students share something expected or unexpected, it can help us see students' conceptions of mathematics, and these opportunities are valuable for other students and the teacher to hear. Furthermore, whether expected or unexpected, both responses require deliberate attention from the teacher to ensure that the student speaking and other students in the classroom are able to make sense of the ideas being shared.

Instances when students say, write, or demonstrate the unexpected have enormous potential to generate cognitive conflict for students and a collaborative environment that encourages controversy. Consequently, their equitable (Nastasi and Clements 1992) and public (Kazemi and Stipek 2001) resolution can have an impact on student learning. If capitalized on, such instances can provide opportunities to reconceptualize a problem, provoke argumentation, generate new questions or problems for students to solve, and fuel new conjectures or strategies, potential that Borasi (1994) said is largely unrecognized and underutilized. She and others (e.g., Stein et al. 2008; Swan 2001) write that those instances where student mathematics or logic does not align with what is expected should not be avoided or diminished but carefully orchestrated (Swan 2001) so as to make existing conceptions and methods explicit.

In the opening vignette, Mrs. Hickey capitalized on unexpected thinking to motivate students to expose more of their logic and mathematical process. By doing so, she enabled students to explore new perspectives on the question of volume and inspired Wyatt to reexamine a mathematical idea that he had previously taken for granted but now thought might be invalid. Her next instructional move might be to invite the three students to return to the water table. There are many ways she might help the students frame their activity. One possibility is to elevate Wyatt to "the leader position" because he has an idea he wants to explore. Another possibility is to give each student the task of trying a new strategy—perhaps one shared by another person in the group. A third possibility is to give the group the task to "find a way to agree," encouraging them to gather and combine evidence from each of the strategies to form one idea or conclusion. Finally, she might choose to move the group on to another activity and suspend the conversation until she has heard from more small groups and is ready to explore these ideas in a whole-class discussion. These possibilities provide Mrs. Hickey the added benefit of more time to think about the mathematics her students are encountering and sharing and to make a more reasoned and thoughtful decision about how to proceed. Mrs. Hickey did not use the thought processes that were shared unexpectedly as examples of what *not* to do, but rather leveraged them as fodder for mathematical discussion, critique, and, ultimately, revision (Bray 2013).

In our own experience as well as in research (Harkness 2009), we have found value in posing this question: Under what conditions could each of these students' statements about volume be true? Seago, Mumme, and Branca (2004) explore this approach in great detail in the context of linear functions in a secondary algebra classroom. Video cases that highlight student thinking about patterns, algebra, and function can help us move away from evaluating the work of students in our classroom and toward unpacking the reasoning behind unexpected statements or representations.

When students act in expected ways, this, too, requires discussion and debate (Jacobs and Ambrose 2008). It may be tempting, after asking students for a solution to a problem, to focus mathematical discussion on highlighting what might have gone awry and to assume that everyone who got the same answer as the back of the book knew exactly what they were doing—and did the exact same thing. It is not just the unexpected that requires unpacking, however. It is certainly possible for students to give an expected answer to a question and *not* understand the material (Wiliam 2007) or be unable to explain why a procedure produced the expected answer or when the procedure would break down. Furthermore, it is possible for two students to give matching solutions based on different strategies and logic. For example, given the Growing Dots problem shown in figure 8.1 (Seago, Mumme, and Branca 2004), two students may report the number of dots at *t* minutes to be "1 plus 4 times *t*." While both students see the center dot as the "+1" extra, one student notices that each arm has *t* dots in it and there are four arms (4*t*), while the other student sees a new ring of four dots forming around the center every minute (also 4*t*). Exploring this pattern from multiple perspectives makes mathematics personal, but it also promotes a sense of flexibility in the classroom as students are asked to consider the equivalence of the algebraic expressions at the same time as the diversity of reasoning supporting each.

When teachers continually adjust their teaching and make instructional decisions during a lesson, Jacobs and Empson (2016) refer to this technique as *responsive teaching*. They identified a series of teaching moves that support and extend student reasoning both before and after a "correct" solution has been given. Teachers can promote reflection on the strategy by asking students to elaborate on their strategies or by asking questions such as "Why did your strategy make sense on this problem?" Teachers can encourage students to explore other strategies and their connections by asking students

to think of different ways to solve the same problem or by comparing and contrasting their strategies with those of other students. This would likely prompt teachers to explore the details of a student's strategy and connect the student's thinking to symbolic notation. Teachers do this by asking students to unpack a symbolic representation and assign meaning to its parts based on the original problem statement or by asking students for symbolic ways to represent verbal or tactile thinking. Last, teachers can pose related problems that create additional opportunities for discussion. By asking students to consider a problem with larger numbers, with fewer constraints, with different assumptions, or even in a different context, teachers can add challenge, encourage more symbolic representations, push for generalization of strategy, and even uncover hidden conceptions that might not have interfered with solving the original problem but emerge nonetheless when conditions change in even slight ways. Jacobs and Empson (2016) provide further elaboration and examples of these strategies, as do Jacobs and Ambrose (2008). See also chapter 4 (discourse) and chapter 5 (questioning) for additional examples of ways to elicit and respond to students' mathematical thinking.

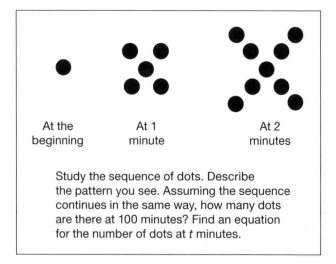

Fig. 8.1. Growing Dots problem. Adapted from Seago, Mumme, and Branca (2004).

Conclusion

When we adopt a stance that student thinking is valuable, it can have an impact on many facets of our teaching practice, notably on two key tensions: time and testing. When we say *time*, we are referring to the tension created when the time we have for math instruction is limited. For us, it is common to glance up at the clock in the midst of a whole-class discussion about mathematics and experience feelings of disappointment, regret, frustration, and even anger. It can be difficult to pull a conversation to a close prior to the ring of a bell, the beginning of lunch, or as the next class shuffles in the hallway, eager to enter.

However, we resolve some of that tension when we elevate the importance of student thinking. We've often employed the "to be continued!" strategy as students pack up their things. In fact, there is great power in leaving a mathematical thought unfinished if we are deliberate about it. Saving time to allow for that dramatic anticipation of the next installment of the conversation is important. Making a digital recording of a student asking a question or stating an idea gives us an entryway into the discussion at a future time. The forced end to a discussion can provide an "academic pause" that has many benefits. Students who may be feeling lost or insecure about their struggle may rally, once given extra time to make sense of the question and to find a way to communicate their thinking. Students who have made great strides in their thinking can be advised to go home and tell someone else about their idea. This puts mathematics forward as a source of pride and encourages students to relate mathematics to others in meaningful ways so that they might appreciate its importance and beauty.

The academic pause also improves our instruction and links lessons rather than leaving them as discrete parcels of math. Once we spend some time understanding the mathematics behind what our students are grappling with, we are better able to get a fresh start on the lesson or find another problem that targets the students' needs. We might also manage small-group instruction based on the strategies that were shared or the questions that were asked. By arranging study groups according to the way students are thinking about the lesson, we target individual needs and can differentiate instruction based on our goals. Sometimes we provoke further unexpected thinking, and sometimes we find great value in helping students adopt more standard (or intended) mathematics. In every event, we plan our instruction around how the previous lesson ended and

where we would like the next lesson to begin, using student thinking as a linking device day to day and lesson to lesson.

We also feel tension around assessment and testing. By *testing*, we mean that we recognize the tension that exists between taking the time to personalize instruction, but also holding those ideas accountable to standards for mathematical learning and practice in the American classroom (Ball 1993; Brown and Campione 1994). To ignore this tension is to set aside the realities of the classroom and take up an idealistic sense of teaching and learning. For us, the tension emerges when we simultaneously recognize the many benefits that curriculum standards offer while still wanting to advocate for the multiplicity of ideas in our lessons and to give students a voice in setting their own mathematical agendas (Wagner and Herbel-Eisenmann 2009).

Standardization supports equity and ensures that all children will have the opportunity to learn solid mathematics. Standardization promotes professional conversations about important mathematical concepts and when it is developmentally appropriate to learn them. Standardization ensures that students will have a coherent mathematical experience as they transition from grade to grade, from classroom to classroom, or even school to school.

Creating lessons that disseminate standardized knowledge while providing opportunities to gauge what students know is a powerful way to ensure that all students have a greater chance of succeeding on end-of-year assessments and in the next mathematics class, a critical component of equity in the classroom. Knowing what our students are thinking helps us become more efficient at constructing activities and conversations that deepen and extend student learning. By eliciting and using evidence of student thinking, we are giving students (and ourselves) autonomy in evaluating our daily progress as well as determining for ourselves how we will achieve the goals that are set for us in the days to come.

References

Ambrose, Rebecca. "Initiating Change in Prospective Elementary School Teachers' Orientations to Mathematics Teaching by Building on Beliefs." *Journal of Mathematics Teacher Education* 7, no. 2 (2004): 91–119.

Ball, Deborah Loewenberg. "With an Eye on the Mathematical Horizon: Dilemmas of Teaching Elementary School Mathematics." *Elementary School Journal* 93, no. 4 (1993): 373–97.

Baron, Reuben M., David Y. H. Tom, and Harris M. Cooper. "Social Class, Race and Teacher Expectations." In *Teacher Expectancies*, edited by Jerome B. Dusek, pp. 251–69. Hillsdale, N.J.: Lawrence Erlbaum, 1985.

Borasi, Raffaella. "Capitalizing on Errors as 'Springboards for Inquiry': A Teaching Experiment." *Journal for Research in Mathematics Education* 25, no. 2 (1994): 166–208.

Bray, Wendy S. "How to Leverage the Potential of Mathematical Errors." *Teaching Children Mathematics* 19, no. 7 (2013): 424–31.

Brown, Ann L., and Joseph C. Campione. "Guided Discovery in a Community of Learners." In *Classroom Lessons: Integrating Cognitive Theory and Classroom Practice*, edited by Kate McGilly, pp. 229–70. Cambridge, Mass.: The MIT Press, 1994.

Clements, Douglas H., and Julie Sarama. "Learning Trajectories in Mathematics Education." *Mathematical Thinking and Learning* 6, no. 2 (2004): 81–89.

Crespo, Sandra. "Seeing More Than Right and Wrong Answers: Prospective Teachers' Interpretations of Students' Mathematical Work." *Journal of Mathematics Teacher Education* 3, no. 2 (2000): 155–81.

D'Ambrosio, Beatriz. "Preparing Teachers to Teach Mathematics within a Constructivist Framework: The Importance of Listening to Children." In *The Work of Mathematics Teacher Educators: Exchanging Ideas for Effective Practice,* edited by Tad Watanabe and Denise R. Thompson, pp. 135–50. Vol. 1, AMTE Monographs. San Diego, Calif.: Association of Mathematics Teacher Educators, 2004.

D'Ambrosio, Beatriz S., and Tânia Maria Mendonça Campos. "Pre-service Teachers' Representations of Children's Understanding of Mathematical Concepts: Conflicts and Conflict Resolution." *Educational Studies in Mathematics* 23, no. 3 (1992): 213–30.

Davis, Brent. "Listening for Differences: An Evolving Conception of Mathematics Teaching." *Journal for Research in Mathematics Education* 28, no. 3 (1997): 355–76.

Doerr, Helen M. "Examining the Tasks of Teaching when Using Students' Mathematical Thinking." *Educational Studies in Mathematics* 62, no. 1 (2006): 3–24.

Duckworth, Eleanor. *The Having of Wonderful Ideas and Other Essays on Teaching and Learning.* New York: Teachers College Press, 1987.

Elbow, Peter. *Embracing Contraries: Explorations in Learning and Teaching.* New York: Oxford University Press, 1986.

Even, Ruhama, and Dina Tirosh. "Subject-matter Knowledge and Knowledge about Students as Sources of Teacher Presentations of the Subject-matter." *Educational Studies in Mathematics* 29, no. 1 (1995): 1–20.

Even, Ruhama, and Tali Wallach. "Between Student Observation and Student Assessment: A Critical Reflection." *Canadian Journal of Math, Science & Technology Education* 4, no. 4 (2004): 483–95.

Fisher, Molly H., Edna O. Schack, Jonathan Thomas, Cindy Jong, Sara Eisenhardt, Janet Tassell, and Margaret Yoder. "Examining the Relationship between Preservice Elementary Teachers' Attitudes toward Mathematics and Professional Noticing Capacities." In *Research Trends in Mathematics Teacher Education*, edited by Jane-Jane Lo, Keith R. Leatham, and Laura R. Van Zoest, pp. 219–37. Cham, Switzerland: Springer International Publishing, 2014.

Gutiérrez, Rochelle. "The Sociopolitical Turn in Mathematics Education." *Journal for Research in Mathematics Education* 44, no. 1 (2013): 37–68.

Harkness, Shelly S. "Social Constructivism and the Believing Game: A Mathematics Teacher's Practice and Its Implications." *Educational Studies in Mathematics* 70, no. 3 (2009): 243–58.

Institute for Mathematics Education, The University of Arizona (IME). "Progressions Documents for the Common Core Math Standards." The Arizona Board of Regents 2007. https:// ime.math.arizona.edu/progressions/

Jacobs, Victoria R., and Rebecca C. Ambrose. "Making the Most of Story Problems." *Teaching Children Mathematics* 15, no. 5 (2008): 260–66.

Jacobs, Victoria R., and Susan B. Empson. "Responding to Children's Mathematical Thinking in the Moment: An Emerging Framework of Teaching Moves." *ZDM* 48, no. 1–2 (2016): 185–97.

Jacobs, Victoria R., Lisa L. C. Lamb, and Randolph A. Philipp. "Professional Noticing of Children's Mathematical Thinking." *Journal for Research in Mathematics Education* 41, no. 2 (2010): 169–202.

Kazemi, Elham, and Deborah Stipek. "Promoting Conceptual Thinking in Four Upper-Elementary Mathematics Classrooms." *Elementary School Journal* 102, no. 1 (2001): 59–80.

Knapp, Nancy F., and Penelope L. Peterson. "Teachers' Interpretations of 'CGI' after Four Years: Meanings and Practices." *Journal for Research in Mathematics Education* 26, no. 1 (1995): 40–65.

Lampert, Magdalene, and Paul Cobb. "Communication and Language." In *A Research Companion to* Principles and Standards for School Mathematics, edited by Jeremy Kilpatrick, W. Gary Martin, and Deborah Schifter, pp. 237–49. Reston, Va.: National Council of Teachers of Mathematics, 2003.

Morrow-Leong, Kimberly. "Evidence-Centered Assessment." *Teaching Children Mathematics* 23, no. 2 (2016): 82–89.

Nastasi, Bonnie K., and Douglas H. Clements. "Social-Cognitive Behaviors and Higher-Order Thinking in Educational Computer Environments." *Learning and Instruction* 2, no. 3 (1992): 215–38.

National Council of Teachers of Mathematics (NCTM). *Principles to Actions: Ensuring Mathematical Success for All.* Reston, Va.: NCTM, 2014.

Seago, Nanette, Judith Mumme, and Nicholas Branca. *Learning and Teaching Linear Functions: Video Cases for Mathematics Professional Development, 6–10.* Portsmouth, N.H.: Heinemann, 2004.

Smith, Margaret S., and Mary Kay Stein. *5 Practices for Orchestrating Productive Mathematics Discussions.* Reston, Va.: National Council of Teachers of Mathematics, 2011.

Stein, Mary Kay, Randi A. Engle, Margaret S. Smith, and Elizabeth K. Hughes. "Orchestrating Productive Mathematical Discussions: Five Practices for Helping Teachers Move Beyond Show and Tell." *Mathematical Thinking and Learning* 10, no. 4 (2008): 313–40.

Swan, Malcolm. "Dealing with Misconceptions in Mathematics." In *Issues in Mathematics Teaching,* edited by Peter Gates, pp. 147–65. New York: Routledge, 2001.

Vacc, Nancy Nesbitt, and George W. Bright. "Elementary Preservice Teachers' Changing Beliefs and Instructional Use of Children's Mathematical Thinking." *Journal for Research in Mathematics Education* 30, no. 1 (1999): 89–110.

Wagner, David, and Beth Herbel-Eisenmann. "Re-Mythologizing Mathematics through Attention to Classroom Positioning." *Educational Studies in Mathematics* 72, no. 1 (2009): 1–15.

Wiliam, Dylan. "Keeping Learning on Track." In *Second Handbook of Research on Mathematics Teaching and Learning,* edited by Frank K. Lester Jr., pp. 1053–98. Charlotte, N.C.: Information Age Publishing, and Reston, Va.: National Council of Teachers of Mathematics, 2007.

Chapter 9

Providing Access to Equitable Mathematics Learning

Anita A. Wager, *University of Wisconsin-Madison*
Barbara Pietz, *Wright Middle School, Madison, Wisconsin*
Mary Klehr, *Madison (Wisconsin) Metropolitan School District*

More than two decades ago, Carey and colleagues (1995) wrote a book chapter entitled "Equity in Mathematics Education." The obstacles to equitable mathematics teaching that they raised then still exist today, yet the field of mathematics education has made some progress in understanding more about practices that can lead to equitable access to high-quality mathematics instruction for all students. Essential elements of equitable mathematics teaching are "that all students have access to a high-quality mathematics curriculum, effective teaching and learning, high expectations, and the support and resources needed to maximize their learning potential" (NCTM 2014, p. 59). In this companion chapter to the section on Access and Equity in *Principles to Actions: Ensuring Mathematical Success for All* (*PtA*), we provide examples of dispositions and practices necessary to provide access to equitable opportunities for learning mathematics. *PtA* elaborates on some obstacles to access—low quality of instruction available to, low expectations for, and negative dispositions toward mathematics—as experienced by African Americans, Latino/as, Indigenous populations, English Language Learners, students with disabilities, girls, and those in poverty. We focus here on suggestions to overcome these obstacles.

We build on the ideas raised in *PtA* by discussing research that identifies equitable approaches to mathematics teaching found to be effective in classrooms and schools. We organized this chapter around the dispositions and practices that *PtA* identifies as necessary to

achieve equitable mathematics teaching: (a) believing that all students are capable and having high expectations of them; (b) valuing student thinking and engaging in practices that support student agency and identity; and (c) identifying possible interventions to achieve the goal of equitable access. Our approach is to address each of these through a brief review of research and accompanying vignettes from classrooms and schools. We conclude by raising other practices that we think are imperative to achieving equity, such as attending explicitly to race and power and to a recognition of the broader structures of privilege and oppression in which mathematics teaching is situated.

First, we provide some background on the authors in order to position ourselves in this work. We are three white, female math educators from the same generation, all teaching and living in the Midwest yet raised under economically, socially, and educationally diverse circumstances. We recognize the irony of a team of white people writing about the inequities that we have not had to face personally and that our whiteness is reflected in how and what we write. What our whiteness affords us, however, is the opportunity to describe how we have interrupted our own assumptions and changed our practices. We are committed to understanding how beliefs and practices of all parties operating in the school system (e.g., administrators, teachers, students, parents, researchers) influence the learning opportunities for students who historically have been denied equitable access to mathematics. Anita Wager is a

The writing of this paper was supported in part by a grant from the National Science Foundation (1019431) and Wisconsin Center for Education Research (WCER). The opinions expressed in this paper do not necessarily reflect the position, policy, or endorsement of the National Science Foundation or WCER.

university mathematics educator and former fifth-grade teacher who teaches and studies ways to support prospective and practicing teachers to engage in equitable mathematics pedagogy. Barbie Pietz is an eighth-grade mathematics teacher in a middle school whose student population has become increasingly diverse. Mary Klehr, a school-based clinical teacher-educator in a joint position between the local university and school district, works with prospective teachers to develop professional agency through opportunities that connect them with others both in and outside of school so that they can recognize and evaluate the effects of their assumptions, choices, and actions on themselves and others.

Beliefs and Expectations

The question is not whether all students can succeed in mathematics but whether the adults organizing mathematics learning opportunities can alter traditional beliefs and practices to promote success for all (NCTM 2014, p. 61).

At the heart of equitable mathematics teaching is the recognition that all students can and should participate in rich mathematics in and out of school. This belief requires a shift in the way students and mathematics learning are framed by focusing on what students bring to the classroom rather than what they lack (Civil 2007) and acknowledging that mathematics is neither culture-free (Bishop 1994; Gerdes 1988) nor politically neutral (Felton 2010). *PtA* uses Dweck's (2006) idea of a growth mindset to refer to the beliefs and dispositions necessary for equitable mathematics teaching and learning.

A growth mindset presupposes that individuals develop intelligence over time, as opposed to a belief that intelligence is innate and fixed (Dweck 2010) or based on race, ethnicity, economic status, country of origin, language proficiency, gender, or special learning needs. This growth mindset provides a foundation from which teachers can shape their teaching practices to provide equitable access to opportunities to learn mathematics. (See chapter 7 for more information about the growth mindset.) Beyond a growth mindset, assets-based (as opposed to deficit-based) views of students are needed. Evident in the work of teachers who recognize

as resources all the experiences students bring from their homes and communities (Drake et al. 2015), assets-based beliefs are illustrated by those who have high academic expectations for all students because they do not accept deficit views about students' intellectual potential (Fine 1986).

Assets-based beliefs can be challenging to develop. For example, despite years of rhetoric about equity in mathematics education, the ways in which African American students have been positioned in research literature and policy statements perpetuates a belief that they are mathematically inferior to their white and Asian classmates (Martin 2003). Martin suggested that teachers cannot simultaneously talk about achievement gaps in terms of race and believe in the "brilliance of black children" (p. 135). Talking about achievement gaps among racial groups ascribes a particular quality to students (e.g., low performing, high performing) based on their race, which is tantamount to making a cause-and-effect claim. But racial achievement gaps are "an artifact of societal racism" (p. 135), so talking about racial achievement gaps adds to the perception that race makes one more or less capable in mathematics (see Lubienski and Gutiérrez 2008). The same can be said with respect to beliefs about so-called gaps based on students' country of origin, economic status, language proficiency, gender, or special learning needs. Disrupting belief in racial and other achievement gaps is imperative if teachers are to provide equitable access to mathematics learning. Reframing one's view of achievement gaps as an education debt (Ladson-Billings 2006) or gaps in access to opportunities to learn (Flores 2007) is a start toward developing an assets-based perspective.

Teachers develop assets-based beliefs (including having a growth mindset) in different ways based on their varied histories and experiences (Wager 2014). Bartell and colleagues (2008) suggest teachers must explore their own conceptions of equity, knowledge of individual students, and their beliefs about and role in closing achievement gaps as their first step in becoming equitable math teachers (p. 607). Educators who reflect and draw on the multiple identities they (and their students) bring to the classroom can reframe instruction to benefit students who have been historically marginalized by race, class, ethnicity, language, gender, or special learning needs (Aguirre, Mayfield-Ingram, and Martin 2013). In the following vignette, Barbie Pietz provides an honest recounting of her own journey as she discovered how her assumptions started from a deficit perspective that kept her from providing one of her students with the learning opportunities he needed to, in Martin's words, "*reach* the ceiling, not just *pass*" (personal communication, July 13, 2015). This discovery led to an overhaul of her beliefs, teaching, and pedagogy.

> My journey began in my third year of teaching. At the time, my classes consisted of mostly white children from working class neighborhoods. The first two years, my two black students failed. I considered myself a social justice activist and was concerned my students were becoming statistics. I wondered if their failing had anything to do with my teaching, but I knew there were many factors involved, including truancy, and felt I had worked hard to teach those two students. In my third year of teaching, I had a black student who was a solid C student. It was a relief to have the confirmation that I wasn't doing something to cause my black students to fail. But my revelation came at parent teacher conferences when his parents shared that he should be an A student, and they were furious no one had

called to raise concerns. I realized I had made a number of assumptions based solely on the color of my student's skin, and I needed to make major changes in my teaching immediately. I began taking classes and reading books on issues of equity to understand how much growth I needed to experience, what perceptions needed to change, and how I needed to rethink my practice with respect to race. While working on my classroom action research around equity, I came to understand that I was the mirror for my students. I must believe that anything is possible for my students, and I must reflect that belief back to them.

Pietz's beliefs shifted from unproductive to productive (see *PtA*, pp. 63–64) and provide evidence of a new mindset with respect to students' abilities based on race. Further, Pietz did not just change her beliefs about students but sought resources to understand how her practice should also change to reflect her new beliefs. Her experience is not uncommon but certainly not common enough. Hers was one of many potential paths that teachers can take toward assets-based beliefs about students and demonstrates not just a shift in beliefs but also a shift in practice. In another account of a teacher's journey toward equitable mathematics teaching,

Table 9.1

Big ideas and practices associated with equitable mathematics teaching

Big ideas	Supporting practices
Pedagogical practices and instructional choices that support students' mathematical identity and agency	• Construct norms for equitable participation and attend explicitly to participation gaps (Cobb and Hodge 2007; Hand, Kirtley, and Matassa 2015; Turner et al. 2013) • Position students as capable (Allen and Schnell 2016; Bartell 2011; Hand 2012; Planas and Civil 2010) • Listen closely to learn about students' mathematical thinking and other experiences (Dominguez 2016; Gutiérrez 2015) • De-track classrooms and schools (Boaler 2011) • Engage in practices that support all students to express their math thinking (Moschkovich 2013; Chval and Chávez 2012) • Build on students' social, cultural, and linguistic resources (e.g., funds of knowledge, multiple forms of discourse and language) (Aguirre et al. 2013; Chval and Chávez 2012; Civil 2007) • Incorporate the Standards for Mathematical Practice with explicit attention to the above (Bartell et al. 2017) and social justice (Cirillo, Bartell, and Wager 2016)
Differentiation, interventions, and support	• Provide extra mathematics learning time (Welner et al. 2008) that focuses on enrichment rather than remediation • Differentiate to meet varying needs of students in the classroom (Christenson and Wager 2012; Gearhart and Saxe 2014)

Amidon and Trevathan (2016) describe a yearlong collaboration to improve practice and raise expectations for Trevathan's middle school mathematics students. Equitable mathematics teachers, like Pietz and Trevathan, express a responsibility to consider how their practice supports student agency and identity; draw on students' cultural, community, and linguistic resources; and recognize that students' access to opportunities to learn in mathematics classrooms is an equity issue (Wager 2014).

Research about beliefs and dispositions that value and honor students' voices, practices, and experience often builds on the ideas of culturally relevant/responsive pedagogy (Ladson-Billings 1995; Gay 2009). An assets-based view starts with the recognition of the inequities students experience in schooling and that the failure to explicitly attend to these inequities makes teachers and schools complicit in perpetuating inequitable systems. In table 9.1, we list some of the supporting practices that teachers enact when they believe all students can learn mathematics. These practices can help overcome three obstacles raised in *PtA*—lack of access to high-quality instruction, low expectations, and negative dispositions toward mathematics—and are discussed in the next two sections.

Pedagogical Practices That Support Students' Mathematical Identity and Agency

Equitable mathematics teachers not only believe in students as equally capable learners and doers of mathematics but also expect all students to participate in rigorous mathematics. "Setting and acting on high expectations and a genuine belief that student effort and effective instruction outweigh 'smarts' and circumstances increase students' opportunities to learn" (NCTM 2014, p. 64). Teachers who believe (and schools that encourage the belief) that all students are capable demonstrate that by engaging in practices that empower all students to have agency in their learning and develop their identity. *Agency* refers to the opportunity for students to take action with respect to their learning (Gresalfi et al. 2009) by participating in mathematics in meaningful and sensible ways (Gresalfi and Cobb 2006; Nasir and Hand 2008). Students who have the oppor-

tunity to participate in mathematical practices that support agency and equal status can "transform how [they] see themselves as mathematical thinkers, how they see the discipline, and ultimately, the mathematics that they learn" (Turner et al. 2013, pp. 228–29). Practices that support student agency include constructing norms for equitable participation, positioning students as capable and competent, and de-tracking schools and classrooms. Dominguez (2016) described four problem-solving strategies that support student agency by allowing them to specify quantities in problems, frame problem questions, pose problems, and interpret representations. Allen and Schnell (2016) and Gutiérrez (2015) provided similar practices for supporting students' identities, including listening to what students are saying and prioritizing their voices.

Establishing Norms for Equitable Participation

A mathematics classroom that provides equitable access for all to learn must be structured to invite participation (Gutiérrez 2012; Hand 2012) by establishing an environment in which students share their ideas, question each other, and respond to teachers' questions (Gresalfi and Cobb 2006). Hand (2012) described one element of inviting participation as fostering dialogic spaces whereby "teachers were attuned to how and when a learner was participating in classroom activity—even by resisting it—and interpreted this meaningful form of participation" (p. 240). In a study of 165 teachers, Jackson and colleagues (2013) identified other norms critical to establishing classrooms in which students were invited to participate. They found that, to provide access, the ways in which tasks were organized needed to include establishment of a common language and a shared expectation that students would provide more than yes or no answers to problems and questions. In a similar vein, Rumsey and Langrall (2016) provided strategies for promoting students' use of argumentation.

One of the things Pietz does in her classroom to establish norms for equitable participation is to develop a community in which students know they are meant to make and learn from mistakes. This type of classroom environment supports students' agency (Turner et al. 2013) and provides space for classroom discussions that build confidence and enable students to develop strong mathematical identities (Hodge 2006). Pietz found this to be true in her class when she hung a banner that stated "Mistakes are expected, respected, and inspected." At the start of the year she pointed it out daily, before students did any sharing of work or thinking. Within a few weeks, students were willing to stand in front of the class to publically share their thinking.

> At the beginning of the year, when a student commented on or ridiculed a mistake, I stepped toward the banner and pointed to it and verbally reminded students that we all will be making mistakes, and it is very important to respect those mistakes. Depending on what was said, I reiterated that it is very important that we create a place where it is safe to make mistakes, because we all are going to make them numerous times throughout the year. Then I asked the student to disagree again but to use respectful language this time. As the year progressed, sometimes all it took was pointing to the banner for them to catch themselves. By the second quarter, when students noticed a peer not respecting mistakes or being concerned about making a mistake, they started stating what was on the banner without prompting from me.

Pietz's interactions with students about their mistakes were similar to the practices that promote effective use of argumentation (Rumsey and Langrall 2016). Further, by developing a norm that mistakes are welcome, Pietz also laid the groundwork for narrowing participation gaps, which are "the differences in the types and rates of participation among groups of students from dominant versus nondominant ethnic, racial, socioeconomic, or linguistic backgrounds" (Hand, Kirtley, and Matassa 2015, p. 262). Her practice provided evidence of the strategies Hand and colleagues suggested to narrow participation gaps: organize students' mathematical contributions; open up what it means to be "smart" in math; and engage students rather than focus on motivating them.

Positioning Students as Capable and Competent

Students are more likely to demonstrate competence when they are treated as competent (Ladson-Billings 1995). Positioning students as capable is not just a mindset but also an explicit practice that requires teachers to purposefully notice and highlight students' strengths rather than attend to what they are lacking. One way to achieve this is to practice the tenets of Complex Instruction (see Featherstone et al. 2011). This approach, in which mathematically rich tasks are designed to be "group-worthy" so that no individual can complete the task alone, highlights students' strengths and makes space to reposition students as capable. Group-worthy tasks are open-ended, require complex problem solving, provide multiple entry points and multiple opportunities to show intellectual competence, deal with mathematically rich content, require interdependence and individual accountability, and include clear criteria for the evaluation of the group's product (Lotan 2003). Group-worthy tasks require all students to be actively involved and work together to build on their different strengths and competencies.

As Civil and Planas (2004) have illustrated, students are well aware of status structures in place that support (or do not support) their participation and learning. Status structures may be school-imposed, such as tracked classes or homogenous groups in de-tracked classrooms, socially imposed by students' group memberships, or societally imposed based on race, gender, language, economic status, or (dis)ability. Thus, it is necessary to give thought to how students take up these structures and to develop practices that debunk them. *PtA* emphasizes the inequities that occur as a result of tracking—in particular the differential opportunities to learn and low expectations associated with the practice (p. 61). Beyond the structures in place, positioning also occurs in interactions between students and between teachers and students as teachers assign competence to some students over others. "Assigning competence is the practice of drawing public attention to a given student's intellectual contribution" (Featherstone et al. 2011, p. 88) and is a way to "help higher-status students appreciate the intellectual contributions of lower-status students" (p. 87). Here, we focus on ways that teachers can address status by positioning students as expert.

Teacher-student interactions that affirm student contributions include revoicing, asking clarifying questions, and soliciting student explanations in ways that legitimize students' expertise (Forman and Ansell 2002). Teachers position students through what Battey (2013) referred to as "relational interactions" that can enable or restrict students' access to math learning. The teacher he worked with enabled access in three ways: by providing a positive framing of students' mathematics ability, acknowledging student contributions through verbal (enthusiastic remarks) and nonverbal (head nods) encouragement, and attending to language and culture by incorporating everyday contexts in word problems (p. 134). In another example of assigning competence, Hand, Kirtley, and Matassa (2015) described how a teacher helped a student engage in a group-worthy task by sharing with the class the way the student set up a problem.

The ways students are positioned (by each other and the teacher) with respect to mathematics competence has a direct impact on students' mathematical identity and therefore access to opportunities to learn (Esmonde 2009; Wager 2014). Students who routinely use ineffective strategies tend to be positioned in negative ways with respect to mathematical competence by both the teacher and fellow students (and themselves). One of the ways Pietz sets up her class to prevent students from positioning one another in negative ways or as low status is to develop a shared practice for redirecting strategies (see fig. 9.1). The chart becomes a way for students to prompt each other to use effective strategies they developed collectively rather than a way to point out when someone's strategy is ineffective. When Pietz has students reflect on how effective strategies support their learning, she is showing them how the choices they make (albeit guided by her) demonstrate how capable they are. These strategies provide differentiated supports so that all students can be successful on the same tasks.

By developing an awareness of the impact of effective and ineffective strategies on mathematical growth and then developing the shared practice for redirecting strategies, the teacher can set up her class to prevent students from positioning one another in negative ways or as low status. All students begin to see themselves and one another as capable. This view then contributes to an environment where it is safe and acceptable to take mathematical risks. Pietz describes one method for encouraging effective problem-solving strategies:

> The first week of school, I do an activity where my classes brainstorm and examine strategies they use when they feel confused or don't understand. Students sort the strategies into effective (get you unstuck) and ineffective (keep you stuck). After compiling the strategies from all my classes, I make a poster and hang it in a prominent place. As I notice students using the ineffective strategies, I point

out the ineffective strategy and have them pick a couple from the effective side that they would be willing to try. As students make the switch to more effective strategies, I have them reflect on how their mathematical understanding grows when they use effective strategies. Throughout the year I have my students reflect on how their strategies have changed and how it has affected their learning.

The students in Pietz's class not only feel confident enough to share their strategies with their classmates, but they are also positioned as competent members of the learning community. Gresalfi and colleagues (2009) challenged the traditional notion of competence as an individual trait to assess and instead offered the idea that competence is an attribute of participation. In their work, they explored how the ways in which participation is structured and tasks are determined can lead to student agency.

Strategies for When I Get Stuck	
EFFECTIVE!!	INEFFECTIVE
Use multiple strategies to solve the problem	Playing w/ pencil,/doodling
Reviews notes and examples	Walking around the room
Raise hand, ask adult for help	Getting frustrated or upset
Re-read the problem	Talking off-task to a peer
Ask a neighbor for help	Putting head down
Persevere!	Sitting and not trying to work

Fig. 9.1. A chart displays students' effective and ineffective strategies "for when I get stuck"

De-tracking Schools and Classrooms

A more systemic way to position students as capable is through de-tracking (see NCTM 2014, p. 61). De-tracking may require schoolwide change but can also happen within a single classroom. Tracked classrooms reinforce the idea that mathematics is attainable for only some people—specifically, white middle-class people (Boaler 2011). In studying de-tracked classrooms, Boaler found that students who had historically been considered "low track" had higher levels of achievement (2002 and 2008), stronger mathematical identities, and a greater sense of agency (2005) when working cooperatively in heterogeneous (de-tracked) classrooms. In the next vignette, Mary Klehr describes what fourth/fifth-grade teacher Carrie does in her classroom to invite all students into the mathematics conversation. In this example, we see how agency is supported as students take on the roles of explaining, justifying, questioning, and making connections (Turner et al. 2013). De-tracked classrooms in which all students feel competent and confident to share these roles provide the opportunity for all to participate equitably. De-tracking serves to counteract the vicious cycle that occurs in tracked classrooms, where student learning is underestimated and students are presented with less challenging work, which results in a decrease in student agency and self-confidence.

> Every morning begins with math in Carrie's classroom when she brings all of her 26 academically and socially diverse fourth- and fifth-graders together and shares a math image [like the one in fig. 9.2] that is accessible to all students and has no clear answer. "What do you notice?" she asks. One at a time, each child shares what she/he notices. This is not about being right or wrong or getting the correct answer; everyone is able to notice something; thus everyone has something to contribute to the conversation.

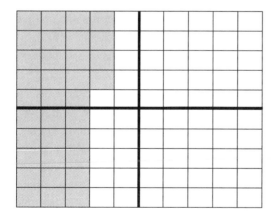

Fig. 9.2. "What do you notice?" example

This practice aligns with what Dominguez (2016) describes as *eliciting students' noticing*, which enables them to see what they already know. This evidence of their competence contributes to student agency.

Instructional Choices That Provide Equitable Access to Learning

In conjunction with the practices discussed above, instructional choices can enhance students' opportunities and access to learning. We focused on the instructional choices that underlie aspects of curricula—the perspective on learning, what or who is included and excluded, and beliefs about what counts as knowledge. We suggest that instructional choices that provide equitable access to learning mathematics build on student thinking; on students' community, cultural, and linguistic resources; and on the Standards for Mathematical Practice (NGA Center and CCSSO 2010). (See also the forthcoming series from NCTM, *Access and Equity: Promoting High-Quality Mathematics*, for preK–grade 2, grades 3–5, grades 6–8, and grades 9–12.)

Building on Students' Mathematical Thinking

Carey et al. (1995) articulated some "universals" about students' mathematical thinking, learning, and practices. An understanding of these universals—that peoples from all cultures use counting and modeling strategies, develop strategies intuitively, and make use of available tools to contextualize and understand their world—supports a growth mindset and, when used in conjunction with other practices discussed here, can lead to equitable mathematics classrooms. Taking these universals and a belief in the importance of learning mathematics with understanding (Hiebert and Carpenter 1992), Carey and colleagues suggested that teachers incorporate into their mathematics teaching the following ideas about students: their culture, the problems they solve informally, and the resources they use to solve problems (Carey et al. p. 98). For younger students, Cognitively Guided Instruction (CGI; Carpenter et al. 2014) can attend to these ideas if it is taken up in a way that also attends to the other practices highlighted in this chapter. Holden (2007) developed a six-step approach for implementing CGI in her first-grade classroom. Her plan was explicitly designed to account for the various needs of all her students. Teachers who engage in CGI plan and enact instruction based on students' thinking and the strategies they are likely to use when solving problems (see Holden 2007 for an example). These tenets also apply when working with older students. (See chapter 8 for more information about building on students' thinking.)

Recognizing and Building on Students' Multiple Mathematical Resources

As has been pointed out for decades, one reason that race, ethnicity, economic status, country of origin, language proficiency, gender, or special learning needs may influence school performance is because schooling, teaching, and assessing are based on white middle-class values (Tate 1995) and fail to represent the practices of students from nondominant backgrounds (Ladson-Billings 1997). To address this, we suggest teachers attend to what Turner and colleagues (2012) refer to as students' multiple mathematical knowledge bases, the "understandings and experiences that have the potential to shape and support children's mathematics learning—including children's mathematical thinking, and children's cultural, home, and community-based knowledge" (p. 67). These knowledge bases include students' understanding of problems, their out-of-school practices, and linguistic and discourse practices. These authors provide some explicit ways to make changes in classroom practice to connect to students' multiple mathematical knowledge bases, including offering choices in problem solving, encouraging multiple representations, and making authentic connections.

To bridge the gap between in- and out-of-school practices, teachers need to make authentic connections to students' lived experiences in ways more meaningful than using assumed experiences and ethnic names in word problems. Ideally, this includes understanding the "deep structures" of students' experiences (Ladson-Billing 1997, p. 700). Connecting to students' lived experiences can also include connecting content to a shared practice in the classroom, as Pietz has done to counter her frustration with mathematics curricula that approach diversity by showing pictures of people from different ethnic backgrounds. In getting beyond problem contexts that remain monoculture, she rewrites the context of the problem but keeps the mathematics content, and she finds that her students became much more engaged and willing to persevere through the

problem. In the vignette below, she describes a familiar problem and how she modified it.

> Two people want to put tiles around their square swimming pool and want to find one or more expressions for the relationship between the side length and the number of tiles. It is a mathematically rich and interesting problem due to the number of possible expressions that can be written and explored for equivalency and the mistakes that arise when considering the corners. I tried to increase engagement by giving manipulatives, by making fancy interactive whiteboard presentations, and by having students act it out. However, year after year, my students were uninterested in the problem. In a school where 90% of the students live in poverty, figuring out tiles for a backyard swimming pool is completely irrelevant. One year, I rewrote the problem and presented it as the school's "Yardening Club" (gardening in the school yard) wanting to add a square goldfish pond to the school yard, and the principal had asked my class to help figure out how many tiles the principal would need to buy to line the pond's perimeter. The size of the pool hadn't been finalized yet, so students needed to come up with expressions that would work no matter what the size of the pool would be. Even though students knew it was a made-up problem, they began discussing the merits of the idea with their partners while trying to find at least one expression to represent the situation. My students then had one of the best discussions of the year, analyzing each other's expressions and determining if they were equivalent. The math content and rigor were the same, but the context made all the difference.

In the above problem, it would have been more authentic if the students were working on a real problem and the goldfish pond was really going to be built or at least recommended to the principal, but it is not always easy to find those contexts, and the one Pietz used was close enough to a relevant situation for her students that they were fully engaged. In other words, teachers do not always have to find a task based on students' cultural experiences but can instead modify curriculum to find a context that has meaning for all students in the class (Wager 2012). Because students may still consider these tasks to reflect mathematical practices connected to schooling, teachers should also bring in individual students' experiences and practices outside of school. To do so, teachers need to know what those mathematical practices are—an undertaking that is not easy given the increasing demands on teacher time and the fact that many teachers have students from multiple ethnic and cultural groups. Ideas for better understanding the kinds of mathematical practices students experience in their homes and communities include doing home visits, interviewing or surveying students and families, attending community events, and participating in professional development to understand others' cultural practices. Gutiérrez (2015) described several ways to "seize the moment" (p. 272) to learn about students beyond the classroom. These activities, including surveys, journals, learning logs, and attending before- and after-school activities, may provide insight into out-of-school (family, community, and cultural) practices. Although this knowledge provides a broader understanding of students' life experiences, mathematizing the activities may be difficult as the actual practice may be lost once brought into school (González et al. 2001; Taylor 2012; Wager 2012). While we recognize the difficulty, we find that these efforts are a fruitful way for students to see their own lives mirrored in the classroom or to provide a window into the lived experiences of other students in their classroom (Gutiérrez 2007).

In addition to building on students' out-of-school experiences, when students' discourse practices and language are recognized as resources rather than something to fix, students not only have greater access to learning, but their cultures are validated (Planas and Civil 2010). For example, a core part of teaching mathematics to English language learners is knowing their language histories and school mathematics histories, yet also understanding that learning mathematics vocabulary is not enough (Moschkovich 2013). Moschkovich outlined several principles for teaching mathematics to English language learners, including focusing on students' mathematical reasoning, rather than accuracy in using language; focusing on mathematical practices, instead of language as single words or vocabulary; recognizing the complexity of language in mathematics classrooms and supporting students in engaging in this complexity; and treating everyday and home languages as resources, not obstacles. Chval and Chávez (2012) provide a similar list of research-based strategies for supporting English language learners' mathematical proficiencies (p. 262). Beyond supporting English language learners, these practices are equitable for all students (Celedon-Patichis and Ramirez 2012). All of these strategies are necessary for students to participate in mathematical discussions and have equitable access to learning.

Building on the Standards for Mathematical Practice

Berry and Ellis (2013) emphasize the importance of attending to cultural contexts when supporting student engagement in the Standards for Mathematical Practice (NGA Center and CCSSO 2010). They make explicit connections between the Standards for Mathematical Practice, NCTM's Process Standards, and the holistic, relational, and contextual characteristics of multi-dimensional mathematics thinking. We caution that supporting the Standards for Mathematical Practice is not enough without explicitly attending to equity; in other words, emphasizing Standards for Mathematical Practice is important but must be done through the other lenses discussed above (Bartell et al. 2017). One way to attend to equity and the Standards for Mathematical Practice is to teach mathematics for social justice through mathematical modeling. Cirillo, Bartell, and Wager (2016) suggest that three features common to mathematical modeling and social justice can open up tasks for students to engage in both ideas. Those features include engaging students in ill-defined problems, leveraging students' real-world knowledge, and raising students' interest.

Interventions on Multiple Levels

PtA identifies the need for explicit interventions that will help students "catch up." Research shows interventions can be done in existing mathematics classrooms with additional time (for example, after school or other times during the day). However, it is important to consider consequences of this type of intervention. If interventions occur during non-math time during the day, what other opportunities are students missing (e.g., art class or recess)? How are students being positioned—is the class obviously for remediation or enrichment? How does this intervention interfere with or support a positive stance toward mathematics—is the intervention reinforcing negative perceptions of mathematics and of the students' mathematical identity? We turn to Pietz's school for an example, where all students in eighth grade either take eighth-grade math or Honors Algebra. However, because so many students are significantly behind in math, Pietz teaches three math intervention classes, which some students take in addition to their eighth-grade math class.

> One class uses a district-mandated, research-based curriculum, meets daily, and either focuses on developing multiplicative reasoning or fractional understanding. The other two meet every other day using a curriculum I created. In the every-other-day intervention classes, I do some pre-teaching and re-teaching. But mostly I analyze where the gaps are in students' mathematical understanding and anticipate when students will need intensive instruction before a concept arises in the daily math class. For example, I discovered that my students in the intervention classes did not have a strong understanding of place value. Two to three weeks before I began teaching scientific notation, I began an intensive study of place value, beginning with numbers larger than 1, to review and solidify what they already understood. Then, we moved to tenths and hundredths, focusing on the connection between how we read a number, write it in expanded form as a fraction, and write it in expanded form as a decimal, using manipulatives to support their thinking. Once students had a strong understanding of tenths and hundredths, they were rapidly able to combine that understanding with what they knew about the place values greater than 1 to understand very small numbers. Then when my classes started scientific notation, they were able to discuss and compare numbers with their peers.

Although Pietz's students received extra mathematics class time and were aware it was different than what other students received, she used this to support their agency and prepare them for class so they could fully participate and be positioned as competent.

On a school level, how could student agency be supported? Klehr's principal is committed to working against tracking and preventing teachers from using a pull-out model—a practice in which students are removed from grade-level classes to do below-grade-level work and are thereby limited to remediation. She looks flexibly and creatively at ways to have more teachers working in individual classrooms, thus lowering student-teacher ratios and providing opportunities for more small-group instruction and individual differentiation. Creating a structure that allows classroom teacher teams to be their own interventionists helps eliminate the inequitable practice of segregating students because of language, achievement, or special education needs (Boaler 2013). This practice encourages collaboration, which supports students' mathematical identities because they are not pulled out of the classroom (Antonovich, Jones, and Hoffman 2012). Klehr makes the following observations about the school.

> Everyone in [this] school works in teams made up of teachers with different licensing areas, such as a regular ed and special ed, or regular ed and ESL, or teachers with dual certifications. This cross-fertilization of licensing areas allows teachers to work closely together around a common group of students, learning with and from each other all year. These teaching teams also engage in weekly coaching sessions to examine and reflect on student work, review resources, and share instructional strategies. Students are brought in for part of these weekly meetings to work through problems or lessons with the coach or one of the teachers while the rest of the team observes and takes notes. These notes are used to identify learning goals and plan the next instructional moves. On a broader scale, cross-team professional development groups meet on a regular basis around curriculum areas such as writing or math, further expanding the intellectual community for classroom teachers and other staff.

This school has success in helping students catch up without tracking or pulling them out of class because they identify ways to differentiate instruction that goes beyond maintaining existing academic differences. More explicit examples of effective, equitable differentiation can be found in research by Gearhart and Saxe (2014), where peers are resources for each other, and Christenson and Wager (2012), where a framework for balanced mathematics instruction provides access and opportunity for all learners to participate. In a similar vein, Nasir and colleagues (2014) described a school-wide framework for equitable mathematics teaching using Complex Instruction.

Conclusion

In 2000, the National Council of Teachers of Mathematics (NCTM 2000) incorporated equity as one of the six *Principles for School Mathematics*—a more explicit reference to equity than was included in the 1989 Standards document. As Martin (2015) pointed out, the same equity message, *mathematics for all,* is now being delineated in *Principles to Actions* (*PtA*) because, despite the well-intentioned solutions that have been offered since equity became a guiding principle, the mathematics education community has yet to address the deep structural issues that continue to result in inequitable outcomes. In this chapter, we have endeavored to provide examples from research, classrooms, and schools of the ideas set forth in *PtA* with respect to equity and access. From our perspective, we need to extend the conversation we started here that responds to the essential element of access and equity in *PtA*. Missing are discussions of critical mathematics pedagogy and how it can be used to understand and challenge the system (Frankenstein 2012; Gutstein 2006; Wager and Stinson 2102); the ways that privilege and oppression play out in math classrooms (Herbel-Eisenmann et al. 2013); explicit attention to race and power (Martin 2009); and the "gender-blind" nature of mathematics and mathematics teaching (Rubel 2016). All of these ideas are salient in the local community in which we work and the mathematics education community globally.

Although *PtA* refers to a growth mindset for teachers, we see a need for systemic attention to assets-based beliefs from multiple perspectives not limited to teachers' views of their work and their students. Rather, assets-based thinking must also be evident in the view of the teaching profession, teachers, and students held by the public and school administrators. Similarly, students must be helped to develop asset-based views of themselves as learners, of their peers, and of their teachers. Toward that end, Pre-K–grade 12 collaboration with higher education in professional development and action research has served to both professionalize the work of teaching and bring value to the role of teachers as researchers. We acknowledge that, taken together, the ideas in this chapter may appear daunting, but without them, we will not attend to the gap in opportunities to learn. Thus, we suggest a recognition that learning to teach equitably takes time, and schools and districts need to invest time and money in teacher learning about equity.

References

Aguirre, Julia, Karen Mayfield-Ingram, and Danny Martin. *The Impact of Identity in K–8 Mathematics: Rethinking Equity-Based Practices*. Reston, Va.: NCTM, 2013.

Aguirre, Julia M., Erin E. Turner, Tonya Gau Bartell, Crystal Kalinec-Craig, Mary Q. Foote, Amy Roth McDuffie, and Corey Drake. "Making Connections in Practice: How Prospective Elementary Teachers Connect to Children's Mathematical Thinking and Community Funds of Knowledge in Mathematics Instruction." *Journal of Teacher Education* 64, no. 2 (2013): 178–92.

Allen, Kasi, and Kemble Schnell. "Developing Mathematics Identity." *Mathematics Teaching in the Middle School* 21, no. 7 (2016): 398–405.

Amidon, Joel C., and Morgan L. Trevathan. "Supporting Mathematics Instruction through Community." *Mathematics Teaching in the Middle School* 21, no. 5 (2016): 288–94.

Antonovich, Jane, Kelly Jones, and Deborah Hoffman. "Eyes on the Prize: A Struggling Wisconsin School Forges a Steady Path toward Academic Achievement." *Journal of Staff Development* 33, no. 1 (2012): 42–45.

Bartell, Tonya Gau. "Caring, Race, Culture, and Power: A Research Synthesis toward Supporting Mathematics Teachers in Caring with Awareness." *Journal of Urban Mathematics Education* 4, no. 1 (2011): 50–74.

Bartell, Tonya G., Margaret R. Meyer, Libby Knott, and Thomas A. Evitts. "Addressing the Equity Principle in the Mathematics Classroom." *Mathematics Teacher* 101, no. 8 (2008): 604–608.

Bartell, Tonya, Anita Wager, Ann Edwards, Dan Battey, Mary Foote, and Joi Spencer. "Research Coomentary: Toward a Framework for Research Linking Equitable Teaching with the Standards for Mathematical Practice." *Journal for Research in Mathematics Education* 48, no. 1 (2017): 7–21.

Battey, Dan. " 'Good' Mathematics Teaching for Students of Color and Those in Poverty: The Importance of Relational Interactions Within Instruction." *Educational Studies in Mathematics* 82, no. 1 (2013): 125–44.

Berry, Robert Q. III, and Mark W. Ellis. "Multidimensional Teaching." *Mathematics Teaching in the Middle School* 19, no. 3 (2013): 172–78.

Bishop, Alan J. "Cultural Conflicts in Mathematics Education: Developing a Research Agenda." *For the Learning of Mathematics* 14, no. 2 (1994): 15–18.

Boaler, Jo. *Experiencing School Mathematics: Traditional and Reform Approaches to Teaching and Their Impact on Student Learning*. New York: Routledge, 2002.

———. "The 'Psychological Prison' from Which They Never Escaped: The Role of Ability Grouping in Reproducing Social Class Inequalities." *Forum* 47, no. 2 (2005): 135–44.

———. "Promoting 'Relational Equity' and High Mathematics Achievement through an Innovative Mixed-Ability Approach." *British Educational Research Journal* 34, no. 2 (2008): 167–94.

———. "Changing Students' Lives Through the De-tracking of Urban Mathematics Classrooms." *Journal of Urban Mathematics Education* 4, no. 1 (2011): 7–14.

———. "Ability and Mathematics: The Mindset Revolution That Is Reshaping Education." *Forum* 55, no. 1 (2013): 143–52.

Carey, Deborah A., Elizabeth Fennema, Thomas P. Carpenter, and Megan L. Franke, "Equity and Mathematics Education." In *New Directions for Equity in Mathematics Education,* edited by Walter G. Secada, Elizabeth Fennema, and Lisa Byrd Adajian, pp. 93–125. Cambridge, U.K.: Cambridge University Press, 1995.

Carpenter, Thomas P., Elizabeth Fennema, Megan Loef Franke, Linda Levi, and Susan Empson. *Children's Mathematics, Second Edition: Cognitively Guided Instruction.* Portsmouth, N.H.: Heinemann, 2014.

Celedon-Pattichis, Sylvia, and Nora G. Ramirez, eds. *Beyond Good Teaching: Advancing Mathematics Education for ELLs.* Reston, Va.: NCTM, 2012.

Christenson, Bridget, and Anita A. Wager. "Increasing Participation through Differentiation." *Teaching Children Mathematics* 19, no. 3 (2012): 194–200.

Chval, Kathryn B., and Óscar Chávez. "Designing Math Lessons for English Language Learners." *Mathematics Teaching in the Middle School* 17, no. 5 (2012): 261–65.

Cirillo, Michelle, Tonya Gau Bartell, and Anita A. Wager. "Teaching Mathematics for Social Justice through Mathematical Modeling." In *Annual Perspectives in Mathematics Education: Mathematical Modeling and Modeling Mathematics,* edited by Christian Hirsh, pp. 87–96. Reston Va.: National Council of Teachers of Mathematics, 2016.

Civil, Marta. "Building on Community Knowledge: An Avenue to Equity in Mathematics Education." In *Improving Access to Mathematics: Diversity and Equity in the Classroom,* edited by Na'ilah Suad Nasir and Paul Cobb, pp. 105–17. New York: Teachers College Press, 2007.

Civil, Marta, and Núria Planas. "Participation in the Mathematics Classroom: Does Every Student Have a Voice?" *For the Learning of Mathematics* 24, no. 1 (2004): 7–12.

Cobb, Paul, and Lynn Hodge. "Culture, Identity, and Equity in Mathematics Classrooms." In *Improving Access in Mathematics: Diversity and Equity in the Classroom,* edited by Na'ilah Nasir and Paul Cobb, pp. 159–72. New York: Teachers College Press, 2007.

Dominguez, Higinio. "Mirrors and Windows into Student Noticing." *Teaching Children Mathematics* 22, no. 6 (2016): 358–65.

Drake, Corey, Tonia J. Land, Tonya Gau Bartell, Julia M. Aguirre, Mary Q. Foote, Amy Roth McDuffie, and Erin E. Turner. "Three Strategies for Opening Curriculum Spaces." *Teaching Children Mathematics* 21, no. 6 (2015): 346–53.

Dweck, Carol S. *Mindset: The New Psychology of Success.* New York: Random House, 2006.

———. "Even Geniuses Work Hard." *Educational Leadership* 68, no. 1 (2010): 16–20.

Esmonde, Indigo. "Mathematics Learning in Groups: Analyzing Equity in Two Cooperative Activity Structures." *Journal of Learning Sciences* 18, no. 2 (2009): 247–84.

Featherstone, Helen, Sandra Crespo, Lisa M. Jilk, Joy A. Oslund, Amy Noelle Parks, and Marcy B. Wood. *Smarter Together! Collaboration and Equity in the Elementary Math Classroom.* Reston, Va.: National Council of Teachers of Mathematics, 2011.

Felton, Mathew D. "Is Math Politically Neutral?" *Teaching Children Mathematics* 17, no. 2 (2010): 60–63.

Fine, Michelle. "Why Urban Adolescents Drop Into and Out of Public High School." *Teachers College Record* 87, no. 3 (1986): 393–409.

Flores, Alfinio. "Examining Disparities in Mathematics Education: Achievement Gap or Opportunity Gap?" *High School Journal* 91, no. 1 (2007): 29–42.

Forman, Ellice Ann, and Ellen Ansell. "Orchestrating the Multiple Voices and Inscriptions of a Mathematics Classroom." *Journal of Learning Sciences* 11, no. 2–3 (2002): 251–74.

Frankenstein, Marilyn. "Beyond Math Content and Process: Proposals for Underlying Aspects of Social Justice Education." In *Teaching Mathematics for Social Justice: Conversations with Educators,* edited by Anita A. Wager and David Stinson, pp. 49–62. Reston, Va.: National Council of Teachers of Mathematics, 2012.

Gay, Geneva. "Preparing Culturally Responsive Mathematics Teachers." In *Culturally Responsive Mathematics Education,* edited by Brian Greer, Swapna Mukhopadhyay, Arthur B. Powell, and Sharon Nelson-Barber, pp. 189–205. New York: Routledge, 2009.

Gearhart, Maryl, and Geoffrey B. Saxe. "Differentiated Instruction in Shared Mathematical Contexts." *Teaching Children Mathematics* 20, no. 7 (2014): 426–35.

Gerdes, Paulus. "On Culture, Geometrical Thinking, and Mathematics Education." *Educational Studies in Mathematics* 19, no. 2 (1988): 137–62.

González, Norma, Rosi Andrade, Marta Civil, and Luis Moll. "Bridging Funds of Distributed Knowledge: Creating Zones of Practices in Mathematics." *Journal of Education for Students Placed at Risk* 6, no. 1–2 (2001): 115–32.

Gresalfi, Melissa Sommerfeld, and Paul Cobb. "Cultivating Students' Discipline-Specific Dispositions as a Critical Goal for Pedagogy and Equity." *Pedagogies* 1, no. 1 (2006): 49–57.

Gresalfi, Melissa, Taylor Martin, Victoria Hand, and James Greeno. "Constructing Competence: An Analysis of Student Participation in the Activity Systems of Mathematics Classrooms." *Educational Studies in Mathematics* 70, no. 1 (2009): 49–70.

Gutiérrez, Rochelle. "Context Matters: Equity, Success, and the Future of Mathematics Education." In *Proceedings of the 29th Annual Meeting of the North American Chapter of the International Group for the Psychology of Mathematics Education,* pp. 1–18. Stateline (Lake Tahoe), Nev.: University of Nevada, Reno, 2007.

———. "Context Matters: How Should We Conceptualize Equity in Mathematics Education?" In *Equity in Discourse for Mathematics Education: Theories, Practices, and Policies,* edited by Beth Herbel-Eisenmann, Jeffrey Choppin, David Wagner, and David Pimm, pp. 28–50. New York: Springer, 2012.

———. "HOLA: Hunt for Opportunities–Learn–Act." *Mathematics Teacher* 109, no. 4 (2015): 270–77.

Gutstein, Eric. *Reading and Writing the World with Mathematics: Toward a Pedagogy for Social Justice*. New York: Routledge, 2006.

Hand, Victoria. "Seeing Culture and Power in Mathematical Learning: Toward a Model of Equitable Instruction." *Educational Studies in Mathematics* 80, no. 1–2 (2012): 233–47.

Hand, Victoria, Karmen Kirtley, and Michael Matassa. "Narrowing Participation Gaps." *Mathematics Teacher* 109, no. 4 (2015): 262–68.

Herbel-Eisenmann, Beth, Tonya Gau Bartell, Mary L. Breyfogle, Kristen Bieda, Sandra Crespo, Higinio Dominguez, and Corey Drake. "Strong Is the Silence: Challenging Interlocking Systems of Privilege and Oppression in Mathematics Teacher Education." *Journal of Urban Mathematics Education* 6, no. 1 (2013): 6–18.

Hiebert, James, and Thomas, P. Carpenter. "Learning and Teaching Mathematics with Understanding." In *Handbook of Research on Mathematics Teaching and Learning,* edited by Doug A. Grouws, pp. 65–97. New York: Macmillan, 1992.

Hodge, Lynn. "An Orientation on the Mathematics Classroom That Emphasizes Power and Identity: Reflecting on Equity Research." *Urban Review* 38, no. 5 (2006): 373–85.

Holden, Becky. "Preparing for Problem Solving." *Teaching Children Mathematics* 14, no. 5 (2007): 290.

Jackson, Kara, Anne Garrison, Jonee Wilson, Lynsey Gibbons, and Emily Shahan. "Exploring Relationships between Setting Up Complex Tasks and Opportunities to Learn in Concluding Whole-Class Discussions in Middle-Grades Mathematics Instruction." *Journal for Research in Mathematics Education* 44, no. 4 (2013): 646–82.

Ladson-Billings, Gloria. "Toward a Theory of Culturally Relevant Pedagogy." *American Educational Research Journal* 32, no. 3 (1995): 465–91.

———. "It Doesn't Add Up: African American Students' Mathematics Achievement." *Journal for Research in Mathematics Education* 28, no. 6 (1997): 697–708.

———. "From the Achievement Gap to the Education Debt: Understanding Achievement in U.S. Schools." *Educational Researcher* 35, no. 7 (2006): 3–12.

Lotan, Rachel A. "Group-Worthy Tasks." *Educational Leadership* 60, no. 6 (2003): 72–75.

Lubienski, Sarah Theule, and Rochelle Gutiérrez. "Bridging the Gaps in Perspectives on Equity in Mathematics Education." *Journal for Research in Mathematics Education* 39, no. 4 (2008): 365–71.

Martin, Danny Bernard. "Hidden Assumptions and Unaddressed Questions in *Mathematics for All* Rhetoric." *Mathematics Educator* 13, no. 2 (2003): 7–21.

———. "Does Race Matter?" *Teaching Children Mathematics* 16, no. 3 (2009): 134–39.

———. "The Collective Black and *Principles to Actions*." *Journal of Urban Mathematics Education* 8, no. 1 (2015): 17–23.

Moschkovich, Judit. "Principles and Guidelines for Equitable Mathematics Teaching Practices and Materials for English Language Learners." *Journal of Urban Mathematics Education* 6, no. 1 (2013): 45–57.

Nasir, Na'ilah Suad, Carlos Cabana, Barbara Shreve, Estelle Woodbury, and Nicole Louie, eds. *Mathematics for Equity: A Framework for Successful Practice*. New York: Teachers College Press, and Reston, Va.: National Council of Teachers of Mathematics, 2014.

Nasir, Na'ilah Suad, and Victoria Hand. "From the Court to the Classroom: Opportunities for Engagement, Learning, and Identity in Basketball and Classroom Mathematics." *Journal of the Learning Sciences* 17, no. 2 (2008): 143–79.

National Council of Teachers of Mathematics (NCTM). *Principles and Standards for School Mathematics*. Reston, Va.: NCTM, 2000.

———. *Principles to Actions: Ensuring Mathematical Success for All*. Reston, Va.: NCTM, 2014.

National Governors Association Center for Best Practices (NGA Center) and Council of Chief State School Officers (CCSSO). *Common Core State Standards for Mathematics*. Washington, D.C.: NGA Center and CCSSO, 2010.

Planas, Núria, and Marta Civil. "Discourse Processes in Critical Mathematics Education." In *Critical Mathematics Education: Past, Present and Future,* edited by Helle Alrø, Ole Ravn, and Paola Valero, pp. 145–59. Rotterdam, the Netherlands: Sense Publishers, 2010.

Rubel, Laurie H. "Speaking Up and Speaking Out about Gender in Mathematics." *Mathematics Teacher* 109, no. 6 (2016): 434–39.

Rumsey, Chepina, and Cynthia W. Langrall. "Promoting Mathematical Argumentation." *Teaching Children Mathematics* 22, no. 7 (2016): 412–19.

Tate, William F. "School Mathematics and African American Students: Thinking Seriously about Opportunities to Learn Standards." *Educational Administrative Quarterly*, 31, no. 3 (1995): 424–48.

Taylor, Edd V. "Supporting Children's Mathematical Understanding: Professional Development Focused on Out-of-School Practices." *Journal of Mathematics Teacher Education* 15, no. 4 (2012): 271–91.

Turner, Erin E., Corey Drake, Amy Roth McDuffie, Julia Aguirre, Tonya Gau Bartell, and Mary Q. Foote. "Promoting Equity in Mathematics Teacher Preparation: A Framework for Advancing Teacher Learning of Children's Multiple Mathematics Knowledge Bases." *Journal of Mathematics Teacher Education* 15, no. 1 (2012): 67–82.

Turner, Erin, Higinio Dominguez, Luz Maldonado, and Susan Empson. "English Learners' Participation in Mathematical

111

Discussion: Shifting Positionings and Dynamic Identities." *Journal for Research in Mathematics Education* 44, no. 1 (2013): 199–234.

Wager, Anita A. "Incorporating Out-of-School Mathematics: From Cultural Context to Embedded Practice." *Journal of Mathematics Teacher Education* 15, no. 1 (2012): 9–23.

———. "Noticing Children's Participation: Insights into Teacher Positionality toward Equitable Mathematics Pedagogy." *Journal for Research in Mathematics Education* 45, no. 3 (2014): 312–50.

Wager, Anita A., and David W. Stinson, eds. *Teaching Mathematics for Social Justice: Conversations with Educators.* Reston, Va.: National Council of Teachers of Mathematics, 2012.

Welner, Kevin, Carol Burris, Ed Wiley, and John Murphy. "Accountability, Rigor, and Detracking: Achievement Effects of Embracing a Challenging Curriculum as a Universal Good for All Students." *Teachers College Record* 110, no. 3 (2008): 571–607.

Chapter 10

"The Right Stuff"
Curriculum to Support the Vision of NCTM and CCSSM

Jill Newton, *Purdue University*
Yvonne Grant, *Michigan State University and Portland (Michigan) Middle School*

A curriculum is more for teachers than it is for pupils. If it cannot change, move, perturb, inform teachers, it will have no effect on those whom they teach. It must be first and foremost a curriculum for teachers. If it has any effect on pupils, it will have it by virtue of having had an effect on teachers.

—Jerome Bruner, *The Process of Education*, p. xv

As Bruner suggests in the quote that opens this chapter, curriculum only has impact insofar as it inspires teachers. Therefore, we address this curriculum chapter to teachers and those who support them (e.g., district leaders, policymakers) in the hopes of empowering stakeholders to make sound curriculum decisions in which students' learning of mathematics is foregrounded. We recommend teacher involvement in every step of the curricular process—adoption, implementation, and evaluation—as no one knows better what is best for their students than those in classrooms with them every day.

The curriculum section in *Principles to Actions: Ensuring Mathematical Success for All* (NCTM 2014) defines curriculum as "the program used to help students meet the standards, including instructional materials, activities, tasks, units, lessons, and assessments" (p. 70). *Principles to Actions* (*PtA*) differentiates the standards from the curriculum by labeling the curriculum as the "means" and the standards as the "end." Therefore, in this chapter we focus on the means—that is, what are the features of curriculum materials and their use that best promote mathematical learning of the

standards for all students? When we speak of standards here, we are referring to both NCTM's Standards as described in a series of documents published over the past four decades (e.g., NCTM 1980, 1989, 2000, 2006, 2009, 2014) and the recently published Common Core State Standards for Mathematics (CCSSM) (NGA Center and CCSSO 2010) currently in use, in some form, by most states.

The good news for those who are committed to the vision of NCTM is that NCTM, along with the National Council of Supervisors of Mathematics (NCSM), the Association of State Supervisors of Mathematics (ASSM), and the Association of Mathematics Teacher Educators (AMTE), has expressed support for CCSSM, stating that "many aspects of the central elements of the CCSS echo the longstanding positions and principles of our organizations" (NCTM, NCSM, ASSM, and AMTE 2010, p. 1). In this chapter, we provide a brief history of mathematics curriculum; discuss teachers' use, development, and selection of curriculum; review research that highlights the complexities of curriculum implementation and evaluation; and describe curriculum-based professional learning experiences for teachers.

Brief History of Curriculum

An excellent mathematics program includes a curriculum that develops important mathematics along coherent learning progressions and develops connections among areas of mathematical study and between mathematics and the real world.

—*Principles to Actions* (NCTM 2014), p. 5

The authors thank Mary Bouck, Kathy Dole, Corey Drake, A. J. Edson, Teri Keusch, Betty Phillips, Barbara Reys, and Megan Staples for reviews of earlier drafts of this manuscript.

John Dewey, in 1916, encouraged teachers to "give the pupils something to do, not something to learn; and the doing is of such a nature as to demand thinking, or the intentional noting of connections; learning naturally results" (p. 181). This call for meaningful activities has been echoed in NCTM's vision, as it supports curriculum that emphasizes attention to mathematical thinking, understanding, and communication and provides students with opportunities that go beyond memorization, symbolic manipulation, and direct teaching of skills. Similarly, Bruner (1966) characterized "knowing" in the following way:

> To instruct someone . . . is not a matter of getting him to commit results to mind. Rather, it is to teach him to participate in the process that makes possible the establishment of knowledge. We teach a subject not to produce little living libraries on that subject, but rather to get a student to think mathematically for himself, to consider matters as an historian does, to take part in the process of knowledge-getting. Knowing is a process, not a product. (p. 72)

Both Bruner and Dewey, and more recently NCTM and CCSSM, made it clear that curriculum has an important task to accomplish: to move students beyond doing mathematics as constructed by others and toward establishing themselves as constructors and meaning makers of mathematics. As NCTM (1989) emphasized, if students have access to this type of learning, they will gain "mathematical power." So, what does curriculum look like that accomplishes these goals, and how can teachers learn to use this curriculum to support student learning?

As early as 1980, NCTM proposed a redesign of mathematics curriculum to focus on a sequencing of "process objectives" as well as content and skill goals. In the classrooms described by NCTM, students would reason about and make sense of problem situations by communicating with others, making connections, and using multiple representations. After the publication of *Curriculum and Evaluation Standards for School Mathematics* (NCTM 1989), the National Science Foundation funded the development of K–grade 12 mathematics curricula to support NCTM's vision; these curricula became known as "Standards-based." This is how we will refer to these curricula, and others that support NCTM's vision, in this chapter. Many textbooks that claim to be aligned to standards are referring, not to the NCTM Standards, but rather to

alignment with state standards and more recently with CCSSM.

To further confuse the matter, other language has been used to reference curricula that serve NCTM's vision—such as *student-centered, inquiry-based, problem-based, or problem-solving* curriculum, to name a few terms. Curriculum researchers have suggested important features of a Standards-based curriculum. For example, Trafton, Reys, and Wasman (2001) suggested that such curricula be comprehensive (i.e., about more than just skills and designed to serve all students) and coherent (i.e., highlight core ideas). They also noted that curricula are designed to develop ideas in depth (i.e., not mile-wide, inch-deep), promote sense making, engage students, and motivate learning. These characteristics can serve as a framework for analysis and selection of curriculum materials and provide guidance for curricular implementation.

Teachers and Curriculum

But only the teacher is there in the classroom, observing and trying to understand her students' mathematical thinking. Individual teachers must continually assess and modify their mathematics program for their own classroom. Thus, curriculum is not a recipe or a compendium of what "should" be taught at a particular grade level. Rather, it provides both a coherent mathematics program for students, based on the best thinking available in the field, and material that supports teachers in making better, more thoughtful, more informed decisions about their students' mathematics learning.

—Susan Jo Russell (1997), p. 248

Much research has focused on teachers' use and interaction with curricula (e.g., Drake 2010; Remillard 2005; Remillard and Bryans 2004; Sherin and Drake 2009). By all accounts, this relationship is complex and varies greatly depending on the teacher, the curriculum, and other factors (e.g., school context). Huntley and Chval (2010) reported that 54 percent of teachers using Standards-based curricula agreed or strongly agreed that "curriculum materials are not prescriptions for practice; rather they are one of many resources teachers turn to for guidance about what content to teach and how to teach it," while 41 percent of the teachers disagreed or strongly disagreed with this statement; this suggests variation among teachers about the role and authority of mathematics curriculum. The need for attention to this variation was emphasized by findings from Stein and Kaufman (2010), which suggested that "how a teacher uses a curriculum may be more important than the education, experience, and knowledge that he or she brings to the table" (p. 688).

Remillard and Bryans (2004) identified a wide range of teacher orientations toward curriculum materials, from little or no use, to using the materials as a guide, to using all suggestions. They found that teachers' orientations had an impact on both their own learning from curricular materials and the opportunities they provided for their students to learn. Sherin and Drake (2009) developed a framework to describe teachers' use of curriculum materials (i.e., a curriculum strategy) with three dimensions: "*reading*, involving a focus on the general outline of a lesson or on the details of a lesson; *evaluating*, involving a focus on students, teachers, or others; and *adapting*, involving creating, replacing, or omitting activities or materials" (p. 490). Their findings suggest that individual teachers maintain a particular curriculum strategy over time. Teachers reported a wide range of methods by which they develop and/or modify curriculum materials, including altering the sequence of topics in the textbooks, omitting topics, and supplementing their curriculum with other resources (Huntley and Chval 2010). Drake (2010) further detailed teachers' supplemental strategies, including the reasons for supplementing, selection of resources, method and duration (e.g., replace, use side by side, integrate), and assessment and reflection. The variation in curricular use by teachers suggests that district and school leaders involved in enhancing curriculum implementation in schools may benefit by surveying teachers concerning both the nature of use and their beliefs about the role of curriculum as they plan professional learning experiences.

Developing Curriculum

In his Curriculum Research Framework, Clements (2007) suggested that the curriculum development process should include ten phases. He classified the phases into three categories for developing research-based instructional materials: drawing from what is known

from existing research; structuring and revising the nature and content of the curriculum components based on children's thinking and learning; and conducting formative and summative evaluations of the effectiveness of the materials (p. 37). Given the many other demands facing teachers and district personnel, these recommendations put the creation of curriculum beyond the scope of most districts and teachers. However, teachers are attempting to do this work; in fact, a survey administered by the Center on Education Policy (Rentner and Kober 2014) reported that more than 80 percent of the districts surveyed were developing curricular materials aligned with the Common Core State Standards locally (by teachers and/or district administrators). Furthermore, 90 percent of responding districts indicated that this work posed a major (45 percent) or minor (45 percent) challenge.

Rather than developing curriculum, teachers should be able to focus their efforts on quality implementation of curriculum. That is, teachers should allocate their time to lesson design, including identifying appropriate learning goals and worthwhile mathematical tasks, engaging students with mathematical content, establishing an environment to both challenge and support students, and assessing students' sense making (Lappan 1997; NCTM 2009; Weiss and Pasley 2004). In a recent survey, teachers described four specific needs as critical to ensuring successful implementation of the Common Core State Standards: instructional materials aligned to the Common Core (86 percent); quality professional development (84 percent); additional planning time (78 percent); and opportunities to collaborate with one another (78 percent) (Scholastic Inc. and the Bill and Melinda Gates Foundation 2014). One elementary teacher respondent noted, "We don't have enough time to search, revise, and align lessons for all of the classes we teach every day" (p. 16). School leaders can support teachers' efforts by providing materials and professional learning opportunities to address the components of quality lessons.

Making Curriculum Decisions

A consideration when selecting curriculum materials must be the district and state expectations for a grade level in conjunction with the development of students' knowledge across the grades. Currently, standards are the primary means of communicating these expectations; as *PtA* emphasized, the standards are the "end" and the curriculum is the "means." However, the alignment of standards to curriculum materials must be carefully assessed. Materials should be "a coherent sequencing of core mathematical ideas that are well articulated within and across grades and courses" (NCTM 2014, p. 72). In a survey of more than 400 middle school mathematics teachers, which asked questions about CCSSM, participants perceived a need to adopt textbooks to reflect the changes in standards. "In the absence of these materials, more than 60% of teacher respondents to a 2013 survey reported that they are 'regularly accessing online resources to supplement their existing textbooks'" (Davis et al. 2013, p. 2). When evaluating materials, consideration should be given not only to how the materials support development of content standards, but also to the standards for mathematical practice. That is, do the materials provide opportunities for students to engage in tasks that require problem solving and reasoning, participate in meaningful discussions of mathematics, and build fluency through conceptual understanding? In addition, curriculum materials should provide opportunities for teacher learning (see Ball and Cohen 1996; Davis and Krajcik 2005). Remillard (2000) suggested materials that create learning opportunities for teachers are those that foster analysis of mathematical tasks, student thinking, and decisions about how to proceed with instruction. Others agree that curriculum materials can support teachers' learning as they read and analyze those materials, enact and then reflect on the materials, and as they discuss and adapt the materials with their colleagues (Choppin 2009; Collopy 2003; Grossman and Thompson 2008).

Many factors influence mathematics textbook adoption (Mark et al. 2010; Seeley 2003). After interviewing more than 150 K–grade 12 mathematics curriculum decision makers from districts in eight states, Mark and colleagues (2010) identified five of the most influential factors in choosing textbooks: alignment with state standards; committee review of textbook quality; additional sources of data (relevant literature, knowledgeable and trusted sources, advice from similar districts, results from piloting); teachers' acceptance; and advocacy (for a particular textbook or selection criteria) by the curriculum leader.

Teachers and district leaders can also access resources for help making informed textbook choices. Tarr and colleagues (2006) offer three areas of focus:

- Mathematics content emphasis: Does the textbook include mathematics concepts that are developmentally appropriate, challenging, and accessible for all students?

- Instructional focus: Are students *doing* mathematics? Stated differently, is there significant "mathematical activity" required of all students?

- Teacher support: Do support materials have the potential to enhance the quality of mathematics instruction? (p. 54)

Hudson, Lahann, and Lee (2010) reinforced these key foci and proposed additional important factors to consider when adopting a textbook: instructional design (challenging tasks that provide a balance of procedural knowledge and conceptual understanding), content emphasis (topics presented in depth and aligned to standards), support for students' learning (a framework for learning that provides opportunities to differentiate), support for teachers' learning (support for instructional decisions and pedagogical support), school and district considerations (support for local needs and values), and research on curricular outcomes and effectiveness (research on efficacy and implementation of materials). Hudson and colleagues also provide a rubric for textbook selection and recommended resources in their chapter. The National Council of Supervisors of Mathematics likewise offers a guide focused on the standards for mathematical practice, grade level content, equity, technology, and assessment to assist in curricular selection for districts looking to adopt materials aligned to CCSSM (NCSM 2011).

Curriculum selection offers opportunities for districts to improve both mathematics teaching and learning for their students, according to former NCTM President Diane Briars. In her November 2014 president's message "Curriculum Materials Matter: Evaluating the Evaluation Process," Briars offered her "Top Lessons Learned" about effective curriculum materials evaluation. She proposed that curriculum selection is one of the most important decisions made by a teacher, school, or district. "Curriculum leaders should view the selection of textbooks as an opportunity to improve and bring coherence to their district's mathematics program" (Mark et al. 2010, p. 209). The process of selection can serve as a rich professional learning experience for teachers and administrators alike, providing an opportunity to create a shared vision, expand teachers' knowledge of mathematics, and further the discussion of quality teaching and learning. In spite of extant research and recommendations related to selecting mathematics curriculum, these decisions are complex, in part, because the curricular options are many and they vary greatly. Next, we provide a summary of research related to the implementation and effectiveness of particular types of curriculum.

Standards-based Curriculum Implementation and Evaluation

The committee [Committee for a Review of the Evaluation Data on the Effectiveness of NSF-Supported and Commercially Generated Mathematics Curriculum Materials] recognizes the complexity and urgency of the challenge the nation faces in establishing effectiveness of mathematics curricula, and argues that we should avoid seemingly attractive, but oversimplified, solutions.

—National Research Council (2004), p. 10

Based on our review of research related to different types of curricula, there is not a simple or straightforward message or obvious best choice; instead, the messages are complex and contextualized. Stein, Remillard, and Smith (2007) provided a foundational starting point, indicating that curricula differ in significant ways; that these differences have an impact on student learning; that no curriculum is self-enacting; that Standards-based curricula are challenging to enact well; and that the success of Standards-based curricula is influenced by multiple factors (pp. 360–61).

Kilpatrick (2003) characterized the early evidence about the effectiveness of Standards-based curricula as "promising and substantial" and concluded the following:

Students studying from Standards-based curricula do as well as students studying from traditional curricula on standardized mathematics tests and other measures of traditional content. They score higher than those who have studied from traditional curricula on tests of newer content

and processes highlighted in the Standards document. (p. 472)

Kilpatrick goes on to highlight the difficulties evaluating the impact of something as complex as curriculum. In more recent research (limited to those published since 2003), this trend continues—promising results for Standards-based curricula, with cautionary tales about the challenges of curricular evaluation. Stein and Smith (2010) used the temporal phases of curriculum use (written curriculum, intended curriculum, enacted curriculum, and students' learning) and the transformations both within and across these phases to account for complexities of curricular evaluation. Many studies connect the written curriculum to students' learning without much more than a nod to the two middle phases (intended and enacted curricula); this may make describing the results less complex, but likely does not provide the whole story. In fact, Stein and Smith (2010) state that, to their knowledge, a study has never been published that traced curriculum through all four phases. Smith and Star (2007) echo the challenges of studying curriculum, including those related to conceptualization, methodology, and analytic issues.

Studying Curricular Impact

We analyzed six studies that investigated the impact of Standards-based curricula, comparing the curricula studied, instrument(s) used, and findings. (See table 10.1 for details about the studies.) Just from these studies, there is much to unpack.

Grouws and colleagues (2013) and Shafer (2014) reported higher achievement for students using Standards-based curricula on all types of items, and Shafer noted that the positive results were enhanced over time. In two additional studies, students using Standards-based curricula performed better on open-ended items and those measuring conceptual understanding, problem solving, and higher-level thinking. The students using Standards-based curricula in the Tarr and colleagues (2008) study also performed better in these areas, but only if the curriculum was accompanied by a Standards-based learning environment in their classrooms.

The Tarr and colleagues (2008) and Cai and colleagues (2011) studies reported no overall difference

Table 10.1
Summary of recent studies of Standards-based curricula

Author(s)	Curricula	Instruments	Findings
Tarr et al. (2008)	Standards-based Connected Mathematics Mathematics in Context MathThematics "Publisher-developed" Addison-Wesley Glencoe Mathematics Harcourt Brace Houghton Mifflin Saxon Southwestern	Balanced Assessment in Mathematics TerraNova Survey	• No significant difference in achievement between middle school students in classrooms using Standards-based curricula and those using "publisher developed" textbooks on either assessment. • When students used a Standards-based curriculum and experienced a "standards-based learning environment," the positive results were significant on the Balanced Assessment in Mathematics.
Post et al. (2008)	Standards-based Connected Mathematics MathThematics	Stanford 9	• Students' achievement on the Stanford 9 subtests with open-ended and problem solving items was greater than the national average while scores on subtests with items focused on mathematical procedures were lower than the national average. • Students in high-SES, native-English-speaker, and white groups outperformed their peers in other groups.
Cai et al. (2011)	Standards-based Connected Mathematics "Traditional" Glencoe Mathematics	Research team-developed (multiple choice and open-ended items to measure students' high-level thinking skills, procedural knowledge and problem-solving skills)	• Students using the Standards-based curriculum demonstrated greater gains in conceptual understanding and comparable gains on procedural tasks. • All ethnic groups showed more growth on open-ended tasks when using the Standards-based curriculum. • The Standards-based curriculum had a positive impact on the Hispanic and white students and a negative impact on the African American students and on procedural tasks.
Grouws et al. (2013)	Integrated/Standards-based Core-Plus Mathematics Subject Specific Glencoe Algebra 1 McDougal Littell Algebra 1 Holt Rinehart & Winston Algebra 1 Prentice Hall Algebra 1	Research team-developed: Test of Common Objectives Problem Solving and Reasoning Test Iowa Test of Educational Development	• Students using the integrated curriculum performed significantly better than students who studied from the subject-specific curricula on the Test of Common Objectives, Problem Solving and Reasoning Test, and the Iowa Test of Educational Development.

Table 10.1
Summary of recent studies of Standards-based curricula

Author(s)	Curricula	Instruments	Findings
Remillard, Harris, and Agodini (2014)	Standards-based Investigations in Number, Data, and Space "Blended" Math Expressions "Traditional" Saxon Math Scott Foresman–Addison Wesley Mathematics	Early Childhood Longitudinal Study-Kindergarten Class of 1998–1999 (ECLS-K)	• Students using *Math Expressions*, a curriculum that blends an NCTM Standards-based approach with explicit instruction, outperformed students using the Standards-based curriculum and the two more traditional curricula in both grades. • The broad mathematical emphasis, blended instructional approach, and teacher guidance provided by *Math Expressions* was beneficial. • The ambitious nature of both the mathematics and instruction presented in *Investigations* (the Standards-based curriculum) and its limited emphasis on procedural fluency may be the reasons for the lower achievement of students using this curriculum. • The procedural nature and lack of intellectual challenge of the more traditional curricula may account for lower student achievement.
Shafer (2014)	Standards-based Mathematics in Context "Conventional" (not named)	Two research team-developed: one to measure performance on multiple-choice and open response tasks used by national and international samples of middle-school students and one to measure conceptual and procedural knowledge; making connections, finding patterns and relationships; and mathematical modeling, analysis, and generalization	• The Standards-based curriculum had an overall positive impact on students' learning of mathematics. • The positive curricular impact was enhanced as students and teachers became more familiar with the curriculum over time.

on procedural items between the groups, which is consistent with prior research. However, the students in the Post and colleagues (2008) study did not perform as well as the national average on procedural items, and Cai and colleagues (2011) reported that results on procedural items varied across racial groups. Remillard and colleagues (2014) found that students using *Math Expressions*, a blended curriculum, performed better than students using either a Standards-based curriculum or more traditional curricula. Several authors pointed to challenges of evaluating curricular effectiveness, including development of instruments, accounting for classroom implementation, and school policies and contexts (Post et al. 2008; Shafer 2014).

Researchers have also suggested that we look beyond student achievement in order to get a broader sense of the impact of Standards-based curriculum (e.g., affective outcomes, problem posing, and conceptions of mathematics). Smith and Star (2007) investigated student achievement, affective outcomes, and the relationships between these two dimensions. They proposed situating student outcomes within their individual experiences to explain relationships between attitudes toward mathematics and mathematical achievement. Cai and colleagues (2013) suggested the use of problem posing (students generating mathematical problems) to measure the impact of a Standards-based curriculum as an alternative to the narrow focus in many studies on student achievement data. The authors found that students using a Standards-based curriculum did at least as well on problem posing as students using a more traditional curriculum. Star and Hoffman (2005) examined students' conceptions of mathematics and found that students using a Standards-based curriculum expressed more sophisticated conceptions of mathematics. The mean response from students using a Standards-based curriculum was greater than the 90th percentile on the Usefulness Scale, which included items such as "Students need mathematics for their future work" and "Mathematics is a worthwhile subject for students."

This review of research suggests a complex picture of curricular effectiveness, including many factors that may contribute to results (e.g., teaching experience, school context, curricular implementation), variation of results on different types of items and with different groups of students, and a range of suggested ways to measure effectiveness (e.g., achievement tests, affective measures, conceptions of mathematics). We turn now to recommendations for curriculum-based professional learning experiences for teachers.

Curriculum-based Professional Learning

Teachers, and those who support teachers, need time—time to learn, time to figure out what reform might mean for their school, time for reformers to build support among administrators and the community, and time to reflect on their attempts to carry out reforms.

—Glenda Lappan (1997), pp. 207–208

Adopting coherent, connected curriculum materials with aligned assessments is not enough; teachers need professional learning opportunities to develop a rich understanding of the curriculum and related standards. In a study that analyzed teachers' instruction and development during a district-wide implementation of mandated curriculum, Stein, Kaufmann, and Kisa (2014) found that "quality was, by far, the most difficult thing to achieve, suggesting that mandates alone cannot dictate transformations of practice. Given that such transformations require teacher learning, additional investments in the professional development of teachers appears to be required" (p. 365).

Teachers who engage in activities with curriculum can become more comfortable with the implementation of the curriculum, increase their understanding of mathematics content, and use this learning to enhance student achievement (Choppin 2011; Collopy 2003; Grossman and Thompson 2008; Gulamhussein 2013; Patel et al. 2012; Remillard 2000; Remillard and Taton forthcoming; Stein and Kaufman 2010). For example, Patel and colleagues (2012) evaluated middle school teachers' knowledge before and after a forty-hour workshop using *Connected Mathematics 2* as their primary resource. Results indicated that the teachers significantly increased both their content knowledge and their skills in problem solving and reasoning as a result of the professional learning experience. After conducting a study to investigate the use of curriculum to enhance student learning, Collopy (2003) suggested that "curriculum materials could be an attractive option for supporting teacher learning on a wide scale because they might offer ongoing support that is intimately connected with practice" (p. 306).

In an effort to synthesize the relationships among various curricular constructs important to guide teachers' work, Breyfogle, Roth McDuffie, and Wohlhuter (2010) developed a framework connecting the knowledge of content and curriculum (Ball, Thames, and Phelps 2008) with curricular reasoning (Roth McDuffie and Mather 2009), curricular vision (Darling-Hammond et al. 2005), and curricular trust (Drake and Sherin 2009). They described curricular reasoning as "the thinking processes that teachers engage in as they work with curriculum materials to plan, implement, and reflect on instruction" (p. 308)—including analyzing, mapping, and reflecting as its primary components. From their perspective, curricular reasoning generates curricular vision (how teachers view curriculum in relation to their students) and influences the development of curricular trust (belief that the curriculum, as written, will support the mathematical goals conceived in the vision).

To stimulate thinking around planning, implementing, and reflecting on curriculum materials, Breyfogle and colleagues (2010) identified three processes for teachers to engage in to enhance curricular reasoning: analyzing curriculum materials from learners' perspectives; mapping learning trajectories; and reflecting on and revising plans. In addition to providing a useful framework for teachers and district leaders developing curriculum-based professional learning experiences, these processes can be implemented regardless of the materials chosen by a district. In the sections that follow, we describe this framework and possible related activities for curriculum-focused professional learning experiences. As *PtA* defines curriculum as "the program used to help students meet the standards, including instructional materials, activities, tasks, units, lessons, and assessments" (p. 70), we have added a section focused on assessing students' learning. We have also added a possible plan for implementing curriculum-based professional learning experiences. Even teachers and district leaders who do not adopt new materials can shape professional learning opportunities to enhance the elements and effectiveness of their current curriculum.

Analyzing Curriculum Materials from Learners' Perspectives

Using the strategies in Smith and Stein's (2011) *5 Practices for Orchestrating Productive Mathematics Discussions*, a professional development leader can simulate classroom practices to help focus a teacher on how a student might interact with the curriculum materials. A mathematical goal, a task from the curriculum materials, and sample student work are useful for this activity. As a first step, the teachers should articulate how the task addresses the mathematical goal and decide what the expectations are for all students. Then, using these resources, teachers could work through the following five steps, then participate in a small-group sharing session for continued generation of ideas, followed by a whole-group discussion.

1. Anticipate: Teachers do the task and then, imagine how different students might solve the same problem. It is important to anticipate diverse strategies and ways of thinking about the mathematics.

2. Monitor: Teachers are given samples of student work. While analyzing the work, teachers note solutions, strategies, and interpretations of the task. Also, teachers generate possible questions that could probe the thinking of each student or small group of students who generated the work.

3. Select: Imagining that the student work represents the work of their own students, teachers decide which student or small group of students would present their thinking to the whole class. Teachers record the selections with a rationale for why and how the thinking of the student(s) can promote the mathematical goal(s) of the lesson.

4. Sequence: After presenters of student thinking are selected, teachers need to decide the order of presentation. Who would present first, second, third, etc.? What is your rationale for choosing that order? How will the order of ideas facilitate the building of the desired mathematical thinking?

5. Connect: In anticipation of students hearing the thinking of others, it is now the teachers' task to plan questions. These questions should encourage students to connect the strategies or ways of think-

ing together. Does the work contain mathematical generalizations, patterns, or structure that could be drawn out with strategic questions?

Analyzing tasks and examples of student work and practicing how they might respond to students can help teachers imagine and plan for students' immersion in the curriculum.

Mapping Learning Trajectories

Mapping the horizontal alignment (within a grade level) of the curriculum helps ensure that all teachers share an understanding of the mathematics to be taught, including the big mathematical ideas to be addressed and how those ideas will be developed over a school year. Mapping mathematical curriculum across grade levels (vertical alignment) can confirm that the curriculum builds mathematical understanding without gaps or overlap over the course of several years. Teachers need to know when and how students have opportunities to begin learning a mathematical concept, explore the concept in depth, and use/extend the concept and related skills to approach new mathematics. Breyfogle and colleagues (2010) suggested the following questions to promote the study of the scope and sequence of a topic:

- When are students first introduced to the topic?

- What relationships are students expected to learn?

- What procedures are important to the topic?

- What models are used to represent the topic? (p. 315)

One way to approach this discussion in a professional learning experience is to select a mathematical topic (e.g., fractions) and map its development within the curriculum across grades to identify gaps and redundancies. For example, teachers would begin in grade level groups by creating posters with answers to the following questions: What do you expect students to know about this topic when they enter your grade level? What will students learn about this topic while in your grade level? Based on what they learned in your grade level, what should they learn next (in the subsequent grade level)? These posters can then be displayed in order of grade level, examined, and discussed. This type of mapping is also helpful beyond specific topics

and can be used to examine the development of big ideas (e.g., ratio/proportion) or standards for mathematical practice (e.g., problem solving) across grade levels.

Reflecting on and Revising Plans

"Becoming a reflective practitioner is necessary for continually improving practice" (Breyfogle et al. 2010, p. 312). To encourage teachers' consideration of the impact of a mathematics lesson, Breyfogle and colleagues suggested investigating questions such as these:

- Did the materials and sequence of tasks support my students in meeting the lesson goals?

- Did I effectively anticipate my students' needs in preparing them to engage in the tasks?

- Did I sequence and connect ideas in the materials to solidify learning and prepare for future lessons? (p. 312)

These questions help teachers consider their lesson design from multiple perspectives. Teachers and leaders across the United States are establishing professional learning communities to more formally collaborate on the design of and reflection on lessons using adaptations of the lesson study model from Japan. In recent years, much has been written about the benefits of the lesson study approach, including the rich learning experiences it provides for teachers and, as a result, their students.

As explained in the case study by Takahashi (2014), teachers, lead teachers, administrators, and supporting personnel first work to develop and implement a research lesson. Teachers carefully study their materials, focusing on the key elements of the lesson and why students need to understand them, then work in collaborative groups over a period of weeks to design a lesson plan. Teachers implement the research lesson while the collaborators observe the teaching. A post-lesson discussion follows immediately after the lesson. The discussion is structured to consist of groups or individuals (including an invited knowledgeable "other") sharing ideas about the lesson, which are summarized by another individual. The discussion focuses on how the shared lesson plan can be improved. A representative from the group is responsible for making sure that issues raised in the discussion are addressed in the next lesson. This model has served to support new learning, collaboration, and the development of teacher leadership. Takahashi pushes us to consider how lesson study can benefit teachers beyond those on the planning team, stating, "Lesson study can be powerful even for teachers who just observe the research lesson and participate in the post-lesson discussion" (pp. 438–39).

Assessing Student Learning

Development of assessments is not addressed explicitly in the curricular reasoning framework; however, *PtA* (NCTM 2014) includes assessment as an important curricular component. Many school districts are using analysis of standardized test data as one way to assess what is learned in classrooms. Teachers might use more intimate analyses to study their students' learning by analyzing student work samples. By analyzing, using, creating, or adapting assessments embedded in curriculum materials, developing accompanying rubrics, and then testing the items with students, teachers can gain insights into student thinking and curriculum development. Many teachers are also experimenting with ways to enhance the quality and quantity of the exhibition of student thinking in their classroom. These teachers use typical paper and pencil tests, but they are also trying alternative strategies such as partner quizzes (students working in pairs to answer more challenging assessment questions), student presentations (students prepare and deliver a summary of learning), student video demonstrations (students create a video to show evidence of mathematical understanding), projects (students perform and describe an experiment or challenge that models their learning), summary posters (students generate a display that summarizes the concepts and procedures learned in a unit of study), and student interviews (teachers interview students to hear them express ideas). Teachers using strategies like these are gaining both formative and summative assessment information beyond the data gleaned from traditional homework, quizzes, and tests.

Preparing for Curriculum-based Professional Learning

Too often, professional learning opportunities and district initiatives are not directly tied to the school curriculum. Teachers may not readily see an overlap between the initiative and their curriculum, lessening the chance that both the curriculum and the initiative will receive the needed attention in the classroom. As new ideas related to mathematical teaching and learning are shared with teachers, integrating the ideas into their current curriculum during professional learning experiences will help teachers find more immediate ways to implement the new ideas in the classroom. Curriculum-based professional learning should not be a one-and-done experience for teachers. Teachers and teacher leaders should be involved in developing priorities, organizing the activities, and evaluating the experiences. Moreover, the learning opportunities should be ongoing.

Table 10.2 presents a plan of action for supporting the ongoing professional learning of teachers as they work to implement curriculum and assess the impact of the curriculum on student learning. The action plan was informed by mathematic education research and policy recommendations related to establishing a plan for student learning (Clements and Sarama 2004; Daro, Mosher, and Corcoran 2011; NCTM 2000, 2014) and analyzing student learning (Arbaugh et al. 2006; Jacobs, Lamb, and Philipp 2010; Wiliam 2007). The proposed action plan can—

- be used by teachers at any level and with any type of curriculum materials;

- offer opportunities for teachers to analyze their use of curriculum and to collaborate with colleagues about their teaching;

- help teachers and leaders articulate and establish a plan for developing professional norms;

- promote an ongoing, shared conversation with common understandings about the school curriculum; and

- serve as a guide for implementing curriculum and assessing the impact of the curriculum on student learning.

Summary

Curriculum resources are tools in the hands of professionals. They cannot replace teachers or quality teaching; moreover, they cannot create professional expertise in schools. Instead, when curriculum resources are well designed and appropriately selected and used, they serve as valuable tools that can enhance professional expertise.

—Janine Remillard and Joshua Taton (forthcoming)

Mathematics curriculum is not a magic bullet—nor is anything else. Teaching and learning mathematics are complex endeavors and should be treated as such. However, curriculum matters in a variety of important ways

Table 10.2
An action plan for curriculum-based professional learning

CURRICULUM WORK	QUESTIONS TO GUIDE A COLLABORATIVE CONVERSATION AMONG COLLEAGUES
MAP GOALS	What do we want students to know at the end of this unit? ("Know" means that they can demonstrate learning in some way.) • What are major ideas and/or learning goals for students? • What are minor ideas? • What are the extended learning ideas?
ALIGN TO STANDARDS	What do the state/national standards say that students should know about these ideas/concepts/skills? • Did we miss anything? • Do we need to add anything to our list?
UNIT OUTLINE AND PLANNING	Where do the unit goals, as mentioned by the authors of the curriculum materials, match the ideas/concepts/skills mentioned above? • What in the unit, and when, do we need to emphasize for students to learn the ideas/concepts/skills indicated above? How can we connect to prior learning? • What is the essential vocabulary to develop?
DEVELOP AND ANALYZE COMMON ASSESSMENTS	What are the essential assessment questions/challenges that achieve demonstration of the knowledge? • Are we giving students sufficient opportunities to show us what they know? • Do the level of questions match the level of ideas? (That is, do most questions focus on the major ideas with less attention to the minor or bonus ideas?)
DEVELOP A COMMON EVALUATION TOOL	How will I rate/score/grade based on the major/minor importance of goals? • What are the important ideas? As an example: Labeling the answer does not have the same "weight" as correctly solving a number sentence. How will I communicate to students (and parents) what has been learned?
ANALYZE STUDENT WORK	What can our students do? Does their work or their assessment results show evidence of learning the goals mentioned above? • If so, how do we repeat that level of learning for other students? • If so, can we increase the level of learning? How? • If not, what can we do differently to assist students' learning?
VERTICAL ALIGNMENT	How do we connect to what is taught in the grade levels above and below? • Is there an overlap with any of the concepts? • Do we have gaps in the development of any concepts? • Do we use the same materials? Same vocabulary?

Note. This action plan was developed by Yvonne Grant for use in teacher professional learning and collaboration.

and therefore deserves the attention of teachers, teacher leaders, administrators at all levels, state leaders, mathematics educators, and researchers. In this chapter, we have provided information about the current nature of curriculum, the language and constructs used to define and describe curriculum, curricular research that tells a complicated story about the role and use of curriculum materials to improve student learning outcomes, and possible frameworks to use for selecting curriculum and planning related professional learning experiences.

Ultimately, teachers and school administrators have the responsibility to make important and challenging curricular decisions, including which textbooks to adopt and which mathematical activities and tasks aligned with CCSSM to use, how to plan lessons that promote higher-level mathematical thinking, and how to assess student learning. There is no current shortage of individuals and groups with opinions about how these decisions should be made; however, in addition to the tools we have suggested in previous sections, we support former NCTM President Diane Briars in her plea to keep students' learning of mathematics central when making these decisions. No one knows your students better than you do. What do they need to know and be able to do, mathematically? How do you want them to think about mathematics, its relevance, and its purpose, when they leave your classroom? And, perhaps most important, how do you want them to feel about themselves as doers and constructors of mathematics? These are certainly not easy questions, but their complex answers may shed light on important considerations when making curricular decisions.

References

Arbaugh, Fran, John Lannin, Dustin L. Jones, and Meredith Park-Rogers. "Examining Instructional Practices in Core-Plus Lessons: Implications for Professional Development." *Journal of Mathematics Teacher Education* 9, no. 6 (2006): 517–50.

Ball, Deborah Loewenberg, and David K. Cohen. "Reform by the Book: What Is—or Might Be—the Role of Curriculum Materials in Teacher Learning and Instructional Reform?" *Educational Researcher* 25, no. 9 (1996): 6–8, 14.

Ball, Deborah Loewenberg, Mark Hoover Thames, and Geoffrey Phelps. "Content Knowledge for Teaching: What Makes It Special?" *Journal of Teacher Education* 59, no. 5 (2008): 389–407.

Breyfogle, M. Lynn, Amy Roth McDuffie, and Kay A. Wohlhuter. "Developing Curricular Reasoning for Grades Pre-K–12 Mathematics Instruction." In *Mathematics Curriculum: Issues, Trends, and Future Directions*, edited by Barbara J. Reys, Robert E. Reys, and Rita Rubenstein, pp. 307–20. Reston, Va.: National Council of Teachers of Mathematics, 2010.

Briars, Diane. J. "Curriculum Materials Matter: Evaluating the Evaluation Process." National Council of Teachers of Mathematics, President's Messages. November 2014. https://www.nctm.org/News-and-Calendar/Messages-from-the-President/Archive/Diane-Briars/Curriculum-Materials-Matter_-Evaluating-the-Evaluation-Process/

Bruner, Jerome. *Toward a Theory of Instruction.* Cambridge, Mass.: Harvard University Press, 1966.

———. *The Process of Education.* 2nd ed. Cambridge, Mass.: Harvard University Press, 1977.

Cai, Jinfa, John C. Moyer, Ning Wang, Stephen Hwang, Bikai Nie, and Tammy Garber. "Mathematical Problem Posing as a Measure of Curricular Effect on Students' Learning." *Educational Studies in Mathematics* 83 (2013): 57–69.

Cai, Jinfa, Ning Wang, John C. Moyer, Chuang Wang, and Bikai Nie. "Longitudinal Investigation of the Curricular Effect: An Analysis of Student Learning Outcomes from the Lie-Cal Project in the United States." *International Journal of Educational Research* 50 (2011): 117–36.

Choppin, Jeffrey. "Curriculum-Context Knowledge: Teacher Learning from Successive Enactments of a Standards-Based Mathematics Curriculum." *Curriculum Inquiry* 39, no. 2 (2009): 287–320.

———. "Learned Adaptations: Teachers' Understanding and Use of Curriculum Resources." *Journal of Mathematics Teacher Education* 14, no. 5 (2011): 331–53.

Clements, Douglas H. "Curriculum Research: Toward a Framework for 'Research-Based Curricula.'" *Journal for Research in Mathematics Education* 38, no. 1 (2007): 35–70.

Clements, Douglas H., and Julie Sarama. "Learning Trajectories in Mathematics Education." *Mathematical Thinking and Learning* 6, no. 2 (2004): 81–89.

Collopy, Rachel. "Curriculum Materials as a Professional Development Tool: How a Mathematics Textbook Affected Two Teachers' Learning." *Elementary School Journal* 103, no. 3 (2003): 227–311.

Darling-Hammond, Linda, James Banks, Karen Zumwalt, Louis Gomez, Miriam Gamoran Sherin, Jacqueline Griesdorn, and Lou-Ellen Finn. "Educational Goals and Purposes: Developing a Curricular Vision for Teaching." In *Preparing Teachers for a Changing World: What Teachers Should Learn and Be Able to Do*, edited by Linda Darling-Hammond and John Bransford, pp. 169–200. San Francisco: John Wiley, 2005.

Daro, Phil, Frederic A. Mosher, and Tom Corcoran. *Learning Trajectories in Mathematics: A Foundation for Standards, Curriculum, Assessment, and Instruction.* Philadelphia: Consortium for Policy Research in Education, 2011.

Davis, Elizabeth A., and Joseph S. Krajcik. "Designing Educative Curriculum Materials to Promote Teacher Learning." *Educational Researcher* 34, no. 3 (2005): 3–14.

Davis, Jon D., Jeffrey Choppin, Amy Roth McDuffie, and Corey Drake. *Common Core State Standards for Mathematics: Middle School Mathematics Tea*. Rochester, N.Y.: University of Rochester, 2013.

Dewey, John. *Democracy and Education: An Introduction to the Philosophy of Education*. New York: Macmillan, 1916.

Drake, Corey. "Understanding Teachers' Strategies for Supplementing Textbooks." In *Mathematics Curriculum: Issues, Trends, and Future Directions*, edited by Barbara J. Reys, Robert E. Reys, and Rita Rubenstein, pp. 307–20. Reston, Va.: National Council of Teachers of Mathematics, 2010.

Drake, Corey, and Miriam Gamoran Sherin. "Developing Curriculum Vision and Trust: Changes in Teachers' Curriculum Strategies." In *Mathematics Teachers at Work: Connecting Curriculum Materials and Classroom Instruction*, edited by Janine T. Remillard, Beth A. Herbel-Eisenmann, and Gwendolyn M. Lloyd, pp. 321–37. New York: Routledge, 2009.

Grossman, Pam, and Clarissa Thompson. "Learning from Curriculum Materials: Scaffolds for New Teachers?" *Teaching and Teacher Education* 24, no. 8 (2008): 2014–26.

Grouws, Douglas A., James E. Tarr, Oscar Chávez, Ruthmae Sears, Victor M. Soria, and Rukiye D. Taylan. "Curriculum and Implementation Effects on High School Students' Mathematics Learning from Curricula Representing Subject-Specific and Integrated Content Organizations." *Journal for Research in Mathematics Education* 44, no. 2 (2013): 416–63.

Gulamhussein, Allison. *Teaching the Teachers: Effective Professional Development in an Era of High Stakes Accountability*. Alexandria, Va.: Center for Public Education, 2013.

Hudson, Rick A., Paula Elmer Lahann, and Jean S. Lee. "Considerations in the Review and Adoption of Mathematics Textbooks." In *Mathematics Curriculum: Issues, Trends, and Future Directions*, edited by Barbara J. Reys, Robert E. Reys, and Rita Rubenstein, pp. 213–25. Reston, Va.: National Council of Teachers of Mathematics, 2010.

Huntley, Mary Ann, and Kathryn Chval. "Teachers' Perspectives on Fidelity of Implementation to Textbooks." In *Mathematics Curriculum: Issues, Trends, and Future Directions*, edited by Barbara J. Reys, Robert E. Reys, and Rita Rubenstein, pp. 289–304. Reston, Va.: National Council of Teachers of Mathematics, 2010.

Jacobs, Victoria R., Lisa L. C. Lamb, and Randolph A. Philipp. "Professional Noticing of Children's Mathematical Thinking." *Journal for Research in Mathematics Education* 41, no. 2 (2010): 169–202.

Kilpatrick, Jeremy. "What Works?" In *Standards-Based School Mathematics Curricula: What Are They? What Do Students Learn?*, edited by Sharon L. Senk and Denisse R.

Thompson, pp. 471–88. Mahwah, N.J.: Lawrence Erlbaum Associates, 2003.

Lappan, Glenda. "The Challenges of Implementation: Supporting Teachers." *American Journal of Education* 106, no. 1 (1997): 207–39.

Mark, June, Deborah Spencer, Julie Koehler Zeringue, and Katherine Schwinden. "How Do Districts Choose Mathematics Textbooks?" In *Mathematics Curriculum: Issues, Trends, and Future Directions*, edited by Barbara J. Reys, Robert E. Reys, and Rita Rubenstein, pp. 199–211. Reston, Va.: National Council of Teachers of Mathematics, 2010.

National Council of Supervisors of Mathematics (NCSM). "Common Core State Standards Materials Analysis Tools." 2011. http://www.mathedleadership.org/ccss/materials.html

National Council of Teachers of Mathematics (NCTM). *An Agenda for Action*. Reston, Va.: NCTM, 1980.

———. *Curriculum and Evaluation Standards for School Mathematics*. Reston, Va.: NCTM, 1989.

———. *Principles and Standards for School Mathematics*. Reston, Va.: NCTM, 2000.

———. *Curriculum Focal Points for Prekindergarten through Grade 8 Mathematics*. Reston, Va.: NCTM, 2006.

———. *Focus in High School Mathematics: Reasoning and Sense Making*. Reston, Va.: NCTM, 2009.

———. *Principles to Actions: Ensuring Mathematical Success for All*. Reston, Va.: NCTM, 2014.

National Council of Teachers of Mathematics (NCTM), National Council of Supervisors of Mathematics (NCSM), Association of State Supervisors of Mathematics (ASSM), and Association of Mathematics Teacher Educators (AMTE). "Mathematics Education Organizations Unite to Support Implementation of Common Core State Standards." 2010. http://www.corestandards.org/assets/k12_statements/NCTM-NCSM-ASSM-AMTE-joint-statement.pdf

National Governors Association Center for Best Practices (NGA Center) and Council of Chief State School Officers (CCSSO). *Common Core State Standards for Mathematics*. Washington, D.C.: NGA Center and CCSSO, 2010.

National Research Council. *On Evaluating Curricular Effectiveness: Judging the Quality of K–12 Mathematics Evaluations*. Washington, D.C.: National Academies Press, 2004.

Patel, Nimisha, Suzanne Franco, Yoko Miura, and Brian Boyd. "Including Curriculum Focus in Mathematics Professional Development for Middle-School Mathematics Teachers." *School Science and Mathematics* 112, no. 5 (2012): 300–309.

Post, Thomas R., Michael R. Harwell, Jon D. Davis, Yukiko Maeda, Arnie Cutler, Edwin Andersen, Jeremy A. Kahan, and Ke Wu Norman. "'Standards'-Based Mathematics Curricula and Middle-Grades Students' Performance on Standardized Achievement Tests." *Journal for Research in Mathematics Education* 39, no. 2 (2008): 184–212.

Remillard, Janine T. "Can Curriculum Materials Support Teachers' Learning? Two Fourth-Grade Teachers' Use of a New Mathematics Text." *Elementary School Journal* 100, no. 4 (2000): 331–50.

———. "Examining Key Concepts in Research on Teachers' Use of Mathematics Curricula." *Review of Educational Research* 75, no. 2 (2005): 211–46.

Remillard, Janine T., and Martha B. Bryans. "Teachers' Orientations toward Mathematics Curriculum Materials: Implications for Teacher Learning." *Journal for Research in Mathematics Education* 35, no. 5 (2004): 352–88.

Remillard, Janine T., Barbara Harris, and Roberto Agodini. "The Influence of Curriculum Material Design on Opportunities for Student Learning." *ZDM* 46, no. 5 (2014): 735–49.

Remillard, Janine, and Joshua Taton. "Rewriting Myths about Curriculum Materials and Teaching to the New Standards." In *Challenging Standards: Navigating Conflict and Building Capacity in the Era of the Common Core*, edited by Jonathan A. Supovitz and James P. Spillane, pp. 49–58. Lanham, Md.: Rowman-Littlefield, forthcoming.

Rentner, Diane Stark, and Nancy Kober. *Common Core State Standards in 2014: Curriculum and Professional Development at the District Level*. Washington, D.C.: Center on Education Policy, The George Washington University, 2014.

Roth McDuffie, Amy, and Martha Mather. "Middle School Mathematics Teachers' Use of Curricular Reasoning in a Collaborative Professional Development Project." In *Mathematics Teachers at Work: Connecting Curriculum Materials and Classroom Instruction*, edited by Janine T. Remillard, Beth A. Herbel-Eisenmann, and Gwendolyn M. Lloyd, pp. 302–20. New York: Routledge, 2009.

Russell, Susan Jo. "The Role of Curriculum in Teacher Development." In *Reflecting on Our Work: NSF Teacher Enhancement in K–6 Mathematics*, edited by Susan N. Friel and George W. Bright, pp. 247–54. Lanham, Md.: University Press of America, 1997.

Scholastic Inc. and the Bill and Melinda Gates Foundation. *Primary Sources Update: Teachers' Views on Common Core State Standards*. New York: Scholastic Inc. and the Bill and Melinda Gates Foundation, 2014.

Seeley, Cathy L. "Mathematics Textbook Adoption in the United States." In *A History of School Mathematics, Volume 1*, edited by George M. Stanic and Jeremy Kilpatrick, pp. 957–88. Reston, Va.: National Council of Teachers of Mathematics, 2003.

Shafer, Mary C. "The Impact of a Standards-Based Mathematics Curriculum on Classroom Instruction and Student Performance: The Case of Mathematics in Context." In *Mathematics Curriculum in School Education*, edited by Yeping Li and Glenda Lappan, pp. 493–514. New York: Springer, 2014.

Sherin, Miriam Gamoran, and Corey Drake. "Curriculum Strategy Framework: Identifying Patterns in Teachers' Use of a Reform-Based Elementary Mathematics Curriculum." *Journal of Curriculum Studies* 41, no. 4 (2009): 467–500.

Smith, John. P., III, and Jon R. Star. "Expanding the Notion of Impact of K–12 Standards-based Mathematics and Reform Calculus Programs." *Journal for Research in Mathematics Education* 38, no. 1 (2007): 3–34.

Smith, Margaret Schwan, and Mary Kay Stein. *5 Practices for Orchestrating Productive Mathematics Discussions*. Reston, Va.: National Council of Teachers of Mathematics, 2011.

Star, Jon R., and Amanda Jansen Hoffman. "Assessing the Impact of Standards-Based Curricula: Investigating Students' Epistemological Conceptions of Mathematics." *Mathematics Educator* 15, no. 2 (2005): 25–34.

Stein, Mary Kay, and Julia H. Kaufman. "Selecting and Supporting the Use of Mathematics Curricula at Scale." *American Educational Research Journal* 47, no. 3 (2010): 663–93.

Stein, Mary Kay, Julia H. Kaufman, and Miray Tekkumru Kisa. "Mathematics Teacher Development in the Context of District Managed Curriculum." In *Mathematics Curriculum in School Education*, edited by Yeping Li and Glenda Lappan, pp. 351–76. New York: Springer, 2014.

Stein, Mary Kay, Janine Remillard, and Margaret Schwan Smith. "How Curriculum Influences Student Learning." In *Second Handbook of Research on Mathematics Teaching and Learning*, edited by Frank K. Lester, Jr., pp. 319–370. Charlotte, N.C.: Information Age Publishing, and Reston, Va.: National Council of Teachers of Mathematics, 2007.

Stein, Mary Kay, and Margaret Schwan Smith. "The Influence of Curriculum on Students' Learning." In *Mathematics Curriculum: Issues, Trends, and Future Directions*, edited by Barbara J. Reys, Robert E. Reys, and Rita Rubenstein, pp. 351–62. Reston, Va.: National Council of Teachers of Mathematics, 2010.

Takahashi, Akihiko. "Supporting the Effective Implementation of a New Mathematics Curriculum: A Case Study of School-Based Lesson Study at a Japanese Public Elementary School." In *Mathematics Curriculum in School Education*, edited by Yeping Li and Glenda Lappan, pp. 417–42. New York: Springer, 2014.

Tarr, James E., Barbara J. Reys, David D. Barker, and Rick Billstein. "Selecting High-Quality Mathematics Textbooks." *Mathematics Teaching in the Middle School* 12, no. 1 (2006): 50–54.

Tarr, James. E., Robert E. Reys, Barbara J. Reys, Oscar Chavez, Jeffrey Shih, and Steven J. Osterlind. "The Impact of Middle-Grades Mathematics Curricula and the Classroom Learning Environment on Student Achievement." *Journal for Research in Mathematics Education* 39, no. 3 (2008): 247–80.

Trafton, Paul R., Barbara J. Reys, and Deanna G. Wasman. "Standards-Based Mathematics Curriculum Materials: A

Phrase in Search of a Definition." *Phi Delta Kappan* 83, no. 3 (2001): 259–64.

Weiss, Iris R., and Joan D. Pasley. "What Is High-Quality Instruction?" *Improving Achievement in Math and Science* 61, no. 5 (2004): 24–28.

Wiliam, Dylan. "Keeping Learning on Track: Classroom Assessment and the Regulation of Learning." In *Second Handbook of Mathematics Teaching and Learning*, edited by Frank K. Lester Jr., pp. 1053–98. Charlotte, N.C.: Information Age Publishing, and Reston, Va.: National Council of Teachers of Mathematics, 2007.

Chapter 11

What (Research on) Technology in the Mathematics Classroom Can and Cannot Do

Keith R. Leatham, *Brigham Young University*
D. Ray Barton, *Olympus High School, Salt Lake City, Utah*

An excellent mathematics program integrates the use of mathematical tools and technology as essential resources to help students learn and make sense of mathematical ideas, reason mathematically, and communicate their mathematical thinking.

—*Principles to Actions: Ensuring Mathematical Success for All*, p. 78

In this chapter, we discuss what research on the use of technology in the teaching and learning of mathematics can and cannot do, considering what research might tell us about what "is," what "could be," and what "should be" happening with technology in mathematics classrooms. We lay the groundwork for that discussion by first describing the complex relationship between the nature of mathematics and the nature of tools. We use *tools* in a broad sense and *technology* as the digital or computer-related subset of tools. Although we focus on technology, the basic arguments we make could easily apply to other tools (e.g., compass and straight edge, manipulatives).

The Nature of Mathematics

There are different perspectives of what it means to know and to do mathematics, and over the past half-century, numerous individuals have characterized these differences (e.g., Davis and Hersh 1981; Ernest 1991; Lakatos 1976). Across the various philosophies, a common distinction emerges between the consumption and the creation of mathematics. From a consumption standpoint, doing mathematics is applying an extant collection of algorithms, generalizations, and solution strategies in order to solve problems. The essence of doing mathematics is consuming it through computation. Alternatively, from a creation standpoint, doing mathematics is solving problems, developing algorithms, generalizing, and proving relationships. From a creation standpoint, the essence of doing mathematics is creating it through problem solving, reasoning, and sense making with respect to quantities and patterns.

This distinction between consumption and creation views of mathematics is important because one's view of the nature of mathematics has serious implications for what it means to learn and teach mathematics. Although focusing on computation can provide students and teachers with immediate and apparent rewards for correct answers (Skemp 1987), with this view of mathematics "too often students leave school with at best a command of a set of facts, procedures, and formulas that they understand in a superficial or disconnected way" (Schoen and Charles 2003, p. xi). Focusing on creation, however, although challenging, can provide students and teachers with mathematical understanding that is both adaptable and sustainable (Skemp 1987). Further, the learning process itself can be "one of the most enjoyable and satisfying intellectual experiences one can have" (Hiebert and Wearne 2003, p. 4).

For decades, advocates for reform in mathematics education have used arguments such as those presented above to call for curriculum and teaching practices that focus more on mathematical reasoning and sense making than on mathematical memorization and computation. For example, the National Council of Teachers of Mathematics envisioned "mathematics as more than a collection of concepts and skills to be mastered; it includes methods of investigating and reasoning, means of communication, and notions of context" (NCTM 1989, p. 5) and later advocated viewing "mathematics as a sense-making discipline rather than one in which rules for working exercises are given by the teacher to be memorized and used by students" (NCTM 2000, p. 334). More recently the contrast has been made using the language of levels of cognitive demand (Henningsen and Stein 1997; Stein et al. 2000), with the doing of mathematics being viewed more as engaging "in active inquiry and exploration" and using "procedures in ways that are meaningfully connected with concepts or understanding" and less as using "procedures, formulas, or algorithms in ways that are not actively linked to meaning" or as consisting "primarily of memorization or the reproduction of previously memorized facts" (NCTM 2014, p. 19).

Throughout this chapter, we embrace and advocate for viewing the doing of mathematics as a creative, ongoing human endeavor. Furthermore, we argue that what makes learning or teaching mathematics with technology either effective or appropriate is inextricably tied to one's view of the nature of mathematics as well as one's view of the nature of tools.

Tools and Mathematics

There have always been tools of one type or another associated with the doing of mathematics. And as different tools come and go, controversies often surround the arrival of the new ones and the departure of the old ones. Such controversies took place with the appearance of the four-function calculator (Dick 1988), when calculators first acquired graphing capabilities (Milou 1999) and then computer algebra capabilities (Herget et al. 2000), and again with the advent of Internet-enabled handheld devices (Kolikant 2010). But earlier challenges arose when pencils with erasers were introduced to pen-dominated classrooms (Baron 2009), and earlier still, even the symbols we use as tools for notating numerals created controversy as we shifted from Roman to Arabic numerals (Stone 1972). Similar challenges have arisen with other categories of tools, such as slates, chalkboards, whiteboards, and interactive whiteboards (Villarreal and Borba 2010).

"Technology is an inescapable fact of life in the

world in which we live and should be embraced as a powerful tool for doing mathematics" (NCTM 2014, p. 82). Furthermore, although technological change is inevitable, that change is only partially outside of our control. The world around us is constantly changing, but we choose how to engage with those changes. Tools do not have intrinsic meaning—only the meaning we give them through the ways and reasons we use them. But different tools do have different characteristics that lend themselves to particular uses. One can use either a wrench or a hammer to drive a nail, but through experience we learn to value the hammer over the wrench for that purpose. Now, which is better, the wrench or the hammer? Absent asking "Better for what?" this question really makes no sense. The hammer does not have "nail pounding" as an intrinsic part of its nature; the user must create that meaning. This process of users creating meaning for tools by the way they use them (turning artifacts into tools) is referred to as "instrumental genesis" (see Artigue 2002; Zbiek et al. 2007). Indeed,

> technology can be used for almost any purpose, including putting students in a passive role or teaching the memorization of facts or rules. Although it carries few intrinsic biases of its own, electronic technology has enormous power to intensify and reinforce almost any bias the user or designer brings to it. (Kaput and Thompson 1994, p. 678)

So we see an important connection between the nature of mathematics and the nature of tools. One's view of what it means to do mathematics significantly influences one's view of the capabilities of a given tool and, most important, whether those capabilities are welcome.

Consider, for example, the oft-heard concern that technology use (usually meaning calculator use) replaces or hinders student thinking (see NCTM 2014, p. 82). Such concern carries with it unspoken assumptions about the nature of mathematics, its teaching, and learning. If mathematics is viewed solely as computation, then technology can indeed replace much of that thinking. However, if mathematics is viewed as creation, communication, and problem solving—of solving problems for which one has not already been given a formula or algorithm, which requires knowing *when* to carry out computations in the service of solving a problem—then technology actually *cannot* replace most of that thinking. Thus, one's vision of the nature of mathematics (what it means to think mathematically or to do mathematics) makes all the difference when it comes to talking about what technology *can* do, as well as what it *should* do. Furthermore, technological changes can prompt us to broaden our vision of the nature of mathematics, to consider reprioritizing various mathematical activities. As Kelly (2003) noted,

> in a pre-computer era, the ability to add a column of figures with lightning speed was an important skill to anyone functioning as a bank teller or a sales clerk. In the age of computers, the ability to identify and execute quickly the correct arithmetic operation on a computer is a much more important skill for that bank teller or sales clerk. (p. 1037)

The very names we have chosen for certain technology illustrate a tendency as a society to view computers as "tools for computing" and calculators as "tools for calculating." If we then view doing mathematics as mostly or solely computing and calculating, using computers and calculators is a problem, as they, not we, do that mathematics. As argued before, tools are defined by what we use them to accomplish. So yes, computers compute and calculators calculate, but they do far more than that. These calculations and computations are both quick and accurate, providing space for us to focus on the meanings of those computations and to generalize beyond those specific calculations. Technology allows us to create complex representations, to dynamically link and manipulate multiple representations, to organize and explore patterns in complex data sets, and to facilitate purposeful communication both across the world and within the classroom. These technological affordances only become visible as we broaden our views of what it means to do mathematics beyond the realm of calculation and computation.

When contemplating technology use in the mathematics classroom, it is important to consider both the nature of mathematics and the nature of tools. We must think about what it means to do mathematics and how technology is being used to engage in mathematical activity. Thus "in the end, tools and technology are only a means, not an end; they cannot supplant student understanding and reasonable levels of computational fluency" (NCTM 2014, p. 84). They *cannot* do so when one views understanding mathematics and being computationally fluent as more than being able to compute, regardless of the means through which one carries out that computation. There seems to be a tendency to want to ensure that new technologies do not hinder or dimin-

ish the skills they are designed to replace (a tendency famously and amusingly explored by Peddiwell 1939). Along with Kelly (2003), however, we propose that "the important question is not, Will student facility with the old skills decline? but rather, What are the basic skills, when students have these new tools?" (p. 1057).

Principles to Actions (NCTM 2014) considers "appropriate tools and technology" as an essential element for "consistent implementation of effective teaching and learning of mathematics" (p. 59). The stance that technology should be used "to help students learn and make sense of mathematical ideas, reason mathematically, and communicate their mathematical thinking" (p. 78) clearly aligns with a creative view of the nature of mathematics. Furthermore, *PtA* aligns with an "instrumental genesis" stance on tools, explaining that "the value of the technology depends on whether students actually engage with specific technologies or tools in ways that promote mathematical reasoning and sense making" (p. 80).

Reality, Possibility, and Vision

Having discussed the complex relationship between the nature of mathematics and the nature of tools, we now consider the role that research can play in exploring and understanding that relationship. To gain insights from research, we must have realistic expectations. Those expectations seem to be influenced in significant ways by our concurrent interest in three states of being: the way things are (our perceived reality), the way things could be (possibility), and the way things should be (vision). As others have noted (e.g., Clements and Sarama 2003; Hiebert 2003; Schoenfeld 2000), research in general (and research on the use of technology in the mathematics classroom in particular) can help us understand reality; it can also reveal numerous possibilities. But it cannot determine vision. In the remainder of this chapter, we discuss what research on the use of technology in the teaching and learning of mathematics can and cannot do with respect to what "is," what "could be," and what "should be."

What Research Cannot Do

Perhaps it is only natural to want to know, plain and simply, what works, but such questions "tend to be unanswerable in principle" because "what a person will think works will depend on what that person *values*" (Schoenfeld 2000, p. 642). There seems to be a tendency to want research to prescribe what "should be" when it cannot do so. As Lynch (2006) put it, "Often, the forms of educational research that are most visible and most persuasive to lay audiences and policy-makers are those that provide simplistic, sometimes misleading, treatments of technology usage" (p. 30). Research can neither prescribe values nor "prove what is best" (Hiebert 2003, p. 6), although it certainly can inform those values and motivate our choices. In the end, research can influence and is influenced by our view of what "should be," but it cannot determine it.

Consider, for example, this question: Is technology good for the mathematics classroom? Research cannot answer this question, in part because "good" is subjective—the answer to the question depends on what one thinks "should be" learned in a mathematics classroom, on one's view of what it means to do and know mathematics. But answering this question is also further complicated by the nature of technology, for, as argued earlier, tools do not carry intrinsic meaning. Technology provides the means to carry out many different activities. Thus, what matters is how that technology is used and what it is used to accomplish. Any consideration of the question (Is technology good for the mathematics classroom?) requires one to consider both the nature of mathematics and the nature of technology. The question then becomes, Does a particular use of technology tend to afford particular mathematical activities?

What Research Can Do

Having discussed what research cannot do, we now turn to what it can do. It is important to note, however, that the argument that vision is not "provable" by research extends here in a slightly different way. We cannot prove vision, but neither can we set it aside. Vision necessarily and significantly influences any research we conduct on the ways things "are" or the way things "could be." Our vision influences the possibilities we seek to explore, the questions we ask, and where and how we look for answers.

Reality Research

Research on the way things "are" has revealed a number of interesting findings when it comes to the use of technology in the mathematics classroom. The following sections describe a few such findings related to technology access and use, particularly as they relate to computation and creation views on the nature of mathematics.

Technology access. A natural place to start when considering the influence of technology in the learning and teaching of mathematics is to determine the access that mathematics students and teachers have to technology, as access certainly must precipitate meaningful use. However, when trying to ascertain levels of access, particularly over time, it quickly becomes apparent that this determination is not as easy as it seems, for technology is a moving target. For example, consider access to computers in schools. Computers began to show up in U.S. schools in the late 1970s. By 1983, about half of all schools had access to at least one computer (Becker 2000). Soon all schools had some computers, and access began to be measured in terms of the ratio of students to computers—shrinking from about 40:1 in 1985 (Becker 2000) to about 4:1 by 2002 (Dunham and Hennessy 2008).

As computers became more widely available, however, the technology that seemed to matter more was whether those computers had Internet access. The past decade has brought further changes to the technology landscape, with mobile devices becoming the new measure for technology access. Furthermore, because of the personalized nature of many mobile devices, smartphones in particular, there is movement toward BYOD (bring-your-own-device) technology integration. In 2013, 73 percent of middle school students and 89 percent of high school students had personal access to a smartphone (Project Tomorrow 2014). In the 2010s, technology access is more about individualized data plans and tablets than about desktops and laptops. Thus, although access to technology in general has continually increased over the years, access to the latest technology is always an issue, as that latest technology is constantly changing. In order to provide equitable access to learning mathematics with technology, schools should prioritize purposeful technology acquisition and provide content-specific teacher development. At the classroom level, a view of mathematics as a creative endeavor implies that all students (at any age or level of preparation) can use technology in meaningful ways to facilitate their mathematics learning (see NCTM 2014, p. 82).

Technology use. Access to technology is a necessary, but by no means sufficient, condition for use of that technology in mathematics classrooms. Unfortunately, one finding related to technology in mathematics classrooms over the years is that the percentage of students who regularly use technology in their classrooms is significantly less than the percentage of students who have access to technology in those classrooms. In 1996, only about 33 percent of fourth graders and 28 percent of eighth graders reported using computers at school at least once a week (Wenglinsky 1998). Just 30 percent of 2012 elementary classroom teachers reported using calculators at least once or twice a month; 75 percent of high school mathematics teachers reported using graphing calculators at least once or twice a month (Fulkerson, Campbell, and Hudson 2013). Given our previous discussion of the complex relationship between the nature of mathematics and the nature of tools, however, access and frequency of use are weak measures when it comes to the influence of technology on the learning and teaching of mathematics. What matters far more is *how* students and teachers are using technology to engage in mathematical activities when they do use technology. We now focus briefly on what research has shown with respect to technology use.

Doerr and Zangor (2000) found a number of different ways that students used graphing calculators to engage in mathematical activity. Such uses ranged from students using the technology solely to perform or check calculations, to students using the technology to create and explore patterns, allowing the calculator to carry out calculations so that they could focus on interpreting the meaning of those calculations. Doerr and Zangor also noted that "the role, knowledge, and

beliefs of the teacher" (p. 143) were critical influences on such student use, and research has begun to explore in greater depth the critical role the teacher plays in orchestrating student use of technology (Drijvers et al. 2010). Various orchestration types have been identified. For example, one type of orchestration (technical-demo) focuses on "the demonstration of tool techniques" (Drijvers et al. 2010, p. 219). When used in isolation, such an orchestration could easily result in an emphasis by students and the teacher on using calculators primarily to calculate, with teachers demonstrating the proper sequence of buttons to push to accomplish a particular procedure and students practicing carrying out this sequence on a number of exercises. In a contrasting type of orchestration (spot-and-show), "student reasoning is brought to the fore" (p. 220) for particular pedagogical purposes. One can see here an orchestration that could support student use related to meaning and interpretation, where technology is the means for both engaging in mathematical exploration and the means for communicating with others about that exploration.

Research on technology in mathematics classrooms reveals that schools in general, and mathematics classrooms in particular, seem to be constantly playing a game of catch-up with emerging technologies, and only a limited number of teachers are in the game. But research is beginning to provide a better picture of just what it looks like for students to engage in meaningful technology-mediated mathematical activity, as well as the role the teacher plays in orchestrating that activity.

Possibility Research

Research can "show what is possible and what looks promising" (Hiebert 2003), in essence providing existence proofs (Schoenfeld 2000). Such research on the way things *could be* has revealed intriguing possibilities when it comes to the use of technology in the mathematics classroom. Much has been said elsewhere about possibilities with respect to mathematical exploration involving dynamic representations. Here, instead, we focus primarily on possibilities related to how technology can help to facilitate meaningful mathematics discourse.

Networking to facilitate meaningful mathematical discourse. Technology now exists that allows a teacher to quickly send a poll to the class and then collect and display results. These polls can be useful tools to facilitate student engagement in mathematical reasoning and communication. In order to facilitate that engagement, however, polls need to be carefully prepared and managed. When preparing the question, it is helpful to keep in mind that the fundamental purposes in asking students questions are to probe or uncover student mathematical understandings or to push or advance student mathematical thinking (Black et al. 2004). Management of the poll results is just as important as preparing effective poll questions. For example, if responses are evenly divided between two answers, it might be tempting for the teacher to simply tell students which response is correct. However, a more effective strategy—one that encourages student reasoning and communication—would be to invite students to find someone with a different response from theirs and talk to them. After the discussion, the teacher could send the poll again to see if responses are migrating toward the correct answer. (This strategy is sometimes called the 50/50 strategy.)

Consider this illustrative example. AP Calculus students were given a quick poll (see fig. 11.1a). Because the results for question 3 were almost evenly divided (see fig. 11.1b) the teacher employed the 50/50 strategy. Figure 11.1c shows the follow-up poll results after students spent several minutes trying to convince their neighbor of the correct response.

In this activity, networking technology was used to

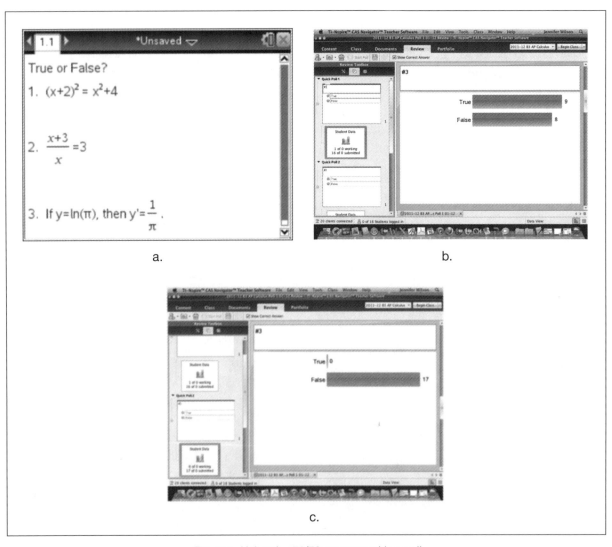

Fig. 11.1. Using the 50/50 strategy with a poll

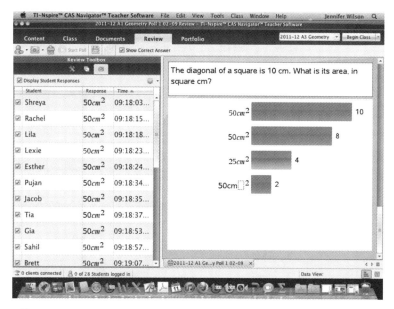

Fig. 11.2. The results of a geometry poll in response to this problem:
The diagonal of a square is 10 cm. What is its area, in square cm?

identify an ideal opportunity for the teacher to facilitate meaningful mathematical discourse among students.

Now consider another intriguing possibility facilitated by technology. Jennifer Wilson, a teacher in Mississippi, asked her students to solve a geometry problem and report their results via a poll (see fig. 11.2). Students' open responses were recorded, along with the time at which they submitted their work, thus providing easy access to how long each student took to do the problem and the order in which they finished.

Here is Wilson's description of the experience:

Lately, I have been deliberately posing problems that provide students with opportunities to look for and make use of structure. A few years ago, I first sent my students the following problem [see fig. 11.2]. When I sent this to my students, I noticed that Shreya marked her response very quickly. When we reviewed the answers, several students shared how they arrived at the answer. Most did what I would do, which was to recognize the 45-45-90 triangles and go backwards from the diagonal to find the side of the square.

Shreya didn't work it that way, however. When we asked her, she said that she recognized that the square was also a rhombus, which has an area of one half of the product of the diagonals. She did one half times ten times ten, and marked her response much quicker than the rest of us. Shreya was a very quiet student and would have never offered her way to work it voluntarily. The time stamp gave her a way so that we knew to ask her how she worked the problem. (Wilson 2016)

Notice how Wilson used technology to elicit and use evidence of student thinking. Without a thoughtful examination of the time stamps, this effective teaching practice might not have happened. For more detailed illustrations of how researchers have explored the possibilities of networking to facilitate meaningful mathematical discourse, see, for example, Roscheele and colleagues (2003), Wright (2010), and Zakrzewski (2016).

Facilitating the orchestration of mathematical discussions. Networking technology tools allow a teacher to capture the calculator screen of each student and then project all the students' screens in one collection for the entire class to view. This screen capture tool has great potential to facilitate meaningful mathematics discourse and the elicitation and use of evidence of student thinking. In particular, this feature can help the teacher manage the discourse. For example, the five practices for managing mathematics discourse (Stein and Smith (2011) can be implemented by capturing shots of all the students' calculator screens, organizing them in a purposeful way, and then presenting them to the class as a springboard for productive classroom discussion.

In the next example, screen capture allowed us to collect and organize student responses (see fig. 11.3) to the Six Degrees of Separation problem:

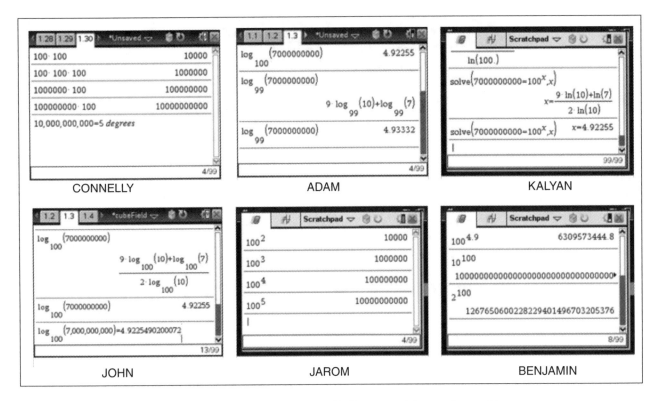

Fig. 11.3. Student responses to the Six Degrees of Separation problem

If you had 100 friends, and each friend had 100 friends and so on, what could be the maximum degree of separation between you and anyone in the world? Assume the world population is 7 billion.

One strategy for sequencing the discussion of these solutions might be to move from basic numeric guess-and-check strategies to strategies involving algebraic representations and solving equations (i.e., Connelly, Jarom, Benjamin, John, Adam, Kalyan). Alternatively, the solutions could be sequenced and discussed in the reverse order (algebraic to numeric strategies). In this example, technology allowed the teacher to elicit student thinking and then use that thinking to facilitate meaningful mathematical discussion among the students. Because the screens showed different mathematical representations, the teacher was able to help the students make connections among the various representations and deepen their understanding of the mathematical concepts involved. Technology also helped students access the problem at multiple entry points that might not have been otherwise possible. For more detailed illustrations of the use of technology to facilitate the orchestration of mathematical discourse,

see, for example, Ares, Stroup, and Schademan (2009), Groth (2015), and Hegedus and Penuel (2008).

CAS as a tool to implement tasks that promote reasoning and problem solving. CAS (Computer Algebra System) technology can be an effective tool to assist students in investigating problems that might otherwise be too difficult or time-consuming to explore, thus elevating students so they can explore the branches of the tree of mathematics (Kennedy 1995). For example, our students use CAS to explore solutions to these related systems of linear equations (see fig. 11.4).

Using CAS, students quickly discover that each of the systems has the same solution, (1, 2). They then find other systems that have this solution and make conjectures about what all of the systems have in common. CAS provides all students access to this rich problem at multiple access points. Some students conjecture that the coefficients need to be consecutive integers, while others find that the coefficients of each row could be arithmetic sequences. CAS helps students generalize their results. Some students may develop a graphical representation of their solution description. Some students may branch out to investigate what happens

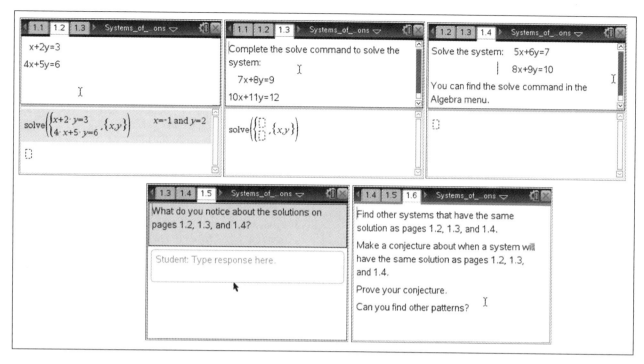

Fig. 11.4. Screenshots of a task for exploring systems of linear equations

when the coefficients are geometric sequences. In this example, technology provides the means for students to explore mathematics that they do not otherwise have access to, and it thus elicits responses and discussion that otherwise would not happen. For other illustrations of how CAS can help student to investigate mathematics they might not otherwise have access to, see, for example, Bowers (2003), Burke and Burroughs (2009), and Fonger (2014).

Conclusion

Technology continues to change at an incredible rate, and it seems impossible to anticipate just where it will take us next. For research to inform the use of technology in the mathematics classroom, we must constantly be aware of the complex relationship between the nature of mathematics and the nature of tools, for such awareness necessarily informs our vision of what it means to do mathematics and how technology might contribute to that endeavor. At the same time, our vision of how technology *should be* used in the learning and teaching of mathematics must both inform and be informed by continued research into not just what *is* but what *could be* as well.

References

Ares, Nancy, Walter M. Stroup, and Alfred R. Schademan. "The Power of Mediating Artifacts in Group-Level Development of Mathematical Discourses." *Cognition and Instruction* 27, no. 1 (2009): 1–24. doi:10.1080/07370000802584497

Artigue, Michèle. "Learning Mathematics in a CAS Environment: The Genesis of a Reflection about Instrumentation and the Dialectics Between Technical and Conceptual Work." *International Journal of Computers for Mathematical Learning* 7, no. 3 (2002): 245–74.

Baron, Dennis. *A Better Pencil: Readers, Writers, and the Digital Revolution.* New York: Oxford University Press, 2009.

Becker, Henry Jay. "Who's Wired and Who's Not: Children's Access to and Use of Computer Technology." *Children and Computer Technology* 10, no. 2 (2000): 44–75. doi:10.2307/1602689

Black, Paul, Christine Harrison, Clare Lee, Bethan Marshall, and Dylan Wiliam. "Working Inside the Black Box: Assessment for Learning in the Classroom." *Phi Delta Kappan* 86, no. 1 (2004): 8–21.

Bowers, David. "Promoting Pure Mathematics through Preliminary Investigational Activities Using Computer Algebra." In *Computer Algebra Systems in Secondary School Mathematics Education*, edited by Jim Fey, pp. 89–95. Reston, Va.: National Council of Teachers of Mathematics, 2003.

Burke, Maurice J., and Elizabeth A. Burroughs. "Using CAS to Solve Classical Mathematics Problems." *Mathematics Teacher* 102, no. 9 (2009): 672–79.

Clements, Douglas H., and Julie Sarama. "Strip Mining for Gold: Research and Policy in Educational Technology—A Response to 'Fool's Gold.'" *AACE Journal* 11, no. 1 (2003): 7–69.

Davis, Philip J., and Reuben Hersh. *The Mathematical Experience.* Boston: Wiley, 1981.

Dick, Thomas. "The Continuing Calculator Controversy." *Arithmetic Teacher* 35, no. 8 (1988): 37–41.

Doerr, Helen M., and Roxana Zangor. "Creating Meaning for and with the Graphing Calculator." *Educational Studies in Mathematics* 41, no. 2 (2000): 143–63.

Drijvers, Paul, Michiel Doorman, Peter Boon, Helen Reed, and Loeno Gravemeijer. "The Teacher and the Tool: Instrumental Orchestrations in the Technology-Rich Mathematics Classroom." *Educational Studies in Mathematics* 75, no. 2 (2010): 213–34. doi:10.1007/s10649-101-9254-5

Dunham, Penelope, and Sara Hennessy. "Equity and Use of Educational Technology in Mathematics." In *Research on Technology and the Teaching and Learning of Mathematics: Vol. 1, Research Syntheses,* edited by Glendon W. Blume and M. Kathleen Heid, pp. 345–418. Charlotte, N.C.: Information Age Publishing, and Reston, Va.: National Council of Teachers of Mathematics, 2008.

Ernest, Paul. *The Philosophy of Mathematics Education, Studies in Mathematics Education.* Bristol, Pa.: Falmer, 1991.

Fonger, Nicole L. "Equivalent Expressions Using CAS and Paper-and-Pencil Techniques." *Mathematics Teacher* 107, no. 9 (2014): 688–93.

Fulkerson, William O., Kiira M. Campbell, and Susan B. Hudson. *2012 National Survey of Science and Mathematics Education: Compendium of Tables.* Chapel Hill, N.C.: Horizon Research, 2013.

Groth, Randall E. "Dynamic Discourse with Dynamic Statistics Software." *Illinois Mathematics Teacher* 63, no. 1 (2015): 1–7.

Hegedus, Stephen J., and William R. Penuel. "Studying New Forms of Participation and Identity in Mathematics Classrooms with Integrated Communication and Representational Infrastructures." *Educational Studies in Mathematics* 68, no. 2 (2008): 171–83.

Henningsen, Marjorie, and Mary Kay Stein. "Mathematical Tasks and Student Cognition: Classroom-Based Factors That Support and Inhibit High-Level Mathematical Thinking and Reasoning." *Journal for Research in Mathematics Education* 28, no. 5 (1997): 524–49.

Herget, Wilfried, Helmut Heugl, Bernhard Kutzler, and Eberhard Lehmann. "Indispensable Manual Calculation Skills in a CAS Environment." In *Proceedings of the Fourth International Derive TI-89/92 Conference,* edited by T. Etchells, C. Leinback, and D. Pountney, pp. 1–7. Liverpool, U.K.: Austrian Center Didactics of Computer Algebra. 2000.

Hiebert, James. "What Research Says about the NCTM Standards." In *A Research Companion to "Principles and Standards for School Mathematics,"* edited by Jeremy Kilpatrick, W. Gary Martin, and Deborah Schifter, pp. 5–23. Reston, Va.: National Council of Teachers of Mathematics, 2003.

Hiebert, James, and Diana Wearne. "Developing Understanding through Problem Solving." In *Teaching Mathematics through Problem Solving: Grades 6–12,* edited by Harold L. Schoen, pp. 3–23. Reston, Va.: National Council of Teachers of Mathematics, 2003.

Kaput, James J., and Patrick W. Thompson. "Technology in Mathematics Education Research: The First 25 Years in the JRME." *Journal for Research in Mathematics Education* 25, no. 6 (1994): 676–84.

Kelly, Brendan. "The Emergence of Technology in Mathematics Education." In *A History of School Mathematics,* edited by George M. A. Stanic and Jeremy Kilpatrick, pp. 1036–81. Reston, Va.: National Council of Teachers of Mathematics, 2003.

Kennedy, Dan. "Climbing around on the Tree of Mathematics." *Mathematics Teacher* 88, no. 6 (1995): 460–65.

Kolikant, Hifat Ben-David. "Digital Natives, Better Learners? Students' Beliefs about How the Internet Influenced Their Ability to Learn." *Computers in Human Behavior* 26, no. 6 (2010): 1384–91. doi:10.1016/j.chb.2010.04.012

Lakatos, Imre. *Proofs and Refutations: The Logic of Mathematical Discovery.* Cambridge, U.K.: Cambridge University Press, 1976.

Lynch, Julianne. "Assessing Effects of Technology Usage on Mathematics Learning." *Mathematics Education Research Journal* 18, no. 3 (2006): 29–43. doi:10.1007/BF03217441

Milou, Eric. "The Graphing Calculator: A Survey of Classroom Usage." *School Science and Mathematics* 99, no. 3 (1999): 133–40.

National Council of Teachers of Mathematics (NCTM). *Curriculum and Evaluation Standards for School Mathematics.* Reston, Va.: NCTM, 1989.

———. *Principles and Standards for School Mathematics.* Reston, Va.: NCTM, 2000.

———. *Principles to Actions: Ensuring Mathematical Success for All.* Reston, Va.: NCTM, 2014.

Peddiwell, J. Abner. *The Saber-Tooth Curriculum.* New York: McGraw-Hill Book Company, 1939.

Project Tomorrow. *The New Digital Learning Playbook: Understanding the Spectrum of Students' Activities and Aspirations.* Irvine, Calif.: Project Tomorrow, 2014. http://www.tomorrow.org/speakup/SU13DigitalLearningPlaybook_StudentReport.html

Roscheele, Jeremy, Phil Vahey, Deborah Tatar, Jim Kaput, and Stephen Hegedus. "Five Key Considerations for Networking in a Handheld-Based Mathematics Classroom." In *Proceedings of the 2003 Joint Meeting of PME and PMENA,* edited by N. A. Pateman, B. J. Dougherty, and J. T. Zilliox, pp. 71–78. Honolulu: University of Hawaii, 2003.

Schoen, Harold L., and Randall I. Charles. Preface. In *Teaching Mathematics through Problem Solving: Grades 6–12*, edited by Harold L. Schoen, pp. ix–xvii. Reston, Va.: National Council of Teachers of Mathematics, 2003.

Schoenfeld, Alan H. "Purposes and Methods of Research in Mathematics Education." *Notices of the American Mathematics Society* 47 (2000): 641–49.

Skemp, Richard R. *The Psychology of Learning Mathematics.* Expanded American ed. Hillsdale, N.J.: Lawrence Erlbaum Associates, 1987.

Stein, Mary Kay, and Margaret S. Smith. *5 Practices for Orchestrating Productive Mathematics Discussions.* Reston, Va.: National Council of Teachers of Mathematics, 2011.

Stein, Mary Kay, Margaret Schwan Smith, Marjorie A. Henningsen, and Edward A. Silver. *Implementing Standards-Based Mathematics Instruction: A Casebook for Professional Development.* New York: Teachers College Press, 2000.

Stone, Williard E. "Abacists versus Algorists." *Journal of Accounting Research* 10, no. 2 (1972): 345–50.

Villarreal, Mónica E., and Marcelo C. Borba. "Collectives of Humans-with-Media in Mathematics Education: Notebooks, Blackboards, Calculators, Computers and ... Notebooks throughout 100 Years of ICMI." *ZDM Mathematics Education* 42, no. 1 (2010): 49–62. doi:10.1007/s11858-009-0207-3

Wenglinsky, Harold. *Does It Compute? The Relationship between Educational Technology and Student Achievement in Mathematics.* Princeton, N.J.: Educational Testing Service, 1998.

Wilson, Jennifer. "The Area of a Square." *Easing the Hurry Syndrome* (blog). March 13, 2016. https://easingthehurrysyndrome.wordpress.com

Wright, David. "Orchestrating the Instruments: Integrating ICT in the Secondary Mathematics Classroom through Handheld Technology Networks." *Technology, Pedagogy and Education* 19, no. 2 (2010): 277–84. doi:10.1080/1475939X.2010.491239

Zakrzewski, Jennifer L. "Using iPads to Your Advantage." *Mathematics Teaching in the Middle School* 21, no. 8 (2016): 480–83.

Zbiek, Rose Mary, M. Kathleen Heid, Glendon W. Blume, and Thomas P. Dick. "Research on Technology in Mathematics Education: A Perspective of Constructs." In *Second Handbook of Research on Mathematics Teaching and Learning,* edited by Frank K. Lester Jr., pp. 1169–1207. Charlotte, N.C.: Information Age Publishing, and Reston, Va.: National Council of Teachers of Mathematics, 2007.

Chapter 12

Using Assessment to Enhance Mathematics Teaching and Learning

Christine Suurtamm, *University of Ottawa*
Ann Arden, *Ottawa Carleton District School Board*

An excellent mathematics program ensures that assessment is an integral part of instruction, provides evidence of proficiency with important mathematics content and practices, includes a variety of strategies and data sources, and informs feedback to students, instructional decisions, and program improvement.

—*Principles to Actions: Ensuring Mathematical*

Success for All, p. 89

The word *assessment* is regularly used to mean many different things. For some, the word *assessment* brings to mind large-scale assessment. For others, *assessment* might mean a focus on classroom assessment or considering differences between formative and summative assessment. In this chapter, we address the diversity of meanings of assessment, as well as how they interact with one another. When speaking of assessment in mathematics education, we also strongly consider the domain that we are assessing, recognizing that understanding mathematics is a complex process that is much more than merely knowing skills and procedures.

In 1989, the *Curriculum and Evaluation Standards for School Mathematics* (NCTM) provided specific standards that had implications for assessment. In 1995, the *Assessment Standards for School Mathematics* (NCTM) went further to clearly outline the assessment standards of mathematics, learning, equity, openness, inferences, and coherence as well as a discussion of the different purposes of assessment. This document reflected a shifting of assessment practices to more

closely reflect a perspective of mathematics teaching and learning that values mathematical understanding through student engagement in mathematical processes such as problem solving and argumentation. These standards emphasized such things as the importance of aligning assessment and instruction, representing the rich array of mathematical actions in assessment tasks, and designing and using assessments in equitable ways. This document, along with contemporary thinking about both assessment and mathematics teaching and learning, called for a move away from assessing merely through paper-and-pencil tests to the use of a range of assessment strategies that provide multiple opportunities for students to show what they know and can do, given the multifaceted mathematical actions that are part of doing mathematics. The vision of mathematics teaching and learning presented in the subsequent *Principles and Standards for School Mathematics* (NCTM 2000) provided further emphasis on this vision of mathematics teaching and learning and the role that assessment plays in furthering that vision. These views were further reflected in state and provincial standards that helped to make mathematical practices explicit and further pushed the implications for assessment (e.g., NGA Center and CCSSO 2010).

Principles to Actions: Ensuring Mathematical Success for All (NCTM 2014) continues to push the agenda, illuminating components of a high-quality mathematics program and positioning assessment as an integral part of such a program. Assessment cannot be viewed in isolation. Assessment is a multidimensional process for examining what students know and can do—and then

The Canada Foundation for Innovation (CFI) supports Dr. Suurtamm's research through an infrastructure grant for the Pi Lab.

using this examination to further enhance teaching and learning. Aspects of sound teaching presented in *PtA* such as focusing on eliciting and using evidence of student thinking, posing purposeful questions, or implementing meaningful tasks are also components of sound assessment.

This chapter expands on the assessment chapter in *PtA* by outlining current research about assessment and describing specific examples of assessment that are aligned with this thinking. The chapter first begins with an overview of purposes and contexts of assessment with respect to both classroom and system-wide assessment. The section on assessment to enhance teaching and learning builds on the "productive beliefs" about assessment put forth in *PtA* (pp. 91–92) and provides examples of these beliefs in action. This discussion emphasizes that sound assessment is ongoing and embedded in instruction, uses a variety of forms, includes students in the process, and reflects meaningful mathematics. The chapter concludes with an examination of assessment issues and obstacles as well as ways to address these issues.

Purposes and Contexts of Assessment

Assessment has been used for multiple purposes, such as providing student grades, national accountability, system monitoring, resource allocation within a district, student placement or monitoring, determining interventions, or providing individual feedback to students and their parents/guardians (Newton 2007). Assessment reform affirms that, while assessment may be conducted for many reasons such as reporting on students' achievement or monitoring the effectiveness of an instructional program, the central purpose of assessment should be to support and enhance student learning (Joint Committee on Standards for Educational Evaluation 2003; Wiliam 2007).

PtA echoes this vision by stating, "The primary purpose of assessment is to inform and improve the teaching and learning of mathematics" (p. 91). This message should guide assessment programs, assessment and instructional planning, and decision making and is reflected in many standards, assessment, and policy documents, both within and outside of the United States (see Ontario Ministry of Education 2005).

Assessment discussions often focus on the distinctions between formative and summative assessments. However, assessments themselves are neither formative nor summative (Wiliam 2015). Rather, it is how the evidence generated by the assessment is used and the types of inferences made that make an assessment formative or summative. If evidence is used to inform teaching and learning with a view to improve learning, then the assessment would be considered to have a formative purpose. Assessment is considered to be formative

> to the extent that evidence about student achievement is elicited, interpreted, and used by teachers, learners, or their peers to make decisions about the next steps in instruction that are likely to be better, or better founded, than the decisions they would have taken in the absence of the evidence that was elicited. (Black and Wiliam, 2009, p. 9)

If, instead, the evidence gathered from an assessment is used to report on student learning at a particular point in time, then the assessment could be considered to be serving a summative purpose (Black and Wiliam 2009; Wiliam 2015).

Because any given assessment task could be used for both summative and formative purposes, blurring of these purposes can occur. For instance, while a teacher might design an end-of-unit test as a summative task, the feedback provided on that assessment might further inform teaching or provide information to students about ways to improve future learning (Brookhart 2001; Earl 2013). Thus, the assessment is serving both formative and summative purposes. Similarly, while a teacher may be collecting what he considers to be formative assessment, information about student learning throughout a unit of study, it is possible that the teacher might draw on this information when determining a report card grade. Thus, if this information provides further evidence of student achievement of learning goals, it may also be considered summative.

Classroom Assessment

Current views on classroom assessment have shifted from viewing assessment as an event that measures the acquisition of knowledge toward a view of assessment as a social practice that provides continual information to support student learning (Gipps 1999; Lund 2008;

Shepard 2001), just as perspectives on mathematics teaching and learning have shifted from a view of learning mathematics as mere memorization of procedures to recognizing that learning mathematics is multidimensional. Thus, rather than relying solely on summative end-of-unit, paper-and-pencil tests, evidence of student learning is useful when students are afforded multiple opportunities to show the complex ways that they engage in mathematics (Even 2005; O'Connor 2007; Suurtamm, Koch, and Arden 2010).

Classroom assessment involves both summative and formative assessment. However, there has been an increased focus on formative assessment because of research that suggests its strong positive impact (e.g., Black and Wiliam 1998; Sadler 2005; Wiliam 2007). Such assessments inform the teacher of next steps, and they inform the student about what areas he or she understands and what areas need to be revisited. It is particularly clear that eliciting evidence of student understanding and using that evidence in a timely fashion to improve instruction has a strong impact on student learning (Wiliam and Leahy 2015). Thus, teachers are encouraged to use formative assessment strategies such as observation, learning logs or journals, and conferencing to better understand their students' learning and to decide on subsequent instructional activities and teacher moves (Moss and Brookhart 2009). Both research in assessment and current perspectives on mathematics teaching and learning emphasize paying close attention to students' mathematical thinking throughout the learning process.

System-wide Assessment

Large-scale, or system-wide, assessment is another part of the assessment package. These assessments have different purposes from classroom assessment, such as accountability or determining system-wide improvements. However, the constructs of sound assessment should also apply to these assessments. For instance, the assessments should be evaluated in terms of what mathematics is valued, whether they are assessing the complex nature of mathematics, and how well they align with the curriculum or standards being assessed (NCTM 1995). Attention must also be paid to ensuring that the interpretation and use of the results of such an assessment align with the purposes for which the

assessment was designed and that the inferences made are appropriate to the test design (Koch 2013; Messick 1989; Rankin 2015). This issue will be further discussed and specific examples provided in the discussion of obstacles.

Assessment to Enhance Teaching and Learning

PtA provides a summary chart (NCTM 2014, p. 91) that contrasts unproductive beliefs about assessment with productive beliefs. Productive beliefs that pertain to classroom assessment practices highlight several aspects of sound assessment that are supported by research. In the following section, we unpack each of these productive beliefs with detail and examples.

Ongoing and Embedded in Instruction

One of the productive beliefs in *PtA* states, "Assessment is an ongoing process that is embedded in instruction to support student learning and make adjustments to instruction" (NCTM 2014, p. 91). Research suggests that assessment should be integrated into all aspects of teaching and learning in a seamless manner and inform teachers' instructional decisions in ways that promote student learning (Carless 2007). Students' learning is supported when the moment-by-moment actions and decisions that teachers make during teaching are informed by evidence of students' understanding (Leahy et al. 2005). However, these actions and decisions require focused attention in order to make students' mathematical thinking and understanding evident.

Ongoing assessment is essential to eliciting and using evidence of student thinking as called for by *PtA*. Some of these actions can be characterized as questioning, listening, and responding to student thinking in order to move that thinking forward (Davis 1996; Suurtamm, Koch, and Arden 2010). Others might speak about these actions as very similar to a focus on professional noticing defined as "(a) attending to children's strategies, (b) interpreting children's understandings, and (c) deciding how to respond on the basis of children's understandings" (Jacobs, Lamb, and Philipp 2010, p. 169). Similarly, Silver and Smith (2015) suggest that formative assessment is embedded in Smith and Stein's (2011) five practices of facilitating mathematical discussions: anticipating, monitoring, selecting, sequencing, and connecting. While the practices are intended to help teachers maintain the high-cognitive demands of tasks, they also encourage teachers to pay close attention to student thinking and to respond appropriately to that thinking, which are sound formative assessment practices.

There are many ways that teachers provide opportunities to elicit and listen to student thinking, such as observations during problem solving, informal interviews during class, or using focused questions during mathematical discussions. These methods allow teachers to be responsive to students' understandings and adjust instruction and to deal with particular understandings with individual students. Liljedahl's research into what he calls "thinking classrooms" provides an example of assessment that is ongoing and embedded in instruction with students' collaborative problem solving (Liljedahl 2016). Class time is used for collaborative problem solving, and all students work on problems in small groups, writing on vertical surfaces in the classroom (e.g., whiteboards, windows). This process allows student thinking to be visible, which enables the teacher to observe what students write, to listen to their conversations, and to provide feedback. The vertical nature also allows students to "borrow" ideas from one another. Liljedahl has found that this approach fosters more discussion, participation, collaboration, and persistence over other modes, such as the use of chart paper and markers. The nonpermanent surface of the whiteboard seems to reduce students' fears of making mistakes, and they seem more willing to take action on a problem.

Reflecting Meaningful Mathematics

The third productive belief in *PtA* suggests that assessment should include assessing students' mathematical understanding and processes. This builds on previous work (e.g., NCTM 1995) that emphasized assessments should reflect the mathematics that is important to know and do and should present a comprehensive picture of what mathematics is. *PtA* values the complexity of mathematics and encourages classrooms where students engage in a range of mathematical practices or processes. Such classroom environments support the development of conceptual understanding, procedural fluency, and mathematical reasoning. The approach

emphasizes instruction using challenging problems, student construction of multiple solution methods, and the discussion and defense of mathematical ideas (Ball 2003; Kilpatrick, Martin, and Schifter 2003; NCTM 2000). Recently, there is a renewed focus on student reasoning and sense making and on the mathematical practices and processes that students engage in when doing mathematics (NCTM 2009; NGA Center and CSSO 2010). If mathematics understanding and the use of mathematical processes are valued, then assessment must take these into account. Assessing mathematical understanding and processes can be a complex task, and many traditional assessments do not adequately address the full range of mathematical actions.

Hunsader, Thompson, and Zorin (2014) emphasize the importance of assessing the mathematical processes or practices to better understand not just what students have learned but how they learn, as this helps teachers determine next steps. In their work, they examined assessments that accompany published textbooks and found that many of the assessment tasks and questions did not adequately address the mathematical practices. In their research, they demonstrated how an item, such as the one shown in figure 12.1, could be adapted to make students' use of mathematical processes more visible.

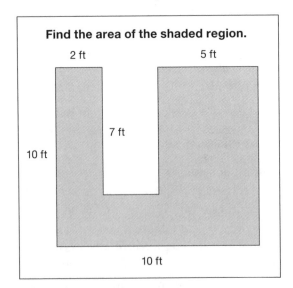

Fig. 12.1. A task that can be adapted to make students' use of mathematical processes more visible. Adapted from Hunsader, Thompson, and Zorin (2014), p. 209.

They offer several adaptations to the task. For instance, they suggest that the following modified question (Modification 1A) accompanying the figure should ask students to communicate, justify, and diagram their thinking. This modification might help to make student thinking visible, which in turn would provide the teacher with insight into the students' processes.

> Modification 1A: Sabrina wants to replace her kitchen counters (the shaded region) with mosaic tiles sold in 1-foot-square sheets. How many tile sheets will she need to complete the job? Use a diagram to show how you know your answer is correct. (Hunsader, Thompson, and Zorin 2014, p. 209)

Use of a Variety of Forms of Assessment

In order to assess the complex process of mathematics, *PtA* suggests that a variety of assessment strategies and tasks be used. Assessment in mathematics must go beyond focusing on how well a student uses a memorized algorithm or procedure and must also elicit, assess, and respond to students' mathematical understandings (NCTM 1995). To do this, assessment strategies need to include more than the traditional practice of relying on end-of-unit tests and mid-unit quizzes, both of which tend to focus on knowledge recall and procedural learning (Shepard 2001). A variety of assessment strategies need to be employed that include innovative ways to assess the full range of mathematical actions and to provide students with multiple opportunities to show what they know and can do (Gipps 1994; Moss 2003; Suurtamm, Koch, and Arden 2010). Using a range of assessment strategies provides teachers with the opportunity to gain insight into students' mathematical thinking (Romagnano 2001). Thus, assessment practices that include observations, interviews, performance tasks, reflective journals, projects, portfolios, presentations, and self-assessments are an essential part of implementing current approaches to teaching mathematics (NCTM 1995; Wiliam 2007).

The work of Young-Loveridge and Bicknell (2015) provides examples of the power of combining interviews with tasks as an assessment technique. In their example, primary school children explain their thinking as they work on tasks focused on operations with numbers. The task work provides familiar settings and artifacts; and as the students work through their task, they explain their thinking to Dog and Rabbit (two soft toys) while the teacher observes and probes with further

questions. The combination of task and interview helps to provide much more evidence of student thinking than merely written evidence. Such techniques should not be limited to young students, however, as students at all levels often struggle with providing written evidence of the depth of their thinking (Brookhart 2003; Liljedahl 2016).

Including Students in the Assessment Process

Current approaches to classroom assessment emphasize the role of the student in the assessment process (Earl 2013). Primarily, students engage with the descriptive feedback that teachers provide, thus allowing students to improve their learning. However, student engagement can move well beyond that. For instance, students can be included in developing and applying assessment criteria or improving their peer- and self-assessment skills (Bleiler et al. 2015; Moss and Brookhart 2009; Shepard 2001). Wiliam suggests that as teachers engage students in formative assessment, students develop ownership for their own learning and act as resources for one another (2007). Engaging students in the co-creation of assessment criteria and using samples of student work to discuss criteria helps students recognize high-quality work and improve their work. When students are clear about criteria, they are able to provide or select evidence of their learning. For instance, many teachers use portfolios that require students to select evidence of their understanding of particular content areas or their use of particular mathematical practices. These portfolios often encourage students to explain why they have selected these pieces of evidence and in what ways they demonstrate their learning. Thus, students develop the metacognitive skills to self-assess.

Students can be involved in the assessment process at all grade levels. In Young-Loveridge and Bicknell's (2015) example of interviews with young children, students were also asked to complete a self-assessment where they circled a face from a set of four faces that ranged from sad to very happy to indicate how they felt about the task they completed. At the other end of the grade range, Bleiler and colleagues (2015) provide evidence of the value of students co-constructing rubrics in college mathematics classes.

Putting It All Together

As a way of showing how these components of assessment might be enacted in practice, we use an example from a mathematics teacher's classroom. Ms. Arden teaches a Grade 10 mathematics course. Within this course, she uses a variety of assessments that include observations with conversations, performance tasks, quizzes, projects, or tests, as well as informal formative assessments that are embedded in instruction as she listens and responds to student thinking. The variety of assessment methods helps her see the range of mathematics content and processes that students are involved in. Planned and purposeful assessment opportunities are recorded to provide evidence of student learning in a more formal way and to help her monitor individual student progress. These multiple data sources provide several opportunities to gain a picture of student performance. Figure 12.2 is a display of this evidence gathered for one particular student. Across the top of the table, we see the range of levels, from incomplete (INC) to level 4. These levels of achievement are described

and outlined in standards documents, with level 2 defined as "approaching the standard" and level 3 defined as "meeting the standard." Level 4 is defined as "surpassing the standard": that is, the student "demonstrates the ability to use the specified knowledge and skills in more sophisticated ways than a student achieving at level 3" (OME 2005, p. 18). Along the left side are the subdomains of the course, with specific standards (e.g., A1, A2) identified. For instance, in this Grade 10 course, there are three strands, each with associated curriculum standards: quadratic functions (with curriculum standards A1, A2, A3, A4); analytic geometry (B1, B2, B3); and trigonometry (C1, C2, C3). The dots on the page represent different types of assessments: observations (OB), tests (T), performance tasks (TK), and their placement on the grid indicates the level of performance. Note that an individual assessment, such as T3, may appear in several places, as the assessment provided evidence of student achievement of several standards.

Ms. Arden uses these data in a variety of ways, such as determining areas where more instruction is

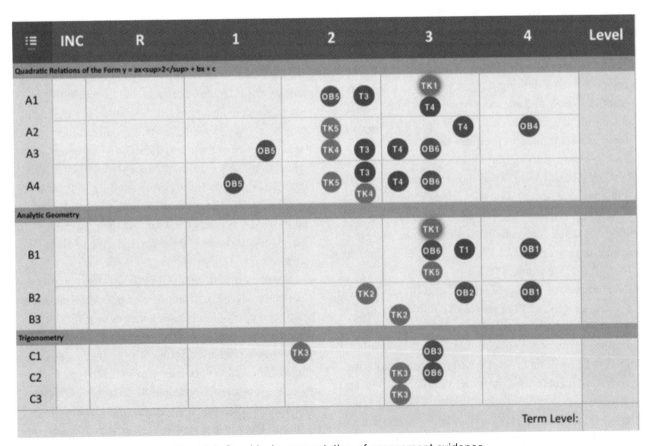

Fig. 12.2. Graphical representation of assessment evidence

necessary or recognizing the need to provide further assessment opportunities, to the whole class, to a small group, or to an individual student. Most important, she shares and discusses each individual student assessment chart with the student. The discussions with students provide further insights into ways to adapt her teaching to better support student learning.

The graphical nature of this presentation makes it easy for students to determine the areas where they need further work. One example of how she provides opportunities for further work is through a "Gap Day." During this time, students work in small groups on areas where they have determined, in consultation with the teacher, they would like to enhance their learning because they perceive a gap in their knowledge. The group activities could take the form of collaborative work on a problem set, peer teaching, or investigating a topic with technology. In the example in figure 12.2, the teacher and student noticed that the student might need to enhance understanding of the trigonometry concepts connected to the standard C1: "Student will use their knowledge of ratio and proportion to investigate similar triangles and solve problems related to similarity" (OME 2005, p. 51). The teacher also noted that several other students had difficulty with this topic, particularly as it related to proportional reasoning. Hence, she designed a small group activity to help them understand that they need to use multiplicative rather than additive thinking when working with proportions. The "Gap Day" is followed by additional opportunities for students to show what they know and can do. These additional opportunities provide Ms. Arden with the latest evidence of student understanding, which helps her determine a student's most recent level of achievement in relation to the standard.

Ms. Arden uses the data in her evidence record at regular intervals to adapt her instruction. She also uses the display of data to determine both a progress mark midway through the course as well as a final mark for reporting purposes. In both cases, she determines an overall level for each of the strands and then uses her professional judgment to determine an overall level of achievement for the student. These interpretations and decisions are made, not in isolation, but in ongoing consultation and discussion with students and other teachers.

Addressing Assessment Issues and Obstacles

While it is clear that productive beliefs about assessment will improve mathematics teaching and learning, several obstacles can stand in the way of enacting those beliefs. In this section, we discuss some of the challenges in adopting new classroom assessment practices. Further, the cultural, political, and educational context that places a large emphasis on accountability and large-scale assessment can often give mixed messages about what is valued in mathematics education. We also offer some potential things to consider in negotiating these issues and obstacles.

Challenges in Adopting New Classroom Assessment Practices

Assessing student learning is a fundamental component of the work of teaching. Using evidence of student learning and making inferences from that evidence plays a role in every phase of instruction. However, assessing students' learning is multifaceted and can pose particular challenges. The process of making sense of students' mathematical thinking is much more complex than might be anticipated and can often challenge teachers' ways of thinking about mathematics (Even 2005; Watson 2006). Current views of assessment also encourage different formats of assessment that might require teachers to develop new practices. Conferencing, observation, performance tasks, choosing or designing rich tasks, the use of rubrics, and involving students in the assessment process, for example, may be new practices for some teachers.

Several researchers look at challenges teachers face through an examination of dilemmas (Adler 1998; Talanquer, Tomanek, and Novodvorsky 2007; Tillema and Kremer-Hayon 2005; Windschitl 2002), including dilemmas in assessment practices (Suurtamm and Koch 2014). Using Windschitl's (2002) framework of four categories of dilemmas—conceptual, pedagogical, political, and cultural—Suurtamm and Koch described the types of dilemmas teachers face in changing assessment practices. Conceptual dilemmas in assessment occur as teachers attempt to understand the conceptual underpinnings of current views of assessment and of mathematics teaching and learning. For instance, they saw teachers grappling with such things as the different purposes of assessment and the value of aligning instruction and assessment; more broadly stated, what it means to understand mathematics. Pedagogical dilemmas arose as teachers created and enacted new assessment opportunities. These dilemmas might focus on how to create or find assessment tasks, design a rubric, or determine ways of recording observations. Finding time to conference or provide descriptive feedback can also be a pedagogical challenge. Cultural dilemmas emerge as new assessment practices challenge the established classroom, school, or general culture. Teachers frequently faced dilemmas when their new assessment practices threatened existing cultural practices within a school or department setting or challenged parents' and students' notions of assessment. Political dilemmas emerge when teachers negotiate their own thinking and practice with state, provincial, district, and school policies around assessment, particularly with regard to accountability. For instance, teachers may be expected to administer frequent multiple-choice tests within their classrooms to prepare for large-scale assessments, even when teachers do not feel that these types of assessments provide them with adequate information about student thinking.

Focus on Accountability and High-Stakes Assessment

While teachers are encouraged to incorporate a range of assessment practices that are responsive to student thinking and that promote learning, they are also situated in a complex landscape of accountability in which they are often portrayed as technicians tasked with implementing prescribed curriculum, policies, and procedures (Cochran-Smith and Lytle 2009). While external assessments help clarify common goals and expectations (Earl 2013), all too often, many stakeholders view success as solely measured by externally created summative assessments. The value placed on results of these assessments can be confusing to educators. For one, the mathematics being assessed is seen as the mathematics that should be valued. However, the format of these assessments often represents only a narrow band of mathematics. Mathematical thinking and actions are difficult to assess with the multiple-choice format often found in these assessments (Delandshere

and Petrosky 1998). Furthermore, as previously stated, in many jurisdictions large-scale assessments are often used for purposes that were not intended by the assessment developers. For instance, in the United States, results on the SAT assessment, a norm-referenced assessment designed to rank students for university admission, are often used to compare student achievement from state to state. Conversely, an assessment that might have been designed for system-wide accountability measures could be used for individual teacher assessment, which puts added stress on teachers.

Addressing Challenges

Using the framework of four categories of dilemmas may help to focus attention on ways to address different types of dilemmas. For instance, pedagogical dilemmas can often be addressed through teachers sharing resources or attending workshops in order to learn new techniques or strategies. However, the other three types of dilemmas are not so easy to address. For instance, conceptual dilemmas may emerge when current beliefs about assessment or mathematics are challenged. According to Wiliam (2015), research has shown "it is often easier to get people to act their way into a new way of thinking than it is to get them to think their way into a new way of acting" (p. 253), suggesting there is evidence that teachers adapt their beliefs as they test out new ideas. Sato, Wei, and Darling-Hammond (2008) claim that when the focus of teachers' professional learning is on their assessment practices, teachers recognize gains in students' learning, which, in turn, encourages their continued use of such practices. Cultural dilemmas often require communication so that stakeholders such as parents, students, colleagues, and administrators understand current thinking in assessment and appreciate the ways it can benefit students and teachers. Communication will also help political dilemmas. As policymakers mandate new assessment practices, they need to be aware of the implications politically, conceptually, pedagogically, and culturally and recognize that a mandate alone will not suffice.

Professional Learning Communities (PLCs) have been shown to strongly support teachers as they enhance their assessment practices (Lee et al. 2015; Suurtamm and Koch 2014). PLCs create an environment and opportunities for teachers to share their experience and work collaboratively to solve assessment dilemmas (Even 2005). In one PLC focused on assessment (Lee et al. 2015), teachers worked together to practice their questioning. They began by role-playing questioning techniques with one another in order to develop questions that probed student thinking. They tested out these new questioning skills in their classrooms. The classroom experiences were then brought back to the PLC and discussed, and the cycle of PLC discussion and classroom experience began again. These collaborative activities help to alleviate teachers' feelings of isolation. Both the de-privatization of practice and working with evidence of students' mathematical thinking are key components to professional learning (Loucks-Horsley and Matsumoto 1999; Vescio, Ross, and Adams 2008). (See chapter 13 for more detail on professional learning communities.)

The interaction between classroom instruction and assessment and system-wide assessment is a complex issue. Caution is needed regarding the limits of what teachers, principals, and others can infer from the results of a large-scale test, whether the emphasis on the results of the assessment strongly influences instruction and whether the assessment evidence is used for purposes that were not intended and may not be valid (Messick 1989; Newton 2007). If an assessment only assesses a narrow band of mathematical skills yet is highly regarded as an accountability measure, this, in turn, may cause "teaching to the test" to only focus on the narrow band that is assessed.

Determining the purpose of an assessment and then using the results for only that purpose is an important component of sound assessment practice. In fact, problems can arise when evidence from assessments that have been designed for one purpose are used for another purpose (Koch 2013; Newton 2007). It is helpful if educators have the opportunity to develop some fluency with assessment results so that they can determine what inferences can be made from assessment results (Rankin 2015). The current trend of educators training and working collaboratively as a data team with results from a variety of sources helps educators understand that a combination of assessments can serve as a barometer of trends rather than a single assessment being seen as a thermometer of the current state of affairs.

Concluding Comments

Assessment is a complex process that cannot be separated from other parts of teaching and learning. In the past, assessments had often been perceived as tests or tasks that concluded a unit of learning. Currently, assessment is understood as a connection between teaching and learning. Assessment is not a separate process but is ongoing and integrated within daily classroom activities in a way that is coherent with mathematical content and practices. Assessment provides opportunities for a student and teacher to engage in meaningful conversations about an individual student's learning and for a teacher to reflect on the activities and processes in his or her classroom. Furthermore, whether at the classroom or system level, in considering the inferences made from assessments, we are reminded that "assessment results are only estimates of what a person knows and can do" (NRC 2001, p. 2).

References

Adler, Jill. "A Language of Teaching Dilemmas: Unlocking the Complex Multilingual Secondary Mathematics Classroom." *For the Learning of Mathematics* 18, no. 1 (1998): 24–33.

Ball, Deborah Loewenberg, ed. *Mathematical Proficiency for All Students: Toward a Strategic Research and Development Program in Mathematics Education*. Santa Monica, Calif.: RAND Institute, 2003.

Black, Paul, and Dylan Wiliam. "Assessment and Classroom Learning." *Assessment in Education: Principles, Policy, and Practice* 5, no. 1 (1998): 7–74.

———. "Developing the Theory of Formative Assessment." *Educational Assessment Evaluation and Accountability* 21 (2009): 5–31.

Bleiler, Sarah K., Yi-Yin (Winnie) Ko, Sean P. Yee, and Justin D. Boyle. "Communal Development and Evaluation of a Course Rubric for Proof Writing." In *Assessment to Enhance Teaching and Learning*, edited by Christine Suurtamm and Amy Roth McDuffie, pp. 97–108. Reston, Va.: National Council of Teachers of Mathematics, 2015.

Brookhart, Susan M. "Successful Students' Formative and Summative Uses of Assessment Information." *Assessment in Education: Principles, Policy, and Practice* 8, no. 2 (2001): 153–69.

———. "Developing Measurement Theory for Classroom Assessment Purposes and Uses." *Educational Measurement: Issues and Practice* 22, no. 4 (2003): 5–12.

Carless, David. "Learning-Oriented Assessment: Conceptual Bases and Practical Implications." *Innovations in Education and Teaching International* 44, no. 1 (2007): 57–66.

Cochran-Smith, Marilyn, and Susan L. Lytle. *Inquiry as Stance: Practitioner Research for the Next Generation.* New York: Teachers College Press, 2009.

Davis, Brent. *Teaching Mathematics: Toward a Sound Alternative.* New York: Routledge, 1996.

Delandshere, Ginette, and Anthony R. Petrosky. "Assessment of Complex Performances: Limitations of Key Measurement Assumptions." *Educational Researcher* 27, no. 2 (1998): 14–24.

Earl, Lorna. *Assessment as Learning: Using Classroom Assessment to Maximize Student Learning.* Thousand Oaks, Calif.: Corwin, 2013.

Even, Ruhama. "Using Assessment to Inform Instructional Decisions: How Hard Can It Be?" *Mathematics Education Research Journal* 17, no. 3 (2005): 45–61.

Gipps, Caroline V. *Beyond Testing: Towards a Theory of Educational Assessment.* London: Falmer Press, 1994.

———. "Socio-Cultural Aspects of Assessment." *Review of Research in Education* 24 (1999): 355–92.

Hunsader, Patricia. D., Denisse R. Thompson, and Barbara Zorin. "Mathematical Practices: Small Changes in Assessments = Big Benefits." In *Using Research to Improve Instruction*, edited by Karen Karp and Amy Roth McDuffie, pp. 205–14. Reston, Va.: National Council of Teachers of Mathematics, 2014.

Jacobs, Victoria, R., Lisa C. Lamb, and Randolph A. Philipp. "Professional Noticing of Children's Mathematical Thinking." *Journal for Research in Mathematics Education* 41, no. 2 (2010): 169–202.

Joint Committee on Standards for Educational Evaluation. *The Student Evaluation Standards: How to Improve Evaluation of Students.* Thousand Oaks, Calif.: Corwin Press and ETS, 2003.

Kilpatrick, Jeremy, W. Gary Martin, and Deborah Schifter, eds. *A Research Companion to* Principles and Standards for School Mathematics. Reston, Va.: National Council of Teachers of Mathematics, 2003.

Koch, Martha J. "The Multiple-Use of Accountability Assessments: Implications for the Process of Validation." *Educational Measurement: Issues and Practice* 32, no. 4 (2013): 2–15.

Leahy, Siobhan, Christine Lyon, Marine Thompson, and Dylan Wiliam. "Classroom Assessment: Minute by Minute, Day by Day." *Educational Leadership* 63, no. 3 (2005): 18–24.

Lee, Ji-Eun, Heather Turner, Coleen Ansara, Jessica Zablocki, Cory Hinks, and Valerie Hanley. "Practicing Questioning in a Professional Learning Community: A Hub of Classroom Assessment." In *Assessment to Enhance Teaching and Learning*, edited by Christine Suurtamm and Amy Roth McDuffie, pp. 133–44. Reston, Va.: National Council of Teachers of Mathematics, 2015.

Liljedahl, Peter. "Building Thinking Classrooms: Conditions for Problem Solving." In *Problem Solving*, edited by Patricio Felmer, Wim Van Dooren, and Jeremy Kilpatrick, pp. 361–86. New York: Springer, 2016.

Loucks-Horsley, Susan and Carolee Matsumoto. "Research on Professional Development for Teachers of Mathematics and Science: The State of the Scene." *School Science and Mathematics* 99, no. 5 (1999): 258–71.

Lund, Andreas. "Assessment Made Visible: Individual and Collective Practices." *Mind, Culture, and Activity* 15, no. 1 (2008): 32–51.

Messick, Samuel. "Validity." In *Educational Measurement*, 3rd ed., edited by Robert. L. Linn, pp. 13–103. New York: Macmillan, 1989.

Moss, Connie M., and Susan M. Brookhart. *Advancing Formative Assessment in Every Classroom.* Alexandria, Va.: ASCD, 2009.

Moss, Pamela. "Reconceptualizing Validity for Classroom Assessment." *Educational Measurement: Issues and Practice* 22, no. 4 (2003): 13–25.

National Council of Teachers of Mathematics (NCTM). *Curriculum and Evaluation Standards for School Mathematics.* Reston, Va.: NCTM, 1989.

———. *Assessment Standards for School Mathematics.* Reston, Va.: NCTM, 1995.

———. *Principles and Standards for School Mathematics.* Reston, Va.: NCTM, 2000.

———. *Focus on High School Mathematics: Reasoning and Sense Making.* Reston, Va.: NCTM, 2009.

———. *Principles to Actions: Ensuring Mathematical Success for All.* Reston, Va.: NCTM, 2014.

National Governors Association Center for Best Practices (NGA Center) and Council of Chief State School Officers (CCSSO). *Common Core State Standards for Mathematics.* Washington, D.C.: NGA Center and CCSSO, 2010. http://www.corestandards.org/assets/CCSSI_Math%20Standards.pdf

National Research Council (NRC). *Knowing What Students Know: The Science and Design of Educational Assessment*, edited by James W. Pellegrino, Naomi Chudowsky, and Robert Glaser. Washington, D.C.: The National Academies Press, 2001.

Newton, Paul. E. "Clarifying the Purposes of Educational Assessment." *Assessment in Education: Principles, Policy, and Practice* 14, no. 2 (2007): 149–70.

O'Connor, Ken. *A Repair Kit for Grading: 15 Fixes for Broken Grades.* Portland, Ore.: ETS/ATI, 2007.

Ontario Ministry of Education (OME). *The Ontario Curriculum: Grades 9 and 10 Mathematics.* Toronto: Queen's Printer for Ontario, 2005.

Rankin, Jenny. "Guidelines for Analyzing Assessment Data to Inform Instruction." In *Assessment to Enhance Teaching and Learning*, edited by Christine Suurtamm and Amy

Roth McDuffie, pp. 191–98. Reston, Va.: National Council of Teachers of Mathematics, 2015.

Romagnano, Lew. "The Myth of Objectivity in Mathematics Assessment." *Mathematics Teacher* 94, no. 1 (2001): 31–37.

Sadler, Royce D. "Interpretations of Criteria-Based Assessment and Grading in Higher Education." *Assessment and Evaluation in Higher Education* 30, no. 2 (2005): 175–94.

Sato, Mistilina, Ruth Chung Wei, and Linda Darling-Hammond. "Improving Teachers' Assessment Practices through Professional Development: The Case of National Board Certification." *American Educational Research Journal* 45, no. 3 (2008): 669–700.

Shepard, Lorrie A. "The Role of Classroom Assessment in Teaching and Learning." In *Handbook of Research on Teaching*, 4th ed., edited by Virginia Richardson, pp. 1066–101. Washington, D.C.: American Educational Research Association, 2001.

Silver, Edward, and Margaret S. Smith. "Integrating Powerful Practices: Formative Assessment and Cognitively Demanding Mathematics Tasks." In *Assessment to Enhance Teaching and Learning*, edited by Christine Suurtamm and Amy Roth McDuffie, pp. 5–14. Reston, Va.: National Council of Teachers of Mathematics, 2015.

Smith, Margaret S., and Mary Kay Stein. *5 Practices for Orchestrating Productive Mathematics Discussions*. Reston, Va.: National Council of Teachers of Mathematics, 2011.

Suurtamm, Christine, and Martha J. Koch. "Navigating Dilemmas in Transforming Assessment Practices: Experiences of Mathematics Teachers in Ontario, Canada." *Educational Assessment, Evaluation & Accountability* 26, no. 3 (2014): 263–87.

Suurtamm, Christine, Martha J. Koch, and Ann Arden. "Teachers' Emerging Assessment Practices in Mathematics: Classrooms in the Context of Reform." *Assessment in Education: Principles, Policy, and Practice* 17, no. 4 (2010): 399–417.

Talanquer, Vicente, Debra Tomanek, and Ingrid Novodvorsky. "Revealing Student Teachers' Thinking through Dilemma Analysis." *Journal of Science Teacher Education* 18 (2007): 399–421.

Tillema, Harm, and Lya Kremer-Hayon. "Facing Dilemmas: Teacher-Educators' Ways of Constructing a Pedagogy of Teacher Education." *Teaching in Higher Education* 10, no. 2 (2005): 203–17.

Vescio, Vicki, Dorene Ross, and Alyson Adams. "A Review of Research on the Impact of Professional Learning Communities on Teaching Practice and Student Learning." *Teaching and Teacher Education* 24, no. 1 (2008): 80–91.

Watson, Anne. "Some Difficulties in Informal Assessment in Mathematics." *Assessment in Education: Principles, Policy, and Practice* 13, no. 3 (2006): 289–303.

Wiliam, Dylan. "Keeping Learning on Track: Classroom Assessment and the Regulation of Learning." In *Second Handbook of Research on Mathematics Teaching and Learning*, edited by Frank K. Lester Jr., pp. 1053–98. Charlotte, N.C.: Information Age Publishing, and Reston, Va.: National Council of Teachers of Mathematics, 2007.

———. "Assessment: A Powerful Focus of the Improvement of Mathematics Education." In *Assessment to Enhance Teaching and Learning*, edited by Christine Suurtamm and Amy Roth McDuffie, pp. 247–54. Reston, Va.: National Council of Teachers of Mathematics, 2015.

Wiliam, Dylan, and Siobhan Leahy. *Embedding Formative Assessment: Practical Techniques for K–12 Classrooms*. West Palm Beach, Fla.: Learning Sciences International, 2015.

Windschitl, Mark. "Framing Constructivism in Practice as the Negotiation of Dilemmas: An Analysis of the Conceptual, Pedagogical, Cultural, and Political Challenges Facing Teachers." *Review of Educational Research* 72, no. 2 (2002): 131–75.

Young-Loveridge, Jenny, and Brenda Bicknell. "Using Task-Based Interviews to Assess Early Understanding of Number." In *Assessment to Enhance Teaching and Learning*, edited by Christine Suurtamm and Amy Roth McDuffie, pp. 67–74. Reston, Va.: National Council of Teachers of Mathematics, 2015.

Chapter 13

Professionalism
Collaborating on Instruction

Robert Q. Berry III, *University of Virginia*
Michelle P. Berry, *Albemarle County Public Schools, Charlottesville, Virginia*

The vignette below describes how one mathematics specialist engaged a team of K–grade 2 teachers (sometimes referred to as a vertical team) in examining ways to improve their instruction for teaching basic facts for addition and subtraction to improve student outcomes. This vignette is a modification of the Domalik, Hodges, and Jaeger (2013) vignette focusing on the work of mathematics specialists.

• •

Near the end of each school year, the teachers at Elk Ridge Elementary School are asked by the mathematics specialist, Ms. Geller, to reflect on their mathematics teaching. They are asked to do two things: first, to make a list of what went well in a recent teaching episode, and second, to identify areas where they and their students struggled. For several years, many teachers at Elk Ridge Elementary School listed basic facts for addition and subtraction as an area that needed attention. Ms. Geller took this as an opportunity to facilitate interactions among K–grade 2 teachers toward addressing this topic. She used the K–grade 2 teachers' vested interest in the success of their students as the starting point for working together toward a common goal of improving instruction of basic addition and subtraction facts. As the mathematics specialist, Ms. Geller was in a position to ask tough questions and guide the teachers to think deeply about their instruction, their common teaching practices, and the overall goal of student achievement. Prior to facilitating interactions with K–grade 2 teachers, Ms. Geller met with the principal to discuss the teaching and learning of basic facts. As she outlined the potential for working with K–grade 2 teachers, the principal envisioned how this work could,

in time, affect not only the K–grade 2 classrooms but all the students in the school.

During the initial stage of meetings with K–grade 2 teachers, Ms. Geller listened and collected information about how individual teachers were teaching the addition and subtraction facts. Additionally, she heard concerns that some students did not know basic facts and that teachers were worried about the long-term impact of this deficiency on their ability to learn mathematics. (See chapter 6 for a detailed discussion of the relationship between procedural fluency and conceptual understanding.) Guided by Ms. Geller, the group of K–grade 2 teachers set the stage for the group's work. They began by asking themselves a number of questions:

- How do children learn their basic facts best?

- What can we do as a team to foster this development?

- How will these strategies develop over time or grade levels?

The K–grade 2 teachers were committed to looking carefully at how they taught basic facts and to begin the process of making improvements. These teachers were excited about the open dialogue. Ms. Geller took on the role of facilitator and shared some research-into-practice recommendations that helped to validate the teachers' work. She continued to ask probing questions to move the teachers' work forward.

Once the group had established some common beliefs and understandings, Ms. Geller and teachers talked about the different strategies typically used for successful recall of basic facts. Ms. Geller took notes and facilitated discussions on how student understanding advanced from one strategy to another and on the connections among strategies. The teachers focused on strategies for generating basic facts. The teachers realized that the children at each level, from kindergarten to first grade and then to second grade, would bring different ideas and skills to their learning. Ms. Geller posed questions to guide the teachers toward seeing how their work at a specific grade level supported the work of the whole team.

As the vertical K–grade 2 team continued their work, they made decisions about how to put their work into action regarding such topics as using common language, visual cues, common tools, assessments, activities, and games. Additionally, the teachers made decisions about additional learning opportunities for struggling and advanced learners. Finally, the team developed parent workshops to help parents understand how to support student learning at home.

• •

Throughout this yearlong process, the K–grade 2 vertical team, with the support of Ms. Geller, engaged in developing cross–grade band instructional strategies, resources, and ways to engage parents, administrators, and other teachers. The teachers discussed and researched instructional strategies, collaborated on developing materials across the grade bands, developed workshops for parents, and worked with Ms. Geller to co-plan and co-teach lessons (Domalik, Hodges, and Jaeger 2013, pp. 73–76).

Teachers can have remarkable flexibility in how they plan and teach mathematics. Many teachers are highly dedicated to their work. They are involved in various kinds of professional development and have access to textbooks and other materials to support their planning and teaching. They care about their students and work long hours preparing lessons and reviewing students' work to move learning and teaching forward. However, some teachers plan their lessons alone, teach behind closed doors, keep ideas and activities to themselves, infrequently observe their colleagues teaching, and rarely review videos of their own teaching (Leinwand 2015). Despite their apparent autonomy—and despite the many resources available to them—some

teachers have limited time to engage with their colleagues to share ideas, observe one another's teaching, and digest professional resources to support their professional growth. One question that arises is this: What kinds of supports and collaborations are needed to help teachers overcome obstacles?

Collaborating on instruction and coaching support are two approaches that support teachers in overcoming obstacles (NCTM 2014). These two approaches are not mutually exclusive, and they overlap in many ways. For example, coaching support helps teachers navigate relationships conducive for collaborating on instruction. In the vignette above, Ms. Geller's coaching support provided a means for teachers to voice their concerns while guiding and leading the teachers toward growth and improvement. The work of Ms. Geller and the K–grade 2 vertical team challenges professional isolation to reduce inconsistencies in teaching practices and to examine inequities in student learning (Feiman-Nemser 2012). By navigating the relationship with the principal, Ms. Geller created space and time for teachers to collaborate and overcome professional isolation. This collaboration situated the vertical team as active participants in their own professional development, as opposed to being passive recipients of professional development activities that may be disconnected from their contexts—including presentations that have little impact on their pedagogical knowledge, practices, or students (Avalos 2011). Active collaboration does not happen spontaneously; rather, it is shared and purposeful. Active collaboration is professional development in which teachers engage in the activities that are contextual and that move their professional growth forward.

Collaborating on instruction and coaching support are two approaches highlighted in NCTM's Professionalism principle in *Principles to Actions: Ensuring Mathematical Success for All* (*PtA*):

> In an excellent mathematics program, educators hold themselves and their colleagues accountable for the mathematical success of every student and for personal and collective professional growth toward effective teaching and learning of mathematics. (p. 99)

Through collaborating on instruction, educators hold themselves and colleagues accountable for professional growth and working to improve student outcomes. Through coaching support, educators learn new instructional strategies, become current with research on mathematics teaching and learning, and navigate relationships for continuous improvement. While elements of professionalism are implied in other NCTM documents (e.g., *Mathematics Teaching Today* [2007], *Principles and Standards for School Mathematics* [2000]), the Professionalism principle is a new and significant addition to NCTM's principles in *PtA* (2014).

An overarching aspect of the professionalism principle is that teachers should recognize that their own learning is never finished and that it is important to build a culture of professional collaboration driven by a sense of interdependence and collective responsibility. The discussion of professionalism in *PtA* suggests several areas of attention, and this chapter will focus on two of the productive beliefs: (a) "Teachers who collaborate with colleagues inside and outside their school are more effective. All mathematics teachers are collectively responsible for student learning, the improvement of the professional knowledge base, and everyone's effectiveness" (p. 102); and (b) "All professionals, even experienced teachers, can benefit from content-focused instructional coaching" (p. 102). At the beginning of this chapter, we used an elementary grade vignette to set the stage for collaborating on instruction; we will use a high school lens near the end of the chapter as the context for describing research and making connections to *PtA*. Consequently, we will make connections across the grade bands where appropriate. We also provide descriptions highlighting critical aspects of these areas and embed the range of productive and unproductive beliefs affecting professionalism. Finally, we discuss the next steps and critical activities that move the Professionalism principle into action.

Collaboration: Changing a Culture

A primary component of collaboration is the building of a culture of professionalism that is resistant to professional isolation that many mathematics teachers experience. Professional isolation is a widespread characteristic of life among teachers that restricts opportunities for professional growth and represents a potential barrier to the implementation of reform initiatives (Hattie 2012). Talbert and McLaughlin (1994) described professional

isolation as norms of privacy that are enacted in schools and classrooms. They contend that strong privacy norms have negative effects on collaboration and collegiality. Norms such as working autonomously and in isolation prohibit teachers from moving into one another's professional spaces and are described in *PtA* (NCTM 2014, p. 102) as an unproductive belief. In schools where norms of privacy prevail, comments on another teacher's classroom appear to be permissible only when aspects of practice, mostly inadequate control or discipline, encroached on another's classroom (Talbert and McLaughlin 1994). Isolation and privacy norms are obstacles that allow "good" and "bad" teaching to go unnoticed—or noticed "silently." Conversely, teachers who collaborate with their colleagues, both inside and outside their school, work together to notice and interpret aspects of effective teaching, share a collective responsibility for student learning, and ensure equitable distribution of resources (van Es and Sherin 2002).

Smith (2009) highlighted five forms of teachers' collaborative interactions, placing them on a continuum ranging from independent interactions, representing individualized teacher work, to interdependence, representing collaborative work in its fullest form. The five forms of interactions follow:

1. Storytelling and scanning—superficial interactions focused on social and personal interests. Storytelling and scanning is on the independence end of the continuum because the interaction is typically less focused on teachers working together.

2. Seeking aid and providing assistance—episodic interactions that are periodic and fragmented. Seeking aid and providing assistance focuses on process and procedures rather than collaborating around teaching and learning.

3. Sharing—routine open exchanges of work, materials, ideas, and pedagogic methods. Sharing is not focused on specific outcomes; rather, teachers might share tasks, strategies, and other ideas around teaching and learning.

4. Joint work—interactions with particular outcomes focused on teaching and learning. Joint work requires identifying outcomes and assumes the use of time, organization, and resources to achieve these particular outcomes.

5. Teamwork—having a strong collaborative ethos. Teamwork is on the interdependence end of the continuum because there is a sense of affinity that teamwork is an important aspect of teachers' jobs in addition to the overall professional culture.

Looking back to the vignette with Ms. Geller and the K–grade 2 vertical team, we see that they engaged in teamwork to improve instruction on basic addition and subtraction facts. Vertical teaming, as described in the vignette, represents the teamwork form of collaboration because the team was invested in the "collective we" rather than focusing on individual teachers' classrooms or specific grade levels. The team developed connections between what was going on in individual teachers' classrooms and how content and instruction spanned across the grade bands (Domalik, Hodges, and Jaeger 2013). Similarly, teachers in middle grades and high school can engage in vertical teams to develop continuity across courses to build coherence in instructional practices and mathematics content. Teamwork is a productive belief, describing a collaborative ethos in which "all mathematics teachers are collectively responsible for student learning, the improvement of the professional knowledge base, and everyone's effectiveness" (NCTM 2014, p. 102). This means that rather than merely exchanging materials—e.g., lessons, tests, and worksheets—mathematics teachers are "collaborat[ing] to design detailed mathematics lessons and materials and then reflect[ing] on the effectiveness of those plans for student learning" (NCTM 2014, p. 103).

Collaboration requires establishing networks and a common ground for joint enterprise in which teachers are not only co-planning lessons but are engaged in efforts to improve instructional practices and recognize practices that increase access to mathematics for each and every student. One way to improve instructional practices and recognize equitable practices is having teachers engage in professional noticing (Jacobs, Lamb, and Philipp 2010; Thomas et al. 2015; van Es and Sherin 2010).

Coaching support through observation of teaching can engage teachers in professional noticing to improve their teaching. Teachers can examine their own teaching and peers' teaching through video recordings to notice aspects of their teaching in need of improvement.

Professional noticing revolves around identifying what is important in the teaching environment. The classroom is a complex structure where many things happen simultaneously, and a teacher cannot attend to everything with equal weight. Jacobs, Lamb, and Philipp (2010) characterize professional noticing as a progression through three interconnected phases: attending, interpreting, and deciding. Attending comprises noting features of a mathematical moment as a way to gather meaningful evidence. For example, a teacher might attend to the use of representations, the use of mathematical language, the implementation of a task, or a number of other aspects of the lesson. Moreover, the goal is to attend closely to actions that are most significant to mathematics teaching and learning.

Interpreting involves making sense of and understanding a mathematical moment with what is known about mathematical development in a particular area. The goal of interpreting is to understand the reason for and meaning behind what occurred. Deciding refers to conceiving and executing an effective tactic drawn from the interpretation of a mathematical moment. Teachers can collaborate on noticing crucial moments of interactions in teaching and then interpreting these moments to make sense of what is important (van Es and Sherin 2010). Many experienced teachers use their knowledge of students and prior teaching interactions to attend, interpret, and decide during mathematical moments, whereas novice teachers need to learn how to attend, interpret, and decide as they grow professionally as teachers of mathematics (Jacobs, Lamb, and Philipp 2010). Through professional noticing, teachers are engaged in the *PtA* productive belief that "highly effective teachers become master teachers over time by continually improving their mathematical knowledge for teaching, mathematical pedagogical skills, and knowledge of students as learners of mathematics" (NCTM 2014, p. 103). Noticing and unpacking one's own teaching, with coaching support, provides a context for teachers to use their own specific practice to examine and notice productive and unproductive teaching, issues of access and equity, and evidence of ways students are engaged.

For example, lesson study is one professional development approach that requires both active collaboration among teachers and coaching support. Lesson study, or *jugyo kenkyu*, is a common method of Japanese professional development that has also been successfully integrated into schools outside of Japan (Corey et al. 2016). While there is no one set way to implement the lesson study process, lesson study typically involves a teacher or a group of teachers preparing a lesson, one teacher teaching the lesson in the presence of observers, and then the group openly discussing the quality of the lesson, so that all participants can learn about teaching mathematics. The common elements of lesson study variations are—

> (1) "a detailed lesson plan to share with observers, containing background information about the lesson and any particular features of teaching they were trying to better understand;
>
> (2) a group of teachers and other professionals observing the lesson in an actual classroom of students; and
>
> (3) a meeting afterward where the teacher and observers could discuss the important aspects of the lesson." (Corey et. al. 2016, pp. 545–46)

Planning, sharing, observing, discussing, and modifying lessons through lesson study deepens teachers' understanding of pedagogy and how students think about mathematics and positions them as continually developing their expertise, as described in the first productive belief in *PtA* (NCTM 2014, p. 102).

Collaborating within a network creates conditions for teachers not only to access rich resources but also to engage with each other in developing pedagogy and learning content. Subject area networks, like those in mathematics, can provide opportunities for innovation and change. Decades of research on teachers' work lives suggests that the local school context plays an important role in both how teachers attend to their students' needs and how networks and collaborations work to help individual teachers make sense of contexts (Gutiérrez 2000). Ingersoll and Smith (2004) recognize three salient components for collaboration in their research on novice teachers: having a mentor from the same field; having common planning time with other teachers in the same subject area and collaborating with other teachers on instruction; and being part of an external network of teachers. These three components do not assume that novice teachers of mathematics leave teacher preparation programs fully prepared. Instead, these components are an essential part of a purposeful network for novice mathematics teachers that are

highly beneficial for their continual professional growth within the context of their schools and communities.

Benefits for both experienced and novice teachers include increased technological skills, improved instruction, enhanced teacher learning, decreased workload, a positive impact on teacher morale, greater efficiency, increased communication, reduced personal isolation, instructional strategies that are more student-centered, and closer alignment between the curriculum and assessments (Vangrieken et al. 2015). Consequently, collaboration among teachers contributes to a career-long process for developing expertise and having a positive impact on teacher effectiveness (NCTM 2014). The benefits of collaboration also appear to address factors like access and equity. Achieving the Access and Equity principle, as described in *PtA*, requires teachers and schools to know the promises and challenges of the students whom they serve, how to deal with potential obstacles that may limit access to high-quality mathematics teaching, and how to address differences that may exist, such as inequitable access to human and material resources. In the vignette with Ms. Geller and the K–grade 2 vertical team, students' opportunities to learn basic addition and subtraction facts were an issue that affected student access and equity because of differential outcomes, which limited student access to opportunities to engage in high-quality mathematics. The teachers examined data and reflected on their practices in order to collaborate on ways to have a positive impact on students' mathematics experiences.

Collaboration: Creating Time and Space

Simply putting teachers together in teams or requiring collaborations among teachers will not improve instruction or student learning (Supovitz 2002). Rather, certain conditions must be fulfilled to facilitate and support collaboration. Vangrieken and colleagues (2015) identify five characteristics of successful collaboration: personal, group, structural, process, and organizational.

Personal characteristics are factors pertaining to individual group members' attitudes, personalities, or capacities. Members must have the willingness and commitment to collaborate, as well as have the necessary skills to make collaboration productive. These include communication skills, self-evaluation skills, and goal-setting skills. Personal characteristics and group characteristics are closely connected because individuals create groups.

Group characteristics are features that are specific to the particular group, which include matching subject area/course interests, diversity considerations (e.g., experience, gender, race, or ethnicity), group efficacy, and a supportive atmosphere. *PtA* takes a homogeneity view of collaboration by focusing on the same grade or same course for collaboration. This view presupposes that teachers with similar characteristics—such as teaching common courses or at a common grade level—can engage in deep collaboration (Fulton and Britton 2011). However, there is also space for collaboration that considers cross-grade and cross-course collaboration. For example, secondary mathematics teachers who teach all levels of geometry may find it beneficial to collaborate, while elementary schools teachers may collaborate by grade level or by vertical teams across grades.

Structural characteristics are components of the collaborative process that mainly relate to time and space issues. These include consistent common planning times, space and proximity of the collaborative team, scheduling, and continuity of the collaborative team. Time is an absolutely essential factor that affects collaboration among teachers. As noted in *PtA*, "A priority for schools and districts is to establish regular content-focused collaborative planning time for teachers at the same grade level or teachers of the same course and to schedule time periodically for vertical articulation" (NCTM 2014, p. 102). In this context, classrooms might be considered communal spaces for teachers to interact and engage in the activities of collaboration.

Process characteristics are critical for teachers working together collaboratively. These include flexibility, relationship building, task emphasis, interdependence, a structured approach with a focus on learning outcomes, and professional autonomy. Collaborative groups must establish norms or a collective commitment of conduct to promote openness and vulnerability for collaborating. Zimmerman and colleagues (2012) recommend that collaborative teams develop collective commitments that focus on teaching and learning and include processes that create a respectful, open environment that encourages a diversity of ideas and invites constructive feedback.

While developing processes for collaboration is important, the organizational characteristics of schools influence the functioning of these collaborations. These characteristics include the school cultural norms of collaboration, commitment to reform/change, creating an environment of mutual trust, monitoring collaboration, school governance, and school leadership.

Mathematics Professional Learning Community: Context

A professional learning community (PLC) often consists of groups of teachers who share and analytically question their practice in an ongoing reflective, collaborative, and learning-oriented way to promote their professional growth and skill (DuFour 2004). PLCs encourage the two approaches (collaborating on instruction and coaching support) described in *PtA* for overcoming obstacles and for supporting professionalism. At Cavalier High School (CHS), a school with an enrollment of about 1,900 students, teachers collaborate on instruction through PLCs with coaching support. The PLCs at CHS are organized by those who teach common courses within the same subject areas—for example, Algebra II teachers collaborate as a PLC. We will focus on the Algebra II PLC as the context for discussing an example of collaboration.

As stated earlier, the structural characteristics of time and space are two factors that have an impact on teachers' collaboration. The Algebra II PLC at CHS is a seven-member team that consists of teachers of advanced and honors level Algebra II. In addition, the PLC has access to an instructional coach who plays an important role with the PLC. At CHS, novice teachers are required to interact with instructional coaches weekly, but experienced teachers can also request the resources of an instructional coach. By design, four teachers have classrooms that are in one common area of the school, and the other three teachers have classrooms in another common area. In fact, most mathematics teachers at CHS share two general spaces within the school building.

The Algebra II PLC has two formal meetings every month—once before school and once on a day when the school has an extended lunch/club period for students—and subsets of teachers in the PLC also interact and collaborate outside of formal meeting times. Within the PLC, teachers share teaching ideas, examine data to prioritize focal topics and set instructional goals, design mathematics projects with rubrics, and collaborate on common formative and summative assessments. The PLC norms include an established team leader, meeting agendas, and expectations that team members will engage in the collaborative process. All of these activities are consistent with *PtA* descriptions of effective PLCs.

At CHS, collaborative conversations happen routinely throughout the year, both during and outside of the formal meeting times. During their interactions, teachers frequently pose questions to one another:

- Are students learning what they need to learn?

- Which strategies are working well, and for whom are they are working and not working?

- What contributed to students' performance on assessments?

- Who needs additional time and support to learn?

Collaborative conversations call on PLC members to make public what has traditionally been private by discussing goals, strategies, materials, pacing, questions, concerns, and results. The established norms of the PLC provide every teacher with someone to talk to, and they are explicitly structured to improve the classroom practice of teachers—individually and collectively.

Subsets of the Algebra II PLC take the lead for collaborating on common quarterly assessments for students enrolled in Algebra II courses. The assessments typically are developed prior to instruction on the associated concepts. Once the quarterly assessment is mostly agreed upon, teachers plan and develop activities to help students meet the goal. The process typically starts with members of the PLC studying the standards and the pacing guide to identify the essential knowledge and skills that all students should learn for the quarter. This process is an adaptation of what McTighe and Wiggins (2004) call "backward design." Starting with designing assessments does not imply that assessment drives the curriculum; rather, this process enables teachers to examine areas within the curriculum needing more or less attention. By collaborating

on the assessment using the backward design process, teachers maintain collective autonomy for planning their units with agreed-upon goals. On the basis of the shared knowledge generated by this joint activity, the PLC agrees on the outcomes that they will use during the quarter.

As an example of collaboration outside of the formal meetings of the PLC, Honors Algebra II teachers collaborated on a project in which students were to use applications to create mathematical models. The mathematics content goal of the project required the use of quadratics, polynomials, exponentials, or logs. After agreeing on the content focus, the teachers explored resources that required students to apply the mathematics content, engage in research, and incorporate writing. The teachers independently researched and found several tasks for the group to consider. The teachers met to discuss the promises and challenges of the tasks. For one of the tasks in this project, the teachers decided to engage students by focusing on the number of deaths due to AIDS in the United States. Students were given preliminary data but were required to do more research to develop a data set that could be modeled using a function. The problem required students to make predictions and discuss whether the model would be a good predictor. In this collaboration, the teachers developed a project, evaluated students' work, and reflected on the process for continuous improvement for future use and adaptations.

The Elk Ridge Elementary and CHS vignettes in this chapter are examples of school-level collaborations that support professionalism. While all teachers do not have similar structures or opportunities to engage in collaboration as described in the vignettes, individual teachers can create and develop collaborative structures to support their professional growth. Teachers can start by engaging in discussion groups centered on articles published in journals such as *Teaching Children Mathematics, Mathematics Teaching in the Middle School,* and *Mathematics Teacher.* Teachers can participate in Twitter discussion groups for each of the NCTM journals, or individual teachers can elicit peers within their schools or across their local area to meet as a group. Building from reading and discussion groups, individual teachers can take actions to collaborate on initiatives to affect their mathematics teaching and learning. Additionally, there are online professional support groups such as the Math Twitter Blogosphere (MTBoS) (https://exploremtbos.wordpress.com/) and The Math Forum at NCTM (http://mathforum.org/). Also, individual teachers can attend local, state, regional, and national conferences to learn about effective instructional practices and to deepen their knowledge of mathematics content.

Next Steps and Actions

Collaboration moves teaching from a solitary experience to a public space where teachers engage in critical conservations about teaching and learning. For meaningful collaboration to occur, some typical practices must evolve. Teachers must stop working in isolation. Isolation restricts professional growth and does not allow educators to improve their teaching nor continue their learning. School administrators have to provide time, support, and other resources that enable teachers to collaborate, for without these tools, teaching will continue to be practiced in isolation. Time for collaboration must be embedded in the daily work of teachers. While scheduling challenges exist, schools can purposefully create spaces for both informal and formal teacher collaboration. Schools and teachers must stop focusing only on what is expected to be taught and start including strategies that are effective and equitable for learning, as well as assessing what students have learned. Finally, school administrators must stop viewing instructional coaching as a luxury and assuming that only novice teachers benefit from general coaching support (Leinwand 2015). As with the case at CHS, many instructional coaches focus their work on novice teachers; however, *PtA* contends that all teachers, including experienced teachers, can benefit from coaching.

Building a culture of professionalism is challenging. It requires that we overcome the unproductive beliefs described in *PtA* and minimize practices that limit meaningful collaboration. Professionalism requires that educators hold themselves and their colleagues accountable for students' success and collective and individual growth (Feiman-Nemser 2012). This means taking collective risks and moving mathematics teaching and learning toward a more public space.

This practice can situate teaching as a risk-taking endeavor, but collaboration provides the support necessary for taking these risks and improving teaching and learning.

References

Avalos, Beatrice. "Teacher Professional Development in Teaching and Teacher Education over Ten Years." *Teaching and Teacher Education* 27, no. 1 (2011): 10–20.

Corey, Douglas Lyman, Travis Lemon, Edward Gilbert, and Hiroyuki Ninomiya. "Japanese Professional Development." *Mathematics Teaching in the Middle School* 21, no. 9 (2016): 544–51.

Domalik, Laura, Vandivere Hodges, and Linda Jaeger. "Supporting Groups of Teachers across Grades." In *The Elementary Mathematics Specialist's Handbook*, edited by Patricia F. Campbell, Aimee J. Ellington, William E. Haver, and Vickie L. Inge, pp. 71–89. Reston, Va.: National Council of Teachers of Mathematics, 2013.

DuFour, Richard. "What Is a Professional Learning Community?" *Educational Leadership* 61, no. 8 (2004): 6–11.

Feiman-Nemser, Sharon. "Beyond Solo Teaching." *Educational Leadership* 69, no. 8 (2012): 10–16.

Fulton, Kathleen, and Ted Britton. *STEM Teachers in Professional Learning Communities: From Good Teachers to Great Teaching.* Washington, D.C.: National Commission on Teaching and America's Future, 2011.

Gutiérrez, Rochelle. "Advancing African-American, Urban Youth in Mathematics: Unpacking the Success of One Math Department." *American Journal of Education* 109, no. 1 (2000): 63–111.

Hattie, John. *Visible Learning for Teachers: Maximizing Impact on Learning.* New York: Routledge, 2012.

Ingersoll, Richard M., and Thomas M. Smith. "Do Teacher Induction and Mentoring Matter?" *NASSP bulletin* 88, no. 638 (2004): 28–40.

Jacobs, Victoria R., Lisa C. Lamb, and Randolph A. Philipp. "Professional Noticing of Children's Mathematical Thinking." *Journal for Research in Mathematics Education* 41, no. 2 (2010): 169–202.

Leinwand, Steven. "Professionalism: The Newest Principle." *New England Mathematics Journal* (2015): 53–63.

McTighe, Jay, and Grant Wiggins. *Understanding by Design: Professional Development Workbook.* Alexandria, Va.: Association for Supervision and Curriculum Development, 2004.

National Council of Teachers of Mathematics (NCTM). *Principles and Standards for School Mathematics.* Reston, Va.: NCTM, 2000.

———. *Mathematics Teaching Today: Improving Practice, Improving Student Learning.* 2nd ed. Reston, Va.: NCTM, 2007.

———. *Principles to Actions: Ensuring Mathematical Success for All.* Reston, Va.: NCTM, 2000.

Smith, Gregory William. "If Teams Are so Good . . . : Science Teachers' Conceptions of Teams and Teamwork." PhD diss., Queensland University of Technology, 2009. http://eprints.qut.edu.au/31734/

Supovitz, Jonathan. "Developing Communities of Instructional Practice." *Teachers College Record* 104, no. 8 (2002): 1591–1626.

Talbert, Joan E., and Milbrey W. McLaughlin. "Teacher Professionalism in Local School Contexts." *American Journal of Education* 102, no. 2 (1994): 123–53.

Thomas, Jonathan N., Sara Eisenhardt, Molly H. Fisher, Edna O. Schack, Janet Tassell, and Margaret Yoder. "Professional Noticing: Developing Responsive Mathematics Teaching." *Teaching Children Mathematics* 21, no. 5 (2015): 294–303.

van Es, Elizabeth A., and Miriam Gamoran Sherin. "Learning to Notice: Scaffolding New Teachers' Interpretations of Classroom Interactions." *Journal of Technology and Teacher Education* 10, no. 4 (2002): 571–96.

———. "The Influence of Video Clubs on Teachers' Thinking and Practice." *Journal of Mathematics Teacher Education* 13, no. 2 (2010): 155–76.

Vangrieken, Katrien, Filip Dochy, Elisabeth Raes, and Eva Kyndt. "Teacher Collaboration: A Systematic Review." *Educational Research Review* 15 (2015): 17–40.

Zimmermann, Gwen, John Carter, Timothy Kanold, and Mona Toncheff. *Common Core Mathematics in a PLC at Work, High School.* Bloomington, Ind.: Solution Tree Press, 2012.